DISCUSSIONS OF THE FARADAY SOCIETY
NO. 43 1967

The Structure and Properties of Liquids

THE FARADAY SOCIETY
LONDON

Distribution arrangements overleaf

THE SOCIETY'S PUBLICATIONS

Transactions of the Faraday Society | Published monthly
Discussions of the Faraday Society | Normally published twice a year
Symposia of the Faraday Society | To be published once a year

MEMBERS

of the Faraday Society receive current issues of both *Transactions* and *Discussions* free on publication, and of *Symposia* at a reduced price on request. Enquiries regarding membership of the Society should be addressed to: **The Secretary, The Faraday Society, 6 Gray's Inn Square, London WC1 (Telephone: 01-242 8101)**

NON-MEMBERS

may obtain the Society's publications *either* through their own bookseller *or* by making application as follows:

FOR

Annual Subscriptions: to current issues of EITHER *Transactions, Discussions* and *Symposium* OR *Transactions* only

Back Issues: Complete Volumes (comprising *Transactions* and *Discussions*) from Vol. 41 (1945) onwards

APPLY TO
**The Aberdeen University Press Ltd
Farmers Hall, Aberdeen, Scotland**

AND FOR

Discussions: All current issues and back numbers

Back Issues: Complete Volumes (comprising *Transactions* and *Discussions*) from Vol. 1 (1905) to Vol. 40 (1944)

APPLY TO
Butterworth & Co. (Publishers) Ltd, 88 Kingsway, London WC2

OVERSEAS ADDRESSES

Australia: Butterworth & Co. (Australia) Ltd.
 Sydney: 20 Loftus Street
Canada: Butterworth & Co. (Canada) Ltd.
 Toronto: 1367 Danforth Avenue 66

New Zealand: Butterworth & Co. (New Zealand) Ltd.
 Wellington: 49/51 Ballance Street
South Africa: Butterworth & Co. (South Africa) Ltd.
 Durban: 33/35 Beach Grove

U.S.A.: Discussions—current and back issues:
 Enquiries to 88 Kingsway, London, WC2.
Complete Volumes 1-40:
 Johnson Reprint Corporation
 New York: 111 Fifth Avenue, 3

A GENERAL DISCUSSION ON

The Structure and Properties of Liquids

11th, 12th and 13th April 1967

A GENERAL DISCUSSION on The Structure and Properties of Liquids was held at The University of Exeter, Exeter, on the 11th, 12th and 13th April 1967. The President, Prof. C. E. H. Bawn, C.B.E., Ph.D., F.R.S., was in the Chair during the opening and closing sessions; Prof. D. H. Everett, Prof. M. L. McGlashan and Prof. J. S. Rowlinson acted as Chairmen during the other sessions. Over 273 members and visitors were present, including the following 99 from overseas:

Dr. Kurt Altenburg *Germany*
Dr. D. Anderson *Sweden*
Prof. and Mrs. F. C. Andrews *U.S.A.*
Dr. V. Ardente *Italy*
Dr. G. D'Arrigo *Italy*
Prof. T. A. Bak *Denmark*
Prof. A. Bellemans *Belgium*
Dr. H.-J. Bittrich *Germany*
Mr. C. Bruin *Netherlands*
Prof. G. Caglioti *Italy*
Mr. A. Compagner *Netherlands*
Dr. G. Döge *Germany*
Dr. D. Dorner *Germany*
Dr. M. Dupuis *France*
Dr. B. Eckstein *Germany*
Prof. H. Eisenberg *Israel*
Dr. T. J. V. Findlay *Australia*
Mr. J. Fischer *Austria*
Dr. D. D. Fitts *U.S.A.*
Prof. M. Fixman *U.S.A.*
Prof. E. Forslind *Sweden*
Prof. E. U. Franck *Germany*
Prof. H. S. Frank *U.S.A.*
Mr. S. Fuks *Belgium*
Dr. and Mrs. J. H. Gisolf *Netherlands*
Dr. J. Chr. Gjaldbaek *Denmark*
Dr. D. Henderson *Australia*
Dr. I. H. S. Henderson *Canada*
Prof. H. G. Hertz *Germany*
Prof. J. B. Hyne *Canada*
Dr. D. Jonah *Sierre Leone*
Mr. O. Jøns *Denmark*
Prof. M. L. Josien *France*
Dr. H. Kehiaian *Poland*
Prof. and Mrs. J. Koefoed *Denmark*
Dr. J. J. Kozak *Belgium*
Prof. K.-E. Larsson *Sweden*
Mr. J. C. Legros *Belgium*
Dr. D. Levesque *France*
Dr. A. Levi *Italy*
Dr. J. W. Lorimer *Canada*
Dr. W. A. P. Luck *Germany*
Dr. H. Lütje, *Germany*
Prof. M. Magat *France*
Miss B. Maijgren *Sweden*
Dr. G. Manfre *Italy*

Dr. P. F. Mijnlieff *Netherlands*
Mr. J. H. Misguich *Belgium*
Dr. L. Mistura *Italy*
Dr. A. H. Narten *U.S.A.*
Mr. L. E. Oden *U.S.A.*
Dr. J. Padova *Israel*
Prof. R. Pecora *U.S.A.*
Mr. E. J. Picard *France*
Prof. C. J. Pings *U.S.A.*
Dr. W. Pistor *Germany*
Mr. T. Plesser *Germany*
Prof. J. A. Pople *U.S.A.*
Dr. E. Praestgaard *Denmark*
Mr. C. Reynolds *Eire*
Dr. F. P. Ricci *Italy*
Dr. H. Richtering *Germany*
Dr. J.-L. Rivail *France*
Dr. E. B. Robertson *Canada*
Mr. J. Rouchard *Congo*
Dr. R. Satterfield *U.S.A.*
Prof. P. Saumagne *France*
Dr. T. Schneider *Switzerland*
Prof. R. L. Scott *U.S.A.*
Dr. K. Sköld *Sweden*
Dr. F. W. Smith *Canada*
Dr. Carel C. Smitskamp *Netherlands*
Prof. N. S. Snider *Canada*
Dr. Stanton *Belgium*
Dr. J. Stecki *Poland*
Dr. D. Stehlik *Germany*
Dr. H. Stiller *Germany*
Mr. D. J. Stufkens *Netherlands*
Dr. G. P. Thomaes *Belgium*
Mr. J. B. van Tricht *Netherlands*
Mr. R. Tufeu *France*
Prof. E. Tunkelo *Finland*
Dr. G. Urbain *France*
Dr. and Mrs. F. Vaslow *U.S.A.*
Prof. L. Verlet *France*
Mr. and Mrs. Vincent *France*
Mr. W. Waeber *Switzerland*
Dr. J. Walkley *Canada*
Prof. A. Weiss *Germany*
Prof. B. Widon *U.S.A.*
Mr. D. A. Young *U.S.A.*

© The Faraday Society and Contributors 1967
Printed in Great Britain at the University Press, Aberdeen

CONTENTS

page 7   Fourteenth Spiers Memorial Lecture—*Structural Theories of Fluids* by G. S. Rushbrooke

16   *Equation of State of a Monatomic Fluid with 6-12 Potential* by S. A. Rice and D. A. Young

26   *Exact and Approximate Values of the Distribution Functions of a Simple Fluid* by D. Henderson, S. Kim and L. Oden

32   *Modified Cell Model for Liquids: Order Defects and Intermolecular Potentials* by F. Kohler and J. Fischer

40   *Calculation of Thermodynamic Properties of Liquid Argon from Lennard-Jones Parameters by a Monte Carlo Method* by I. R. McDonald and K. Singer

50   GENERAL DISCUSSION—Dr. J. A. Barker, Dr. D. Henderson, Dr. P. Hutchinson, Prof. J. S. Rowlinson, Dr. S. Levine, Mr. A. Moreton, Prof. G. H. A. Cole, Prof. S. A. Rice, Dr. D. A. Young, Prof. J. Walkley, Dr. W. Y. Ng, Prof. U.v. Weber.

60   *Random Close-Packed Hard-Sphere Model.*
I. Effect of Introducing Holes by J. D. Bernal and S. V. King
II. Geometry of Random Packing of Hard Spheres by J. D. Bernal and J. L. Finney

70   *Hidden Variables in the Critical Region* by M. Fixman

75   GENERAL DISCUSSION—Mr. G. Mason, Mr. R. H. Beresford, Prof. J. Walkley, Dr. I. H. Hillier, Mr. R. Collins, Prof. D. H. Everett, Dr. J. Finney, Prof. C. Domb, Dr. B. L. Smith

89   *Structure of Liquids. Part 7.—Determination of Intermolecular Potential Functions and Correlation Functions in Fluid Argon by X-Ray Diffraction Techniques* by C. J. Pings

97   *X-Ray Diffraction Study of Liquid Water in the Temperature Range 4-200°C* by A. H. Narten, M. D. Danford and H. A. Levy

108   *Infra-Red Absorption of HDO in Water at High Pressures and Temperatures* by E. U. Franck and K. Roth

115   *Spectroscopic Studies Concerning the Structure and the Thermodynamic Behaviour of H_2O, CH_3OH and C_2H_5OH* by W. A. P. Luck

128   GENERAL DISCUSSION.—Dr. M. Davies, Dr. J. N. Sherwood, Dr. G. Caglioti, Dr. M. Corchia, Dr. G. Rizzi, Dr. D. I. Page, Mr. J. W. Perram, Dr. S. Levine, Dr. W. A. P. Luck, Prof. H. S. Frank, Dr. J. Padova, Prof. M. L. Josien, Prof. M. Magat, Dr. B. Eckstein, Prof. J. B. Hyne

149   *Radiation Scattering Studies of the Structure and Transport Properties of Liquids* by P. A. Egelstaff

160   *Brillouin Scattering of Neutrons from Liquids* by B. Dorner, Th. Plesser and H. Stiller

- **169** *Neutron Scattering Spectroscopy of Liquids* by B. K. Aldred, R. C. Eden and J. W. White
- **184** GENERAL DISCUSSION.—Dr. M. Davies, Prof. K.-E. Larsson, Prof. J. Stecki, Dr. A. Levi
- **192** *Nuclear Magnetic Resonance in the Study of Liquids* by J. A. Pople
- **196** *Study of Molecular Motion in Liquids by Measurement of Nuclear Relaxation* by R. A. Dwek and R. E. Richards
- **205** *Angular Correlation in Liquids* by A. D. Buckingham
- **212** *Frequency-Dependent Direct Correlation Function* by J. Stecki
- **216** *Influence of Molecular Rotation on Some Physical Properties of Liquids* by D. B. Davies and A. J. Matheson
- **223** *Viscoelastic Relaxation in Supercooled Liquids* by A. J. Barlow and J. Lamb
- **231** *Euclidean Geometry and the Flow of Generalized Liquids* by F. W. Smith
- **235** GENERAL DISCUSSION.—Dr. M. Davies, Prof. A. Bellemans, Prof. H. G. Hertz, Prof. A. D. Buckingham, Dr. G. H. Findenegg, Dr. A. J. Matheson, Dr. R. A. Dwek, Dr. I. Henderson, Dr. F. W. Smith, Dr. B. Cleaver
- **243** *Summarizing Remarks* by J. S. Rowlinson
- **248** AUTHOR INDEX

FOURTEENTH SPIERS MEMORIAL LECTURE
Structural Theories of Fluids

By G. S. Rushbrooke

Dept. of Theoretical Physics, The University, Newcastle-upon-Tyne

Received 13th April, 1967

To have the honour of giving the Spiers Memorial Lecture at this General Discussion of the Faraday Society on the Structure and Properties of Liquids is a privilege which I prize: but to respond responsibly I must keep to the one aspect of the subject with which I have some familiarity, namely, the equilibrium structural theories as they relate to monatomic fluids. In speaking on these I shall hope to give a convenient background to some of the papers with which we shall later be concerned in the earlier half of this meeting.

The last Faraday Society Discussion concerned with the structure and properties of pure liquids was that held at Edinburgh in 1936. The date coincides, rather precisely, with the start of the transition from theories of interpretation to theories of prediction as regards the structure of simple fluids. Of course, there is still, and always will be, room for theories of interpretation: it would be foolish, for example, to attempt to predict the structure of water from first principles. I am glad that later we have papers on so important a fluid. But for the really simple fluids, in particular (perhaps exclusively) for the inert gases, the last thirty years have seen increasingly successful attempts to predict scattering intensities, X-ray or neutron, directly from assumptions about the interatomic forces. And for liquid metals also, there is hope that the attempt will be profitable.

If we ignore multiple scattering, the scattering function $i(s)$ is essentially the Fourier transform of the pair correlation function $h(r)$, or $g(r)-1$, where $g(r)$ is the radial distribution function. For the customary assumption that the interatomic forces may be represented by additive pair potentials, all thermodynamic properties can be derived from this correlation function $h(r)$, if it is known over an appropriate range of density and temperature. The theory of the structure of simple liquids is thus intimately enmeshed in the theory of the equation of state and, more particularly, in the theory of phase-changes. This is very satisfactory for those theoreticians, like myself, to whom the most remarkable thing about the liquid state is that it exists.

The three theories, customarily called Born-Green, hyperchain, and Percus-Yevick, of which any discussion of the theory of fluids must take account, had very different origins: though the last two are sufficiently alike in structure to be classed together. It is the Born-Green theory which dates back to the mid-thirties, its two equations,

$$\kappa T \nabla_1 g(1,2) = -g(1,2)\nabla_1 \phi(1,2) - \rho \int g(1,2,3)\nabla_1 \phi(1,3) d3, \tag{1}$$

and

$$g(1,2,3) = g(1,2)g(2,3)g(1,3), \tag{2}$$

having been given, by Yvon [1] and Kirkwood [2] respectively, in 1935. The first, in which $g(1,2)$ and $g(1,2,3)$ denote the pair and triplet distribution functions and

$\phi(1,2)$ the interatomic potential, is an exact equation: one of a heirarchy of equations linking successive distribution functions, it is a consequence of Boltzmann's distribution law. The second is an approximation, the superposition approximation, expressing the additivity of potentials of mean force, which can be argued on physical grounds. They were brought together by Yvon [3] in 1937. Yvon also gave (1935) the pressure, or virial, equation,

$$p = \rho\kappa T - \tfrac{1}{2}\rho^2 \int r\phi'(r)g(r)\mathrm{d}^3 r, \qquad (3)$$

enabling us to pass from the distribution function $g(r)$ to the equation of state. But the time was not yet ripe for the exploitation of these equations. Some ten years later (1946) the theory was redeveloped, independently of Yvon's work, both by Bogolyubov [4] and by Born and Green.[5] Within four years (1950), Kirkwood, Maun and Alder [6] had solved the equations, and those of the very similar theory developed by Kirkwood himself, for hard spheres, on an I.B.M. computer: and with this we enter the modern era. For without machine calculations, and machine experiments, no progress in the structural theory of fluids is possible.

Although quantitatively, the Born-Green theory is very much inferior to its later rivals, perhaps no theory has yet had greater consequences. For it was the discovery by Kirkwood, Maun and Alder that the equations did not have integrable solutions for densities greater than $\rho\sigma^3 = 0.95$, where ρ is the number density and σ the sphere diameter,* which led Alder and Wainwright [7] to embark on machine calculations, by the method now known as molecular dynamics, to produce an experimental equation of state for a hard sphere fluid. The results, first published in 1957, and supported by independent Monte Carlo calculations by Wood and Jacobson,[8] gave rather clear evidence of a transition from a fluid to a solid phase at a density approximately that predicted by the Born-Green theory. The Born-Green theory gives appreciably too low a pressure, perhaps 30 % too low at the limit $\rho\sigma^3 = 0.95$; but the later theories, while they do justice to the experimental fluid isotherm, would not have predicted the fluid-solid transition.

One may legitimately question the reliability of these machine calculations, inevitably based on the dynamics of a comparatively small number of particles. But our confidence is restored by the close agreement between the fluid branch of this experimental equation of state and that calculated by the quite independent method of evaluating successive virial coefficients. It is a sobering thought that whereas Boltzmann,[9] in 1899, using some calculations of von Laar, could write

$$P + a\rho^2 = \kappa T\rho[1 + b\rho + 0.625 b^2\rho^2 + 0.2869 b^3\rho^3 + \ldots$$

(where $b = 2\pi\sigma^3/3$), and regard it as a more precise form of van der Waals's equation, even now, with the indispensable advantages of the Ursell-Mayer theory and high-speed computers, we can add only three more terms [10]

$$+ 0.1103 b^4\rho^4 + 0.0386 b^5\rho^5 + 0.0138 b^6$$

(with some uncertainty in the last digits). Nevertheless, extrapolation of the extended series by the method of Padé approximants, gives nice agreement with the fluid branch of the experimental isotherm: which thus constitutes a firm, if artificial, base line for testing theories at high temperatures. And probably few of us today would disbelieve that freezing, or melting, is essentially an excluded volume problem: as was indeed foreshadowed by the considerations of Bernal at the Edinburgh Conference in 1936, in one of the earliest papers of the predictive type.

---

* In these units, close packing corresponds to $\rho\sigma^3 = 1.414$.

But we must turn to the other theories. Perhaps their most attractive feature is that both of them incorporate the Ornstein-Zernike [11] equation

$$h(1,2) = c(1,2) + \rho \int c(1,3)h(2,3)d3, \tag{4}$$

relating the total correlation function $h(r)$, or $g(r)-1$, to the direct correlation function $c(r)$. Essentially this equation provides the definition of one function in terms of another, and nothing more. It has the consequence, of course, that the compressibility equation of Zernike and Prins (1927) [12]

$$\kappa T \partial \rho / \partial p = 1 + \rho \int h(1,2)d2 = I(0), \tag{5}$$

where $I(0)$ is the structure factor, $1+i(s)$, for limitingly small scattering angles, and which is a second route to thermodynamic behaviour, can be written in the alternative form,

$$\frac{1}{\kappa T} \frac{\partial p}{\partial \rho} = 1 - \rho \int c(1,2)d2 \tag{6}$$

This shows that for a highly compressible fluid, near its critical point, $c(r)$ is short-ranged compared with $h(r)$. But whether we have gained anything, whether $c(r)$ is a useful physical concept, can be judged only by whether $c(r)$ is more simply, or transparently, related to the interatomic potential than is $h(r)$. A definition is not a theory.

The simplest possible theory, of hyperchain or Percus-Yevick type, is to assume that $c(r)$ is simply the Mayer f-function, i.e., to write

$$c(r) = \exp[-\phi(r)/\kappa T] - 1. \tag{7}$$

This gives the direct correlation function the range of the interatomic potential, and incorporates a temperature dependence of the correct Boltzmann form. The assumption is intuitively appealing: and both Ornstein and Debye, in their work on critical opalescence, argue very much along these lines. In the theory of liquids, however, it is not good enough. It leads,[13] essentially, to the crudest form of the linearized Born-Green equations. Nevertheless, it corresponds precisely to what Montroll and Mayer [14] did in the theory of ionic solutions, when they derived the Debye-Hückel theory by summing over a certain class of interaction-graphs (in the Ursell-Mayer formalism): namely the chain, or ring, diagrams. And it was the achievement of Montroll and Mayer in showing that physically interesting theories could result from summing over subsets of interaction-graphs in a low density expansion which ultimately led to the hyperchain equation: though we must not lay the defects of this theory at their door.

The set of graphs over which we sum to obtain the hyperchain equation is dictated *faute de mieux*, rather than on physical grounds. It is just the largest subset, complete within its topological class, which we can handle conveniently. But the result, obtained independently by many people some eight years ago,[15] is a theory which retains the Ornstein-Zernike equation together with a second equation for $c(r)$, namely,

$$c(r) = h(r) - \ln[1 + h(r)] - \phi(r)/\kappa T. \tag{8}$$

The Percus-Yevick theory,[16] although of the same structure, had an entirely different origin. It could have arisen, as Stell later showed, out of the graphical analysis that led to the hyperchain theory: retaining a different, but equally plausible, set of interaction graphs. In fact, it arose out of an attempt to define collective coordinates for a fluid, in a paper (1959) which I am probably not alone in finding obscure. Its best derivation is undoubtedly that which Percus later gave (1962) using the mathematical technique of functional differentiation recently introduced, in the theory of liquids, by Yvon.[17] This, which examines the change in density at one point produced by a change in force field at another, brings us closest to thinking physically, and furthest both from the dilute gas and from arbitrary assumptions of mathematical convenience. Fortunately, as Percus showed, all our theories can in fact be derived this way: though the Born-Green theory then appears as something of a *tour de force*. But however it is derived, the Percus-Yevick theory joins to the Ornstein-Zernike equation the second prescription for $c(r)$,

$$c(r) = [1 - \exp\{\phi(r)/\kappa T\}][1 + h(r)]. \tag{9}$$

We must now turn to the testing of these theories. They can be used in three rather different ways. Assuming a knowledge of $\phi(r)$, we can calculate the thermodynamic properties: or we can calculate the correlation functions and structure factors. Alternatively, we can use the theories to determine $\phi(r)$ from scattering experiments.

Not unnaturally, the earliest calculations, with any theory, are the simplest: in this case calculating the predicted values of successive virial coefficients for hard spheres. These are not exact theories, nor are they entirely internally consistent. Different routes to any thermodynamic property will lead to different answers. The two routes most commonly used are based, respectively, on the virial equation and the compressibility equation. Ultimately we may have to be content with the most satisfactory prescription (preferably understanding why it succeeds); but a serious lack of internal consistency is certainly a defect in any theory.

At first, for hard spheres, the test was mainly one of internal consistency, since the true virial coefficients were not known beyond the fourth. But now that we know the rigid sphere isotherm with some confidence, it is more satisfactory to compare the theories directly with it rather than with low density expansions.[18] Judged in this way, the Percus-Yevick theory is incomparably the best: in respect of both internal consistency and agreement with the true isotherm. There is the added advantage, as Thiele [19] and Wertheim [20] have shown, that, for hard spheres, the Percus-Yevick equations can be solved exactly, in closed form. The compressibility prescription accords with the known isotherm to within perhaps 2 % over the whole fluid range. But the thermodynamic properties show no evidence of a phase transition: indeed the Thiele-Wertheim solutions show no singularity until we reach the quite unphysical density $\rho\sigma^3 = 1.9$, far greater than that of close packing ($\rho\sigma^3 = 1.4$). The Thiele-Wertheim solution, however, enables us also to find the correlation functions; and we now know [21] that for $\rho\sigma^3 \geqslant 1.18$, $g(r)$ takes on negative values. Since this is physically impossible, it gives us an excuse for disregarding the more implausible predictions of the Percus-Yevick theory.

A hard sphere gas, however, though it provides a useful high-temperature base line, is far removed from a real liquid. To separate the fluid phase, at low enough temperatures, into gas and liquid regions, we must add an attractive potential: and we should soften the repulsive core. Quite appropriately, most further work has been based on the Lennard-Jones potential

$$\phi(r) = 4\varepsilon[(\sigma/r)^{12} - (\sigma/r)^6].$$

For this potential, all three theories have been compared with a high-temperature Monte Carlo isotherm, for $T^*(= \kappa T/\varepsilon) = 2.74$, obtained ten years ago by Wood and Parker [22]: there is quantitative agreement, or disagreement, of the same order as in the hard sphere case. But this is still at twice the critical temperature; and we must next turn to the critical constants themselves.

These critical constants have now been found for all three theories, notably by Levesque,[23] whose recent paper is the source of the numbers I shall quote. For the hyperchain theory, hitherto the most studied, Levesque's estimates agree, within their limits of error, with those of Klein and Green,[24] and de Boer et al.[25] Table 1 shows T_c^*, $\rho_c\sigma^3$, and the ratio $(p/\rho\kappa T)_c$, for the Lennard-Jones potential,

TABLE 1

	T_c^*	$\rho_c\sigma^3$	$(p/\rho\kappa T)_c$
B.G.	1·45	0·40	0·44
h.c.	1·25	0·26	0·35
P.Y.	1·25	0·29	0·30
"argon"	1·26	0·32	0·30

together with values customarily quoted for argon, assuming the Lennard-Jones parameters $\varepsilon/k = 120°$, $\sigma = 3\cdot 4$ Å. Bearing in mind that T_c^*, for the theoretical predictions, is uncertain to perhaps 2 %, and that the uncertainty in ρ_c is greater, we might well conclude that the modern theories were by no means inadequate. But this is not the whole story: first, because I have deliberately chosen the values obtained from the virial equation, and not from the compressibility equation; secondly, because we do not really know what the true experimental values are for a Lennard-Jones gas.

To take the second point first, Levesque has also determined the critical constants predicted by the hyperchain and Percus-Yevick theories for the hard core with square well potential, $\phi(r) = -\varepsilon$, $\sigma \leqslant r \leqslant 1\cdot 5\sigma$, and the corresponding results are shown in table 2. This table shows also the predictions of Verlet's P.Y.II equation [26] (a

TABLE 2

	T_c^*	$\rho_c\sigma^3$	$(p/\rho\kappa T)_c$
h.c.	1·16	0·25	0·32
P.Y.	1·16	0·21	0·30
P.Y. II	1·28	0·32	0·32
M.D.	1·28	0·33	0·31

natural extension of the Percus-Yevick theory, when approached through functional differentiation), together with recent "experimental" results, for this potential, found by Alder from molecular dynamic studies (and quoted by Levesque). It now looks as if both hyperchain and Percus-Yevick theories do only scant justice to the critical region, yielding T_c^* to within perhaps 10 %. The P.Y.II equation, however, seems to be appreciably more accurate.

I shall not discuss the corresponding figures obtained by use of the compressibility equation, save to say that the internal inconsistency in the theories is of the same order as their inaccuracy. It is already clear both that first-order theories give only a moderately satisfactory account of thermodynamic properties in the critical region, and that there is need for caution before drawing conclusions for real fluids.

At greater densities and, more particularly, at lower temperatures, in the true liquid region not far from the triple point, the thermodynamic situation is much worse: certainly if the virial equation is used to find the pressure. To take an extreme example, Gaskell [27] has shown that were we to use the hyperchain equations to infer the pressure from accurate scattering experiments on liquid argon, essentially by solving (8) for $\phi(r)$ and substituting in (3), we should overestimate the pressure at the triple point by a factor of about 10^3. But it does not follow from this that the theories are useless. We are far from being able to calculate a vapour pressure curve from first principles: but we may yet have a good theory of liquid structure. The virial equation is exceptionally sensitive to the precise form of $g(r)$ in the liquid region. If we look at the internal energy the results are much more encouraging; indeed, as Levesque shows, hyperchain and Percus-Yevick predictions are in very close agreement with Monte-Carlo results for the Lennard-Jones potential. And there is the observation by Ashcroft and Lekner,[28] that if the neutron diffraction data on alkali metals are fitted, as regards the first peak, by the first peak of the Percus-Yevick hard sphere theory, which for Na at 100°C means choosing the density value $\rho\sigma^3 = 0.85$, then the compressibility from zero-angle scattering on Percus-Yevick theory is extraordinarily close to the experimental, thermodynamic, value (within 5 %). While this may tell us more about metals than about our theories, it at least suggests that the Percus-Yevick theory does good justice to the excluded volume problem in the liquid state, even at effectively high densities.

Perhaps our greatest present need is to be able to answer for the structural properties the questions we have already largely answered for the thermodynamic ones, namely, over what regions of the fluid phase, gas, liquid, or supercritical, equations such as (8) and (9) adequately interrelate the structural properties, $h(r)$ and $c(r)$, or their Fourier transforms, and the interatomic potential, $\phi(r)$. We may ask, of course, adequately for what? Here, surely, the most physically important question is whether current theories enable us to infer properties of the potential $\phi(r)$ from the best experimental measurements of the structure factors of real fluids. I am not thinking of the oscillatory potentials found by Johnson, Hutchinson and March[29] in this way from the structure factors of liquid metals, oscillations which have been only partially confirmed by the later work of Ascarelli[30]: though it is to the credit of the theories if they can point to significant differences between metals and inert gases. The issue, rather, is whether we can attach quantitative significance to such predictions of $\phi(r)$ for the inert gases themselves.

This question can be answered only by computer studies of the kind on which Verlet[31] has recently embarked. For a chosen $\phi(r)$, $h(r)$ and $c(r)$ must be determined by machine experiments over a wide range of ρ and T: then equations such as (8) and (9) can be tested by seeing to what extent, and over what range of ρ and T, they successfully reproduce $\phi(r)$. A preliminary report from Verlet is encouraging, for although at large densities or low temperatures the shape of $\phi(r)$ is not well reproduced, nevertheless for temperatures of the order of T_c, and for a range of density extending well beyond ρ_c, the depth of the potential minimum in $\phi(r)$ is reproduced by (9) to within 2 %. The analysis, by Mikolaj and Pings,[32] of their experimental measurements on argon, suggests that the hyperchain equation, (8), may have an approximately equal validity in this region. More importantly, if these results can be trusted, the finding by Mikolaj and Pings that the depth of the potential minimum so deduced for argon varies linearly with ρ must afford evidence of the inadequacy of the assumption of additive pair potentials, and demonstrate that for real liquids we are concerned also with multibody forces. If, and when, our theories of dense fluids enable us to say this with complete confidence, and with some quantitative precision, they will have been justified.

Attempts to improve on the present theories usually bring us back to the problem of the triplet distribution function, $g(1,2,3)$. This is inevitably true of the Born-Green theory, where it must be the superposition approximation that is inadequate since the other, Yvon, equation is exact: and it is the very essence of Born-Green theory to use this exact equation. Prof. Rice will later be telling of his work with Lekner to replace eqn. (2) by a more adequate approximation. But it is true also of the hyperchain and Percus-Yevick theories, which successfully by-pass the triplet distribution problem in their original forms. If we proceed systematically along the path indicated by the functional differentiation approach of Yvon, Percus and Verlet, the Ornstein-Zernike equation is retained, but the correction to the second expression for $c(r)$ involves $g(1,2,3)$: and the theory is not self-contained without an additional assumption. Though a crude approximation may suffice for calculating a small correction, and good though Verlet's P.Y.II theory appears to be, we do not know how sensitive the predictions are to the element of arbitrariness here, and may doubt if these second-order theories are yet in their final form.

We are also faced with the triplet distribution function if we attempt to bring three-body forces, or triplet potentials, into the theory of fluids. For although the compressibility equation (5) or (6), is unmodified, the pressure equation (3), must now include the virial of the three-body forces: which implies a term involving $g(1,2,3)$. Nevertheless, if we are content with predicting the scattering functions, triplet potentials can be introduced at the level of the hyperchain and Percus-Yevick theories: though it is less certain that the theories are quite strong enough to stand the strain.

On the hyperchain theory, the inclusion of triplet potentials is particularly simple.[33] For eqn. (8) is just a truncated form of the exact equation

$$h(1,2) - c(1,2) = \ln[1 + h(1,2)] + \phi(1,2)/\kappa T - x(1,2) \qquad (10)$$

where, in the graphical analysis, $x(1,2)$ corresponds to the so-called "elementary" graphs: which are neglected in the hyperchain theory. With only two-body forces, the first elementary graph has two field-points, and is proportional to a term in ρ^2. With triplet potentials, however, there is a new class of elementary graph having only one field-point, and summing to give

$$x_1(1,2) = \rho \int f(1,2,3) e(1,3) e(2,3) d3$$

where $e(i,j)$ is the Boltzmann factor for the pair potential, $\exp[-\phi(i,j)/\kappa T]$ and $f(i,j,k)$ is the Mayer function for the triplet potential, $\exp[-\phi(i,j,k)/\kappa T] - 1$. Thus, at the level of hyperchain theory, the use of (8) to infer $\phi(r)$ from $h(r)$ and $c(r)$ will lead not to the true pair potential $\phi(1,2)$ but to an effective pair potential

$$\phi^*(1,2) = \phi(1,2) - \kappa T x_1(1,2),$$

I would expect this result to have the same range of validity as the hyperchain theory: but shall not pursue the matter further since Prof. Pings will be describing an alternative, and possibly sounder, approach to what I think are essentially the same conclusions.

But even if we refine our theories, by going to a higher order of approximation or including triplet potentials, there remain two outstanding problems: the problem of asymptotic behaviour and the problem of freezing. It is ironic that whereas Ornstein and Zernike introduced the direct correlation function $c(r)$ to argue intuitively that this is short-ranged compared with $h(r)$, and consequently that for large r

$$h(r) \sim \exp(-\alpha r)/r,$$

where $\alpha \to 0$ at the critical point (or wherever the compressibility becomes infinite) it is just this classic conclusion that is today most open to attack.[34] All our approximate theories suggest that $c(r)$ decays like $\phi(r)$, (more accurately, $-\phi(r)/\kappa T$), which for real fluids, in the absence of triplet potentials, means like $1/r^6$: i.e., more slowly than does $h(r)$ on the Ornstein-Zernike theory. Even if we try to salvage, and refine, the Ornstein-Zernike result by supposing that perhaps

$$h(r) \sim A\phi(r) + B \exp(-\alpha r) \cos(\beta r + \gamma)/r,$$

(where the coefficients are functions of ρ and T, and α and β vanish at the critical point), we know that the two-dimensional analogue of this is disproved by the work of Onsager and Kaufman on the Ising problem.[35] One technical comment may be permitted. Since

$$I(s) = 1 + i(s) = 1 + \rho\tilde{h}(s) = 1/[1 - \rho\tilde{c}(s)] \qquad (11)$$

[where $\tilde{h}(s)$ is the Fourier transform of $h(r)$, and in scattering experiments $s = (4\pi/\lambda) \sin(\theta/2)$] it is clear that $1 - \rho\tilde{c}(s)$ cannot become negative for real s: we cannot have a negative intensity of scattered radiation. On the Ornstein-Zernike theory, for $\rho = \rho_c$ and $T = T_c$ the equation, $1 - \rho\tilde{c}(s) = 0$, has a double root at the origin. It would seem that any heuristic theory must consider the roots of $1 - \rho\tilde{c}(s) = 0$ in the complex plane, without assuming that $\tilde{c}(s)$ is an analytic function of s^2 near the origin: since this last assumption leads to the Ornstein-Zernike result. Fisher's hypothesis, that (in three dimensions)

$$h(r) \sim \exp(-\alpha r)/r^{1+\eta}, \quad \text{where} \quad 0 < \eta < 1$$

avoids this assumption: and its two-dimensional analogue can be made to cover the known behaviour of the Ising model. Nevertheless, for van der Waals forces, it does not avoid the conceptual difficulty of a correlation function which decays more rapidly than do the interatomic forces which produce it.[36] While this may not be inherently impossible, certainly the theory is not yet so firmly rooted as to force us to so surprising a conclusion.

Writing eqn. (5) and (6) as

$$\kappa T \frac{\partial \rho}{\partial p} = 1 + \rho\tilde{h}(0) = \frac{1}{1 - \rho\tilde{c}(0)}, \qquad (12)$$

we see that near freezing, indeed anywhere in the true liquid region, when the fluid is comparatively incompressible, $1 - \rho\tilde{c}(0)$ is large (though we are not now concerned with infinities) and it is $1 + \rho\tilde{h}(0)$ which is small. The question whether our theories of liquids give us any real indication of the onset of freezing, or are capable in principle of so doing, is, I think, the most important with which we are at present faced. Is it accidental, or significant, that the Born-Green theory suggested a phase-change for a hard-sphere gas? It was, of course, $\tilde{h}(0)$ which ceased to exist: though without the divergence which would indicate infinite compressibility. If freezing is essentially an excluded volume problem, can we approach a theory of freezing against a continuum background, or must we discuss the excluded volume problem against the background of a lattice-gas? Are there other, physically acceptable, solutions of the Percus-Yevick equations for hard spheres,[37] besides that found by Wertheim and Thiele? I think we do not know the answers to these questions: and although the non-equilibrium, or dynamic properties of fluids offer a richer experimental field, there is certainly still work to be done in the development of a satisfactory equilibrium theory.

[1] J. Yvon, *Actualites Sci. Ind.*, (Hermann et Cie, Paris, 1935), p. 203.
[2] J. G. Kirkwood, *J. Chem. Physics*, 1935, **3**, 300.
[3] J. Yvon, *Actualites Sci. Ind.* (Hermann et Cie, Paris, 1937), 542, 543.
[4] N. N. Bogolyubov, *J. Phys. U.R.S.S.*, 1946, **10**, 257, 265.
[5] M. Born and M. S. Green, *A General Kinetic Theory of Liquids* (Cambridge University Press, 1949).
[6] J. G. Kirkwood, E. K. Maun and B. J. Alder, *J. Chem. Physics*, 1950, **18**, 1040.
[7] T. Wainwright and B. J. Alder, *Suppl. Nuovo Cimento*, 1958, **9**, 116.
B. J. Alder and T. Wainwright, *J. Chem. Physics*, 1957, **27**, 1209; 1959, **31**, 459.
[8] W. W. Wood and J. D. Jacobson, *J. Chem. Physics*, 1957, **27**, 1207.
W. W. Wood, F. R. Parker and J. D. Jacobson, *Suppl. Nuovo Cimento*, 1958, **9**, 133.
[9] L. Boltzmann, *Proc. Roy. Acad. Sci. Amst.*, 1899, **1**, 398.
[10] F. N. Ree and W. G. Hoover, *J. Chem. Physics*, 1964, **40**, 939 and private communication.
[11] L. S. Ornstein and F. Zernike, *Proc. Acad. Sci. Amst.*, 1914, **17**, 793.
F. Zernike, *Proc. Acad. Sci. Amst.*, 1916, **19**, 1520.
[12] F. Zernike and J. A. Prins, *Z. Physik*, 1927, **41**, 184.
[13] G. S. Rushbrooke and H. I. Scoins, *Proc. Roy. Soc. A*, 1953, **216**, 203.
[14] E. W. Montroll and J. E. Mayer, *J. Chem. Physics*, 1941, **9**, 626.
[15] M. S. Green, *J. Chem. Physics*, 1960, **33**, 1403.
J. M. J. van Leeuwen, J. Groeneveld and J. de Boer, *Physica*, 1959, **25**, 792.
E. Meeron, *J. Math. Physics*, 1960, **1**, 192.
T. Morita and K. Hiroike, *Progr. Theor. Physics*, 1960, **23**, 1003.
G. S. Rushbrooke, *Physica*, 1960, **26**, 259.
L. Verlet, *Nuovo Cimento*, 1960, **18**, 77.
[16] J. K. Percus and G. J. Yevick, *Physic. Rev.*, 1958, **110**, 1.
G. Stell, *Physica*, 1963, **29**, 517.
J. K. Percus, *Physic. Rev. Letters*, 1962, **8**, 462.
[17] J. Yvon, *Suppl. Nuovo Cimento*, 1958, **9**, 144.
[18] J. S. Rowlinson, *Report Prog. Physics*, 1965, **28**, 169.
[19] E. Thiele, *J. Chem. Physics*, 1963, **39**, 474.
[20] M. S. Wertheim, *J. Math. Physics*, 1964, **5**, 643.
[21] G. Throop and R. J. Bearman, *J. Chem. Physics*, 1965, **42**, 2408.
[22] W. W. Wood and F. R. Parker, *J. Chem. Physics*, 1957, **27**, 720.
[23] D. Levesque, *Physica*, 1966, **32**, 1985.
[24] M. Klein and M. S. Green, *J. Chem. Physics*, 1963, **39**, 1367.
[25] J. de Boer, J. M. J. van Leeuwen and J. Groeneveld, *Physica*, 1964, **30**, 2265.
[26] L. Verlet, *Physica*, 1965, **31**, 959.
[27] T. Gaskell, *Proc. Physic. Soc.*, 1966, **89**, 231.
[28] N. W. Ashcroft and J. Lekner, *Physic. Rev.*, 1966, **175**, 83.
[29] M. D. Johnson, P. Hutchinson and N. H. March, *Proc. Roy. Soc. A*, 1964, **282**, 283.
[30] P. Ascarelli, *Physic. Rev.*, 1966, **143**, 36.
[31] L. Verlet, Preprint, 1966.
[32] P. G. Mikolaj and C. J. Pings, *Physic. Rev. Letters*, 1965, **15**, 849.
[33] G. S. Rushbrooke and M. Silbert, *Mol. Physics*, 1967, in press.
[34] M. E. Fisher, *J. Math. Physics*, 1964, **5**, 944.
[35] B. Kaufman and L. Onsager, *Physic. Rev.*, 1949, **76**, 1244.
[36] B. Widom, *J. Chem. Physics*, 1964, **41**, 74.
[37] H. N. V. Temperley, *Proc. Physic. Soc.*, 1964, **84**, 339.
R. J. Baxter, *Physic. Rev.*, 1967, **154**, 170.

Equation of State of a Monatomic Fluid with 6-12 Potential

By Stuart A. Rice and David A. Young*

Institute for the Study of Metals and Dept. of Chemistry,
The University of Chicago, Chicago, Illinois 60637

Received 24th October, 1967

The modified Yvon-Born-Green equation of Rice and Lekner is solved for a monatomic fluid with 6-12 potential at $kT/\varepsilon = 2\cdot 74$. The equation of state and excess internal energy are calculated and compared with Monte Carlo calculations; the agreement is good. Calculations with hard-sphere modifications and with the Kihara potential are also discussed. The Kirkwood limit of stability for the fluid phase is calculated.

A study,[1] by Rice and Lekner, of the equation of state of a rigid-sphere fluid, has shown that the Yvon-Born-Green equation may be so improved as to yield an equation of state in close agreement with the molecular dynamics data of Alder and Wainwright.[2] In this paper we present an analogous study of a fluid with molecules which interact through a 6-12 Lennard-Jones potential. Monte Carlo calculations [3] of the equation of state corresponding to this potential have been reported for a supercritical isotherm at $kT/\varepsilon = 2\cdot 74$, where ε is the depth of the potential well. Our calculations, based on the improved YBG equation, will be at this temperature so as to permit comparison of theory and "experiment".

Recent work [4] has provided the solutions of the Yvon-Born-Green (YBG), Percus-Yevick (PY), and the Convolution Hypernetted Chain (CHNC) equations for the 6-12 potential at $kT/\varepsilon = 2\cdot 74$. As for the hard sphere potential, the PY theory yields the best agreement with experiment over a wide density range, but gives no explicit evidence for a liquid-solid phase transition. Our motive for choosing to extend the YBG theory is that it predicts a transition to occur at high density, while the PY and CHNC theories do not.† Hence we regard the YBG equation to contain the qualitative features necessary to describe the limits of stability of the fluid phase.

TRIPLET DISTRIBUTION FUNCTION

The exact, formal, expression for the triplet distribution function of a fluid is

$$g^{(3)}(\mathbf{123}) = g^{(2)}(\mathbf{12})g^{(2)}(\mathbf{13})g^{(2)}(\mathbf{23}) \exp \tau(\mathbf{123}, \rho), \tag{1}$$

where

$$\tau(\mathbf{123}, \rho) = \sum_{n=1}^{\infty} \rho^n \delta_{n+3}(\mathbf{123}). \tag{2}$$

Here ρ is the fluid number density. The δ_m are expansion terms developed and discussed by Meeron [5] and Salpeter.[6] The superposition approximation may be obtained by placing $\tau = 0$. This approximation yields the correct third virial coefficient for a fluid, but incorrect higher virial coefficients. Inclusion of terms up to δ_m yields correct virial coefficients up to B_m.

*Fannie and John Hertz Fellow.
†*Note added in proof*: The PY equation admits solid-like solutions above a critical density but does not prohibit simultaneous fluid-like solutions.

For the hard sphere potential, Rice and Lekner (referred to as RL henceforth) found that δ_4 and δ_5 could be calculated with a reasonably small amount of computer time, but that δ_6 could not. For the 6-12 potential we find that δ_4 can be calculated accurately, that δ_5 can be estimated fairly well, and that δ_6 cannot be calculated at all, again owing to the computer time involved. Starting with δ_4 and δ_5, we shall use the technique of the Padé approximant to achieve an estimate of the entire δ_m series. The derivation of the diagrams corresponding to the δ is fully explained in RL and here we only point out those aspects of the calculation which are special to the 6-12 potential.

The calculation of $\delta_4(\mathbf{123})$ was carried out numerically by means of Gaussian quadrature. Now

$$\delta_4(\mathbf{123}) = \quad\quad = \int d\mathbf{4}\, f_{14} f_{24} f_{34}, \tag{3}$$

where $f_{ij} = \exp(-u(\mathbf{ij})/kT) - 1$ and $d\mathbf{4}$ is the element of volume swept out by particle number 4. There are no boundary problems such as arise in the hard sphere case because the 6-12 potential is continuous. Since for moderately large distances r, $f_{ij}(r)$ is small, the integration in (3) may be carried out over a small region. Taking advantage of the symmetry of the plane of the triplet (**123**) with respect to the perpendicular z axis, we find that a hemisphere of radius 3·0 molecular diameters serves the purpose adequately. All distances will be given in units of the molecular diameter, the diameter being defined as the distance σ for which the potential $u(\sigma) = 0$.

The integration (3) was divided into three parts. In the interior region $(0\cdot0 \leqslant r \leqslant 1\cdot0)$, where the integrand is large, the integral was evaluated by using Cartesian coordinates and 16 point Gaussian quadrature. Then the contributions from the two spherical shells $(1\cdot0 \leqslant r \leqslant 1\cdot5)$ and $(1\cdot5 \leqslant r \leqslant 3\cdot0)$ were evaluated in spherical polar coordinates using 12 point Gaussian quadrature. The results compare favourably with those obtained by using larger numbers of Gaussian points, viz., 20, 16, and 16. The average error is about 1 %. The integrations required in (3) were carried out for all triplet configurations (R,S,T) such that $0\cdot0 \leqslant R,S,T \leqslant 2\cdot6$ and $\Delta R = \Delta S = \Delta T = 0\cdot20$. $R = 2\cdot6$ was found to be satisfactory cutoff since $\delta_4(2\cdot6, 2\cdot6, 2\cdot6) = 0\cdot0015$, which is close enough to zero to be negligible.

The $\delta_5(\mathbf{123})$ diagrams were grouped and evaluated using the same techniques as in RL. There are 13 diagrams to evaluate. By using the functions

$$p_{ij} = \int d\mathbf{5}\, f_{i5} f_{j5}; \quad t_{ijk} = \delta_4(\mathbf{ijk}); \quad e_{ij} = f_{ij} + 1 = \exp[-u(\mathbf{ij})/kT],$$

the calculation may be reduced to three 3-fold integrations and one 6-fold integration;

$$\delta_5(\mathbf{123}) = \int d\mathbf{4}\{f_{14}f_{24}e_{34}(p_{34}+t_{134}) + f_{14}f_{34}e_{24}(p_{24}+t_{234}) + f_{24}f_{34}e_{14}(p_{14}+t_{124})\} +$$
$$\tfrac{1}{2}\int d\mathbf{4}\, f_{14}f_{24}f_{34} \int d\mathbf{5}\, f_{15}f_{25}f_{35}f_{45}. \tag{4}$$

The first three integrals may be evaluated by using values of δ_4 tabulated with an interval of 0·1. Since the storage of δ_4 in this state in the computer required approximately 19,700 locations, it was not feasible to increase the state of subdivision of δ_4. Hence the t_{ijk} required in the integrand had to be truncated to the nearest tabulated value, at the expense of accuracy.

This difficulty was avoided in the work with hard spheres because δ_4 is known in terms of elementary functions and can be rapidly computed for any desired triplet configuration. Exactly how much accuracy is lost by the truncation is not known.

However, very accurate values of p_{ij} were calculated and these were often much larger than the t_{ijk} which appeared with them in the integrands. Hence the inaccuracies in t_{ijk} are masked to some extent by this discrepancy in size.

Again the individual integrals were divided into three parts, this time using 12, 12, and 8-point Gaussian quadrature in a sphere of radius 3·0. Comparison with more accurate calculations shows an average error of 5 % due to imprecise integration. The total error is not known because of the truncation of the t_{ijk} terms. Once again $\delta_5(R,S,T)$ was obtained for all configurations up to $R = S = T = 2·6$ and $\Delta R = \Delta S = \Delta T = 0·2$.

δ_4 and δ_5 are thus obtained as three-dimensional arrays with a spacing of 0·2 diam. units. These values were interpolated by using a linear Taylor expansion. In the examples below, R, S, and T are the tabulated triplet lengths (multiples of 0·2) and x, y,

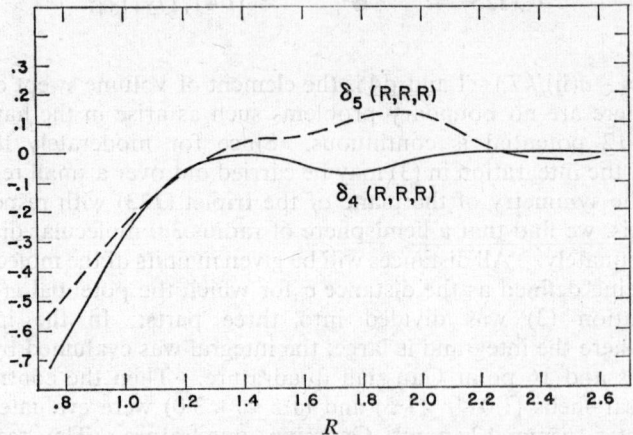

Fig. 1.—δ_4 and δ_5 for the 6-12 potential at $kT/\varepsilon = 2·74$ in the equilateral configuration (R,R,R).

and z are the interpolated lengths (odd multiples of 0·1). Both δ_4 and δ_5 are tabulated in this way. There are three cases to be considered :

I. $\quad \delta(R,S,z) = ·5\{\delta[R, S, (z+·1)] + \delta[R, S, (z-·1)]\}$, $\hfill (5a)$

II. $\quad \delta(R,y,z) = ·5\{\delta[R, (y+·1), (z-·1)] + \delta[R, (y-·1), (z+·1)]\}$, $\hfill (5b)$

III. $\quad \delta(x,y,z) = ·5\{\delta[(x+·1), (y-·1), (z-·1)] + \delta[(x-·1), (y+·1), (z-·1)] +$

$\delta[(x-·1), (y-·1), (z+·1)] - \delta[(x-·1), (y-·1), (z-·1)]\}$. $\hfill (5c)$

In each case the δ in the parentheses on the right side are tabulated values, or they are nonexistent owing to the violation of the restriction that R, S, and T must be the sides of a triangle. In the event that one of the δ necessary for the interpolation does not exist, a simpler approximation is used. The result is some 2700 pieces of data for each of δ_4 and δ_5.

Several special values of δ_4 were calculated and checked against interpolated results in order to test the interpolation scheme. The error ranged from 3 to 20 % (for case III), with an overall average error of 5 %. Hence the overall picture of the tabulated δ_4 and δ_5 values is one of fair but not high accuracy.

Both δ_4 and δ_5 take on positive and negative values, and both are large and negative near (0,0,0). In this sense they differ strongly from the hard sphere terms in which $\delta_4 \leqslant 0$ and $\delta_5 \geqslant 0$ over their respective ranges. δ_4 and δ_5 for the equilateral triplet configuration are shown in fig. 1.

YVON-BORN-GREEN-EQUATION

The YBG equation has been reduced to a form which can be used for numerical computation. Details of the reduction are described by Hill.[7] We write, following the same arguments,

$$kT \ln g(R) = -u(R) + \pi\rho \int_0^\infty u'(y)g(y)\mathrm{d}y \int_{R-y}^{R+y} \frac{y^2 - (R-X)^2}{R}[g(x)-1]x\mathrm{d}x +$$

$$\pi\rho \int_0^\infty u'(z)g(z)\mathrm{d}z \int_R^\infty \frac{\mathrm{d}y}{y^2} \int_{y-z}^{y+z} (z^2 + y^2 - x^2)g(x)x[\exp \tau(x,y,z) - 1]\mathrm{d}x, \quad (6)$$

$$u(R) = 4\varepsilon\left(\frac{1}{R^{12}} - \frac{1}{R^6}\right).$$

Here R, x, y and z are reduced distances with units of molecular diameters. Eqn. (6) is exact, but since only the first two terms of $\tau(x,y,z)$ are known, we must resort to approximation if a solution is to be found. A good approximation to the entire series is the Padé approximant

$$\tau(\mathbf{123}) \cong \frac{\rho\delta_4}{1 - \rho\delta_5/\delta_4}, \quad (7)$$

which we henceforth adopt.

NUMERICAL INTEGRATION OF THE MODIFIED YBG EQUATION

We have obtained numerical solutions over a range of densities for

(i) $\tau = 0$ (superposition); (ii) $\tau = \rho\delta_4$;

(iii) $\tau = \rho\delta_4 + \rho^2\delta_5$; (iv) $\tau = \rho\delta_4/(1-\rho\delta_5/\delta_4) = \tau(\text{Padé})$.

Also we have tried mixing terms for hard spheres and the 6-12 potential:

(v) $\tau = \rho\delta_4(\text{HS})$; (vi) $\tau = \rho\delta_4(\text{HS}) + \rho^2\delta_5(\text{HS})$;

(vii) $\tau = \text{Padé (HS)}$; (viii) $\tau = \rho\delta_4(6\text{-}12) + \rho^2\delta_5(\text{HS})$.

Of the terms (v)-(viii) only (v) turns out to be of real interest.

In each of the above calculations the parameter ρ was selected in the range $0.1 \leqslant \rho \leqslant 1.2$, and kT/ε was fixed at 2.74. Solutions of the YBG equation were obtained by the iteration procedure commonly used in solving nonlinear integral equations. This is discussed in RL. The input for the $(k+1)$th iteration is taken to be

$$g_{\text{in}}^{k+1}(r) = g_{\text{in}}^k(r) + \alpha[g_{\text{out}}^k(r) - g_{\text{in}}^k(r)]. \quad (8)$$

For low densities, we found that the optimum α can be as high as 0.75, and that for high densities α must be reduced to 0.2, where convergence is correspondingly slower. If α is too large for a given value of ρ the iterative solution undergoes a divergent oscillation. For a given τ and ρ the first input used was the convergent solution of the previously chosen density in the series of calculations.

Convergence was observed by calculating the reduced pressure for each iteration:

$$\frac{p}{\rho kT} = 1 - \frac{\rho}{6kT} \int_0^\infty u'(r)g(r)r 4\pi r^2 \mathrm{d}r. \quad (9)$$

The approach to a stable solution could be either monotonic or oscillatory. The larger the value of α the greater the tendency for oscillatory behaviour. Convergence was usually taken to mean that the input and output $g(r)$ differed by not more than 0·5 % at the highest density. The accuracy of the solutions depends on : (i) the interval Δr used in the numerical integration; (ii) the maximum value of R to which the integration is carried; (iii) the number of iterations performed; (iv) the accuracy of $\tau(x,y,z)$.

For the superposition approximation, some solutions were obtained for $\Delta r = 0·05$. The pressures calculated from these results differed from results interpolated from $\Delta r = 0·1$ by about 3 % for $\rho = 0·8$. The superposition pressures at high density coincide with those of Broyles [4] to within 2-3 %. Hence it may be assumed that the results obtained for $\Delta r = 0·1$ are reasonably accurate.

Interpolations of $g(r)$ were quadratic (i.e. second order in the Taylor expansion) and the pressures obtained from interpolation ($\Delta r = 0·05$) differ from those of the original results ($\Delta r = 0·1$) by about $+5$ %. Most of the contribution to the pressure occurs near $r = 1·0$ where the function $g(r)$ is steep. A special interpolation technique was used to achieve an increment of 0·05 in the integration of the triple integral in eqn. (6). For $\tau = \rho\delta_4 + \rho^2\delta_5$, for densities above $\rho = 0·6$, divergent results were obtained with the increment 0·1. These divergences disappeared when the smaller increment was used, showing that they were numerical in origin. Comparison of the pressures obtained for the two increments showed that at $\rho = 0·6$ the accuracy obtained is approximately 1 %.

Condition (ii) was significant only for the high density solutions in the superposition approximation. All solutions were obtained with $R(\max) = 4·0$, and in addition $R(\max)$ for $\rho = 1·1$ and 1·2 was extended to 5·0. The discrepancy in pressures between the two limits in the latter cases are 5 % for $\rho = 1·2$ and 2 % for $\rho = 1·1$. Condition (iii) was met by iterating until the desired convergence was obtained, viz., a self-consistency of better than 0·5 % in the reduced pressure.

TABLE 1.—YBG REDUCED PRESSURES $p/\rho kT$ FOR A SERIES OF τ FUNCTIONS. VALUES IN PARENTHESES ARE NOT EXACT OWING TO SLOW CONVERGENCE. THE SUPERPOSITION PRESSURE AT $\rho = 1·2$ IS PROBABLY DIVERGENT.

	superposition	$\delta\delta_4$	$\rho\delta_4 + \rho^2\delta_5$	Padé	$\rho\delta_4$(HS)	Kihara	obs. (Levelt)
·1	·975	·979	·979	·979	·979	—	·976
·4	1·154	1·215	1·212	1·206	1·226	1·30	1·21
·6	1·537	2·013	1·973	2·079	1·912	2·03	1·89
·7	—	2·946	2·803				2·55
·8	2·259	(5·06)	(4·44)		3·360		
·9	2·724				4·372		
1·0	3·229				5·626		
1·1	3·683						
1·2	4·074						

The accuracy of the τ functions may be checked by evaluating virial coefficients. According to the theory, inclusion of terms in τ up to δ_m should result in correct virial coefficients up to B_m. For the superposition approximation B_3 was calculated to be 0·365 B^2. The exact value is 0·365 B^2. B_4 was found to be 0·104 B^3. The correct value is found, by interpolation of Barker's results,[8] to be 0·116 B^3. Similarly for B_5 we calculate 0·056 B^4 and Barker's value is 0·049 B^4. Here $B = 2\pi\sigma^3/3$. The discrepancies cited reflect the limited accuracy of δ_4 and δ_5.

Table 1 contains values of $p/\rho kT$ for $\tau = 0$ (superposition), $\tau = \rho\delta_4$, $\tau = \rho\delta_4 + \rho^2\delta_5$ and $\tau = $ Padé. Also $\tau = \rho\delta_4$(HS) is included. These results are shown in fig. 2 and

3. The excess internal energy of the fluid may be calculated from the pair distribution function, i.e.,

$$\frac{U}{NkT} = \frac{\rho}{2kT}\int_0^\infty u(r)g(r)4\pi r^2 dr. \qquad (10)$$

The calculated excess internal energy U/NkT is given in table 2 for each of the cases

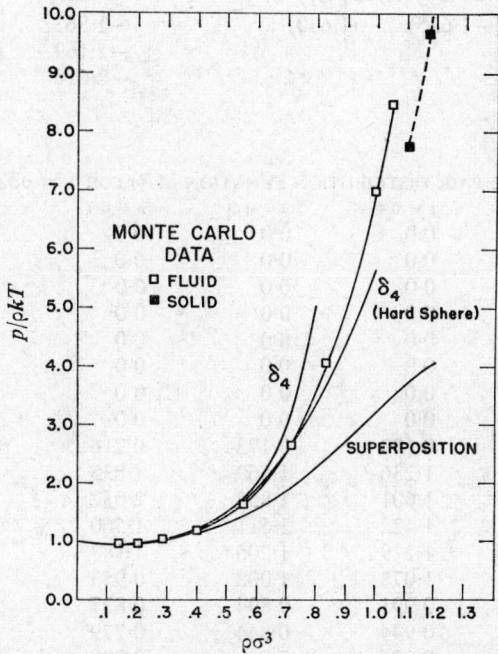

FIG. 2.—Equation of state for the 6-12 potential fluid at $kT/\varepsilon = 2\cdot74$. The Monte Carlo data are taken from ref. (3).

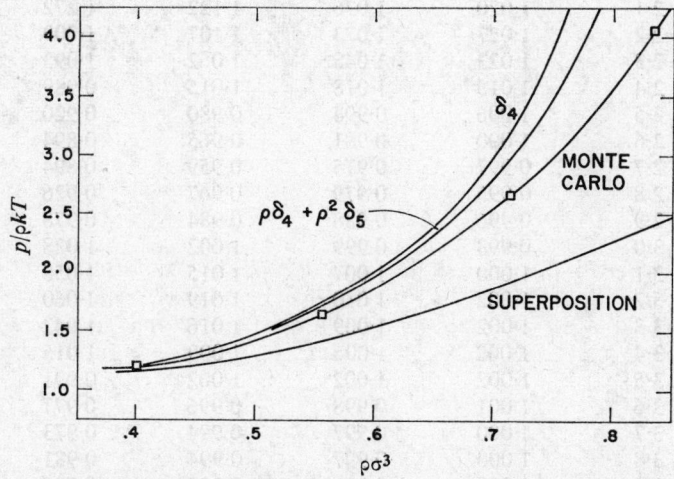

FIG. 3.—Detail of the fluid branch of the equation of state at $kT/\varepsilon = 2\cdot74$.

TABLE 2.—YBG EXCESS INTERNAL ENERGIES U/NkT FOR A SERIES OF τ FUNCTIONS. VALUES IN PARENTHESES ARE NOT EXACT OWING TO SLOW CONVERGENCE. THE SUPERPOSITION ENERGY AT $\rho = 1\cdot2$ IS PROBABLY DIVERGENT.

ρ	superposition	$\rho\delta_4$	$\rho\delta_4+\rho^2\delta_5$	Padé	$\rho\delta_4$(HS)	Kihara	obs. (Levelt)
·1	−·223	−·222	−·222	−·222	−·222	—	−·218
·4	−·877	−·859	−·865	−·858	−·889	−·744	−·829
·6	−1·310	−1·267	−1·286	−1·269	−1·357	−1·118	−1·205
·7	—	−1·455	−1·477		—		
·8	−1·758	(−1·625)	−(1·630)		−1·863		
·9	−1·989				−2·169		
1·0	−2·234				−2·616		
1·1	−2·517						
1·2	(−2·84)						

TABLE 3.—THE PAIR DISTRIBUTION FUNCTION $g(R)$ FOR $\tau = \rho\delta_4+\rho^2\delta_5$.

R	$\rho = 0.4$	$\rho = 0.6$	$\rho = 0.7$	$\rho = 0.8$
0·1	0·0	0·0	0·0	0·0
0·2	0·0	0·0	0·0	0·0
0·3	0·0	0·0	0·0	0·0
0·4	0·0	0·0	0·0	0·0
0·5	0·0	0·0	0·0	0·0
0·6	0·0	0·0	0·0	0·0
0·7	0·0	0·0	0·0	0·0
0·8	0·0	0·0	0·0	0·0
0·9	0·123	0·173	0·216	0·290
1·0	1·236	1·569	1·835	2·337
1·1	1·601	1·854	2·032	2·380
1·2	1·422	1·511	1·560	1·640
1·3	1·219	1·205	1·183	1·112
1·4	1·078	1·008	0·953	0·815
1·5	0·991	0·894	0·827	0·668
1·6	0·944	0·844	0·779	0·628
1·7	0·926	0·840	0·788	0·666
1·8	0·933	0·880	0·853	0·791
1·9	0·960	0·955	0·964	1·000
2·0	0·995	1·034	1·072	1·200
2·1	1·020	1·076	1·122	1·272
2·2	1·027	1·073	1·107	1·209
2·3	1·023	1·048	1·062	1·093
2·4	1·015	1·018	1·015	0·989
2·5	1·006	0·994	0·980	0·920
2·6	1·000	0·981	0·965	0·894
2·7	0·997	0·975	0·959	0·894
2·8	0·995	0·979	0·967	0·926
2·9	0·996	0·988	0·984	0·978
3·0	0·998	0·999	1·002	1·028
3·1	1·000	1·007	1·015	1·058
3·2	1·002	1·010	1·019	1·060
3·3	1·002	1·009	1·016	1·042
3·4	1·002	1·006	1·009	1·015
3·5	1·002	1·002	1·002	0·991
3·6	1·001	0·998	0·996	0·977
3·7	1·000	0·997	0·994	0·973
3·8	1·000	0·997	0·994	0·981
3·9	1·000	0·998	0·996	0·995
4·0	1·000	1·000	1·000	1·011

cited, and is plotted in figs. 4 and 5. For $0 \leqslant \rho \leqslant 0.8$, the superposition excess internal energy is nearly linear in density, with an equation $U/NkT = -2.1975\rho\sigma^3$. Pair distribution functions are listed in table 3.

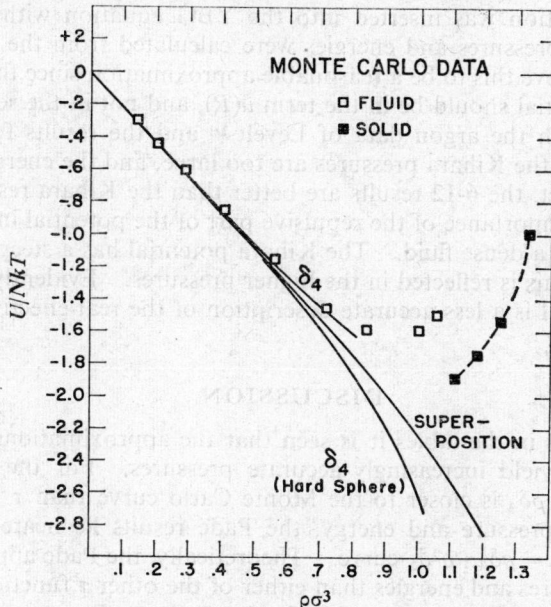

FIG. 4.—Excess internal energy of the 6-12 potential fluid at $kT/\varepsilon = 2.74$. The Monte Carlo data are taken from ref. (3).

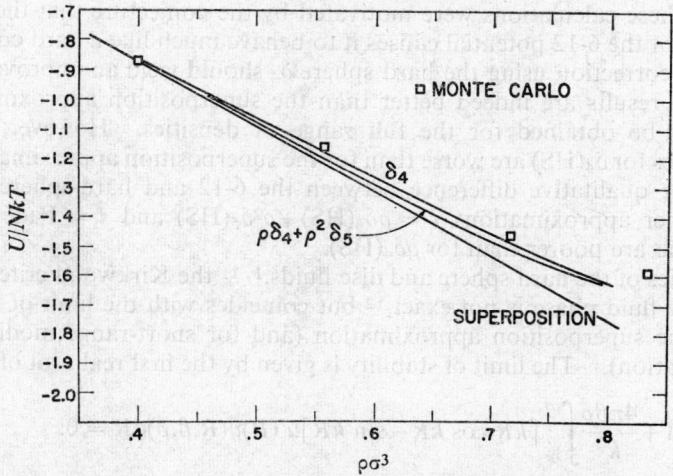

FIG. 5.—Detail of the excess internal energy of the fluid at $kT/\varepsilon = 2.74$.

COMPARISON WITH EXPERIMENT

The 6-12 potential, although qualitatively sound, is inadequate to describe quantitatively potential functions in real gases. One of the best pair potential functions is that due to Kihara. In particular, we have chosen the form used by

Barker:[9]

$$U(R) = 4\varepsilon\left[\left(\frac{\cdot 9}{R-\cdot 1}\right)^{12} - \left(\frac{\cdot 9}{R-\cdot 1}\right)^{6}\right]. \tag{11}$$

This potential function was inserted into the YBG equation with $\tau = \rho\delta_4(6\text{-}12) + \rho^2\delta_5(6\text{-}12)$ and the pressures and energies were calculated from the solutions of this equation. We believe this to be a reasonable approximation since the main effects of the change in potential should be in the term $u(R)$, and not in the several δ_m.

Comparison with the argon data of Levelt [10] and the results for the pure 6-12 potential show that the Kihara pressures are too large, and the energies too small (in magnitude). In fact, the 6-12 results are better than the Kihara results. This is an illustration of the importance of the repulsive part of the potential in determining the equation of state of a dense fluid. The Kihara potential has a steeper repulsive part than the 6-12 and this is reflected in the higher pressures. Evidently in a dense fluid the Kihara potential is a less accurate description of the real effective potential than the 6-12.

DISCUSSION

From the entries in the tables it is seen that the approximations $\tau = 0$, $\tau = \rho\delta_4$, and $\tau = \rho\delta_4 + \rho^2\delta_5$ yield increasingly accurate pressures. For the internal energy, it appears that $\tau = \rho\delta_4$ is closer to the Monte Carlo curve than $\tau = \rho\delta_4 + \rho^2\delta_5$. In both the calculated pressure and energy, the Padé results lie nearer to the $\tau = \rho\delta_4$ curve than to the $\tau = \rho\delta_4 + \rho^2\delta_5$ curve. Theoretically, the Padé approximant should lead to better pressures and energies than either of the other τ functions. We believe that it is the inaccuracies in the δ_4 and δ_5 functions that are responsible for the failure of the Padé approximant to provide good agreement with experiment.

The results with δ_4(HS) represent a "mixture" of the 6-12 and hard-sphere potentials. These calculations were motivated by the conjecture that the very steep repulsive part of the 6-12 potential causes it to behave much like a hard core. Hence the first-order correction using the hard sphere δ_4 should yield an improved equation of state. The results are indeed better than the superposition approximation, and solutions may be obtained for the full range of densities. However, the excess internal energies for δ_4(HS) are worse than for the superposition approximation. This emphasizes the qualitative difference between the 6-12 and hard-sphere potentials. Also, the higher approximations $\tau = \rho\delta_4$(HS)$+\rho^2\delta_5$(HS) and $\tau = $ Padé (HS) yield pressures which are poorer than for $\rho\delta_4$(HS).

From studies of the hard sphere and disc fluids,[1, 11] the Kirkwood criterion for the stability of the fluid phase is not exact,[12] but coincides with the limit of stability for the fluid in the superposition approximation (and for short-range modifications of this approximation). The limit of stability is given by the first real root of

$$1 + \frac{4\pi\beta\rho}{k^3}\int_0^\infty [kR\cos kR - \sin kR]u'(R)g(R,\beta,\rho)\mathrm{d}R = 0. \tag{12}$$

By evaluating the left-hand side with a series of $g(R)$, we obtain a function of k with damped oscillations. This function resembles the Bessel functions obtained from this equation for hard spheres and disks. At some density ρ_c, the first minimum of the function will become zero, defining the upper limit of stability of the fluid. Since we do not have $g(R,\rho)$ for a continuous range of densities, we must use interpolation to locate the density cut-off. For the 6-12 potential, the superposition approximation leads to $k_c = 6\cdot 0$ and $\rho_c = 1\cdot 12$. For $\tau = \rho\delta_4 + \rho^2\delta_5$, $k_c = 6\cdot 0$ and

$\rho_c = 0.83$. Although these results are approximate, they are supported by the fact that we have found the solutions of the superposition approximation for $\rho > 1.2$ to be definitely divergent.

At the highest fluid densities the YBG equation of state diverges markedly from the Monte Carlo equation of state. Although some of this discrepancy is probably due to inaccuracies in the calculations, it seems likely that δ_4 and δ_5 are not adequate to account for all of the important long-range interactions in the 6-12 fluid. Clearly, a different approach is needed.

We conclude that an adequate theory of the fluid must: (a) treat the short-range repulsions accurately, i.e., more accurately than by using the hard-sphere potential; (b) take into account relatively long-range correlations, i.e., of the order of 3-5 atomic diameters. A mean field treatment, superimposed on the δ_4, δ_5 fluctuation terms described herein, is indicated.

We thank the Directorate of Chemical Sciences, AFOSR for financial support. We have also benefited from the use of facilities provided by ARPA for materials research at the University of Chicago. We are indebted to John Lekner for helpful discussions. One of us (D. A. Y.) thanks the Hertz Foundation for generous financial assistance.

[1] S. A. Rice and J. Lekner, *J. Chem. Physics*, 1965, **42**, 3559.
[2] B. J. Alder and T. E. Wainwright, *J. Chem. Physics*, 1960, **33**, 1439.
[3] W. W. Wood and F. R. Parker, *J. Chem. Physics*, 1957, **27**, 720.
[4] A. A. Broyles, S. U. Chung, and H. L. Sahlin, *J. Chem. Physics*, 1962, **37**, 2462.
[5] E. Meeron, *J. Chem. Physics*, 1957, **27**, 1238.
[6] E. E. Salpeter, *Ann. Physics*, 1958, **5**, 183.
[7] T. L. Hill, *Statistical Mechanics* (McGraw-Hill Book Co., Inc., New York, 1956).
[8] J. A. Barker, P. J. Leonard, and A. Pompe, *J. Chem. Physics*, 1966, **44**, 4206.
[9] J. A. Barker, W. Fock, and F. Smith, *Physics Fluids*, 1964, **7**, 897.
[10] J. M. H. Levelt, *Physica*, 1960, **26**, 361.
[11] D. A. Young and S. A. Rice, to be published.
[12] J. G. Kirkwood, in *Phase Transformations in Solids*, ed. R. Smoluchowski, J. E. Mayer, and W. A. Weyl (John Wiley and Sons, Inc., New York, 1951), chap. 3.

Exact and Approximate Values of the Distribution Functions of a Simple Fluid *

By Douglas Henderson †

Division of Applied Chemistry, C.S.I.R.O. Chemical Research Laboratories, Melbourne, Victoria, Australia

Sungwoon Kim and Lynn Oden ‡

Department of Physics, University of Waterloo, Waterloo, Ontario, Canada

Received 29th *December*, 1966

The terms which are proportional to the cube of the density in the expansions of the pair distribution function $g(r)$, and the direct correlation function $c(r)$, have been evaluated for the 6 : 12 potential. In addition, these terms have been evaluated using the Percus-Yevick (PY), hyper-netted chain (HNC), PY2, and HNC2 theories. Comparison of these approximate and exact values for $g(r)$ and $c(r)$ and of the resulting approximate and exact values of the fifth virial coefficient shows that, to this order in the density, the PY2 and HNC2 theories are very reliable. Extensions of the PY and HNC theories which are simpler thean the PY2 and HNC2 theories are also considered.

If only pair interactions are considered,[1] the equation of state of a fluid of N molecules in a volume V can be calculated from the pair distribution function $g(r)$ by means of the pressure equation, or from the direct correlation function $c(r)$ by means of the compressibility equation. These two functions are related by the equation:

$$h_{12} = c_{12} + \rho \int h_{13} c_{23} d\mathbf{r}_3, \qquad (1)$$

where $c_{12} = c(r_{12})$, etc., $\rho = N/V$, and $h(r) = g(r) - 1$.

The problem is to calculate $g(r)$ and $c(r)$. An approximate theory may be obtained by postulating an equation, in addition to (1), relating $g(r)$ and $c(r)$. If such a theory is tested by comparing the resulting approximate equation of state with experiment it is difficult to make conclusions because of inexact knowledge of the intermolecular potential $u(r)$ and because of the perturbations resulting from the presence of three-body forces in real systems.

An alternate procedure is to expand $g(r)$ and $c(r)$ in a power series in ρ and calculate the coefficients both exactly and on the basis of the approximate theory. A comparison of these coefficients and the resulting virial coefficient B_k involves no assumptions other than those inherent in the theory itself. The conclusions reached from such a comparison are only valid at low densities but they do not appear to be sensitive to the number of terms included in the expansion and are of interest in a discussion of the liquid state.

---

* This work has been supported by grants from the National Research Council of Canada and the Office of Saline Water, United States Department of the Interior.

† Alfred P. Sloan Foundation Fellow and Ian Potter Foundation Fellow; permanent address: Department of Physics, University of Waterloo, Waterloo, Ontario, Canada.

‡ present address: Fresno State College, Fresno, California, U.S.A.

EXACT RESULTS

We denote the coefficients of ρ^n in the expansions of $y(r) = \exp\{\beta u(r)\}g(r)$ and $c(r)$ by $g_n(r)$ and $c_n(r)$, respectively. The lowest-order coefficients are $g_0 = 1$ and $c_0(r) = f(r) = \exp\{-\beta u(r)\} - 1$. In previous publications [2,3] we have presented results for g_1, g_2, c_1, and c_2 using the 6 : 12 potential. In this paper we present our

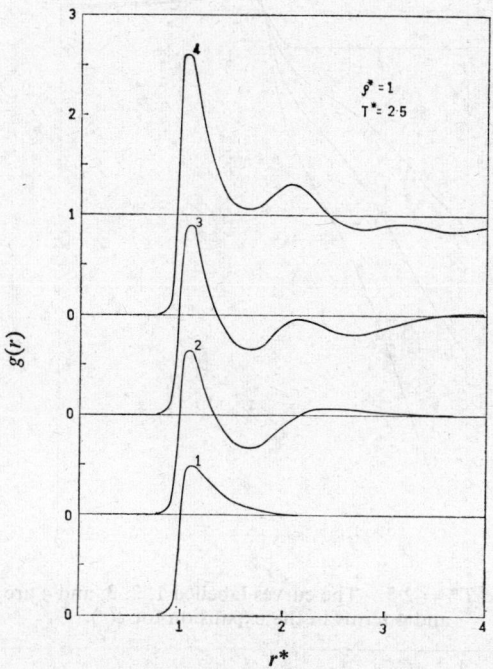

FIG. 1.—$g(r)$ for $\rho^* = 1$ and $T^* = 2 \cdot 5$. The curves labelled 1, 2, 3, and 4 are obtained using 1, 2, 3 and 4 terms in the expansion for $g(r)$.

results for g_3 and c_3. Values for $g(r)$, obtained using a four-term expansion, are plotted in fig. 1 for $T^* = kT/\varepsilon = 2 \cdot 5$ and $\rho^* = \rho\sigma^3 = 1$. This high density was chosen so as to magnify the contributions of the higher-order terms. In fig. 2 a similar plot of $c(r)$ is given. Unfortunately, our calculations for g_3 and c_3 are not complete so that it is not yet possible to show results for lower temperatures.

PY AND HNC THEORIES

It is well-known [4] that
$$c(r) = f(r)y(r) + d(r), \qquad (2)$$
and [5] that $c(r)$ can be written in the form,
$$c(r) = f(r)y(r) + y(r) - 1 - \ln y(r) + E(r). \qquad (3)$$
Eqn. (2) and (3) are little more than definitions of $d(r)$ and $E(r)$, and are useful only if $d(r)$ or $E(r)$ can be approximated.

The Percus-Yevick (PY) approximation is $d(r) = 0$ and the hyper-netted chain (HNC) approximation is $E(r) = 0$. Both approximations give correct results for g_0 and g_1 and thus give exact B_2 and B_3. However, they give approximate results for the higher g_n. In fig. 3 and 4 the errors in the PY and HNC values for $g_2^* = g_2/\sigma^3$ and $g_3^* = g_3/\sigma^6$ at $T^* = 2\cdot 5$ are shown. At this temperature the HNC theory gives the least error for $r^* = r/\sigma$ small but the PY theory gives the least error in the important region $r^* \sim 1$.

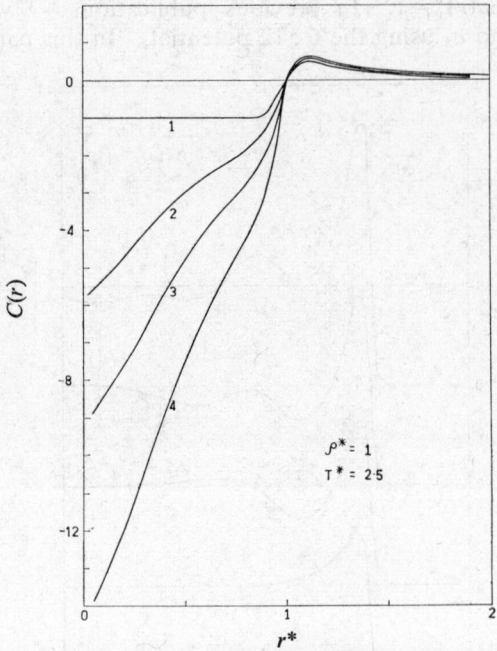

FIG. 2.—$c(r)$ for $\rho^* = 1$ and $T^* = 2\cdot 5$. The curves labelled 1, 2, 3, and 4 are obtained using 1, 2, 3, and 4 terms in the expansion for $c(r)$.

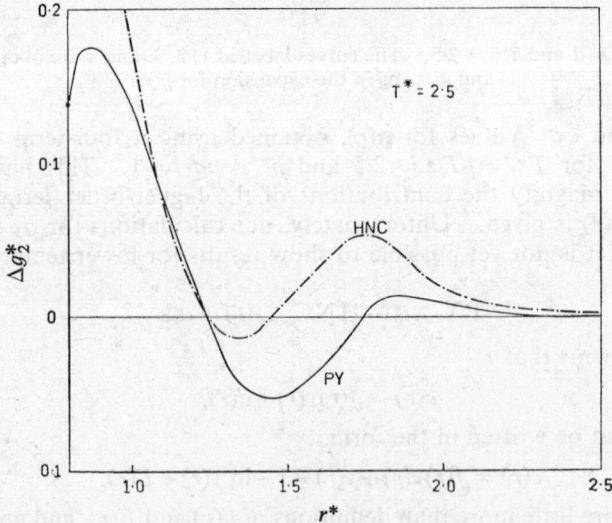

FIG. 3.—$\Delta g_2^* = g_2^*$ (approximate) $- g_2^*$ for $T^* = 2\cdot 5$.

In tables 1 and 2, B_4 and B_4, obtained from these theories, are compared with the exact values. The parameter $b = 2\pi\sigma^3/3$. The necessary cluster integrals have been tabulated previously.[3, 6, 7] The compressibility equation yields the best B_4 and B_5 at

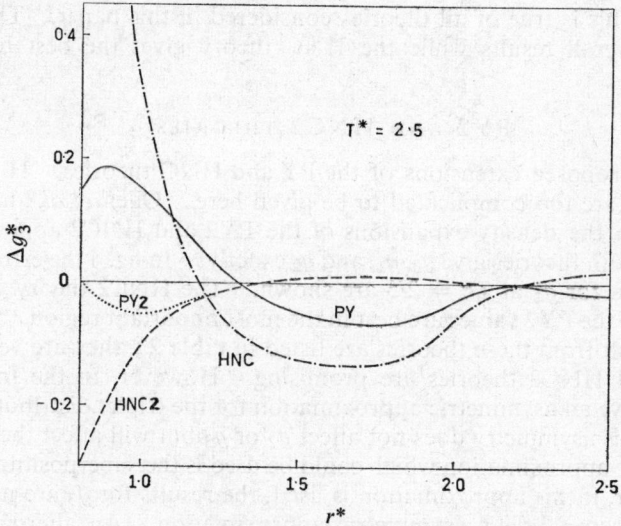

FIG. 4.—$\Delta g_3^* = g_3^*$ (approximate)$-g_3^*$ for $T^* = 2\cdot 5$.

TABLE 1.—FOURTH VIRIAL COEFFICIENTS FOR 6 : 12 POTENTIAL
(in units of b^3)

T^*	exact	PY(c)	PY(p)	HNC(c)	HNC(p)
0·6	−182·17	−130·89	−194·87	−193·40	−196·33
0·8	−9·327	−7·179	−11·699	−12·597	−10·768
1·0	−0·265	−0·3184	−0·7213	−1·2473	−0·4776
1·2	0·3393	0·2170	0·2789	−0·0502	0·3347
1·4	0·2705	0·2028	0·3087	0·0777	0·3043
1·6	0·1898	0·1591	0·2529	0·0765	0·2387
2·0	0·1230	0·1205	0·1872	0·0666	0·1807
2·5	0·1131	0·1160	0·1658	0·0775	0·1739
3·0	0·1198	0·1210	0·1621	0·0912	0·1815
5·0	0·1342	0·1299	0·1534	0·1109	0·1949
10·0	0·1156	0·1120	0·1177	0·0937	0·1681

TABLE 2.—FIFTH COMPRESSIBILITY VIRIAL COEFFICIENTS FOR 6 : 12 POTENTIAL
(in units of b^4)

T^*	exact	PY	PY2	HNC	HNC2	V	E
0·6		−1845·4	−3818·1	−3689·8	−3836·8	−3614·0	−3580·6
0·8	−76·6	−44·8	−81·6	−105·0	−80·8	−85·9	−99·2
1·0	−2·77	−1·93	−3·09	−6·61	−3·02	−4·14	−6·08
1·2	0·023	0·002	0·009	−0·502	0·001	−0·191	−0·478
1·4	−0·0021	0·0341	0·0062	−0·0130	−0·0040	−0·0227	−0·0370
1·6	−0·0415	0·0119	−0·0348	0·0222	−0·0413	−0·0290	−0·0003
2·0	−0·0099	0·0218	−0·0067	0·0370	−0·0086	0·0033	0·0254
2·5	0·0365	0·0441	0·0387	0·0549	0·0387	0·0436	0·0511
3·0	0·0579	0·0547	0·0598	0·0609	0·0607	0·0618	0·0614
5·0	0·0629	0·0550	0·0642	0·0472	0·0665	0·0645	0·0551
10·0	0·0390	0·0365	0·0393	0·0214	0·0422	0·0418	0·0331

high temperatures while the pressure equation yields the best B_4 and B_5 at low temperatures. This is true of all theories considered in this paper. The PY theory gives the best overall results while the HNC theory gives the best results at low temperatures.

PY2 AND HNC2 THEORIES

Verlet [8] has proposed extensions of the PY and HNC theories. His expressions for $d(r)$ and $E(r)$ are too complicated to be given here. Oden et al.[9] have given the first two terms in the density expansions of the PY2 and HNC2 approximations to $d(r)$ and $E(r)$. Both theories give g_0, g_1, and g_2 exactly. In fig. 4 the errors in the PY2 and HNC2 values for g_3^* at $T^* = 2 \cdot 5$ are shown. The HNC2 theory gives the best overall values but the PY2 values are best in the most important region $r^* \sim 1$. Values for B_5 which result from these theories are listed in table 2; they are very good.

The PY2 and HNC2 theories are promising. However, in the form given by Verlet, they involve an asymmetric approximation for the triplet distribution function, $g^{(3)}(r_1,r_2,r_3)$. This asymmetry does not affect g_2 or g_3 but will affect the higher-order g_n. A symmetric approximation which could be used is the superposition approximation.[10] However, if this approximation is used, the results for g_3 are not as good as those obtained from Verlet's asymmetric approximation. An alternate symmetric expression is

$$g^{(3)}(\mathbf{r}_1,\mathbf{r}_2,\mathbf{r}_3) = g_{12}g_{13}g_{23}\{1 + \rho \int h_{14}h_{24}h_{34}\mathrm{d}\mathbf{r}_4\}. \qquad (4)$$

Eqn. (4) yields the same g_3 as does Verlet's approximation to $g^{(3)}$ and should be more satisfactory for the higher-order g_n. We have not yet tested this approximation for the 6 : 12 potential. However, our calculations [11] for Gaussian molecules and hard spheres indicate that eqn. (4) is a considerable improvement over the superposition approximation.

SIMPLER EXTENSIONS

The PY2 and HNC2 theories are complicated. It would be useful to have some simpler extensions of the PY and HNC theories. Each of these extensions yields an exact g_2 and B_4. Verlet [12] and Rowlinson [13] have proposed the approximation:

$$d_{12} = \tfrac{1}{2}\rho^2 \int c_{13}c_{14}h_{23}h_{24}g_{34}\mathrm{d}\mathbf{r}_3\mathrm{d}\mathbf{r}_4. \qquad (5)$$

We refer to this as the V approximation. In table 2 values for B_5 which result from this approximation are listed. In general, the results are worse than PY values. However, at low temperatures the results are good and eqn. (5) may be of some value at low temperatures. Green [14] has proposed an approximation which is similar to (5) but which yields poor values for B_5.

An approximation would be to truncate the series expansion for E after one term. Thus

$$E_{12} = \tfrac{1}{2}\rho^2 \int f_{13}f_{14}f_{23}f_{24}f_{34}\mathrm{d}\mathbf{r}_3\mathrm{d}\mathbf{r}_4. \qquad (6)$$

This approximation, which we call the E1 approximation, corrects the HNC expression for g_2 but does not greatly affect the higher-order g_n. This can be seen from table 2. The E1 values for B_5 are slightly improved over the HNC results. The advantage of this approximation is that it can be continued. When our calculations of g_3 are complete it will be possible to add a second term to (6) and obtain the E2 approximation. The E2 approximation will yield g_3 exactly and should give reasonably good values for the higher-order g_n.

A similar series of approximations could be based on the PY theory and could be referred to as d1, d2, etc. approximations. However, in view of the superiority of the HNC results at low temperatures it would probably be better to use the HNC theory as a basis. Van Leeuwen et al.[5] have proposed an approximation where $E(r)$ is given by (6) with each $f(r)$ replaced by $h(r)$. However, the g_3 and B_5 which result from this approximation are disappointing.

The PY2 and HNC2 theories are promising theories of the liquid state. However, they are complicated and it is harder to obtain numerical values for $g(r)$ from these theories than from the simpler PY and HNC theories. On the other hand, the E2 and d2 theories, although probably less satisfactory than the PY2 and HNC2 theories, are no more difficult to use than are the PY and HNC theories.

One of us (D. H.) is grateful to the staff of the C.S.I.R.O. Chemical Research Laboratories for their hospitality during his visit.

[1] J. S. Rowlinson, *Reports Prog. Physics*, 1965, **28**, 169.
[2] D. Henderson, *Mol. Physics*, 1966, **10**, 73.
[3] D. Henderson and L. Oden, *Mol. Physics*, 1966, **10**, 405.
[4] G. Stell, *Physica*, 1963, **29**, 517.
[5] J. M. J. van Leeuwen, J. Groeneveld and J. de Boer, *Physica*, 1959, **25**, 792.
[6] S. Kim, D. Henderson and L. Oden, *J. Chem. Physics*, 1966, **45**.
[7] J. A. Barker, P. J. Leonard and A. Pompe, *J. Chem. Physics*, 1966, **44**, 4206.
[8] L. Verlet, *Physica*, 1964, **30**, 95.
[9] L. Oden, D. Henderson and R. Chen, *Physics Letters*, 1966, **21**, 420.
[10] J. G. Kirkwood, *J. Chem. Physics*, 1935, **3**, 300.
[11] D. Henderson, *J. Chem. Physics*, 1967, (in press).
[12] L. Verlet, *Physica*, 1965, **31**, 959.
[13] J. S. Rowlinson, *Mol. Physics*, 1966, **10**, 533.
[14] H. S. Green, *Physics Fluids*, 1965, **8**, 1.

Modified Cell Model for Liquids: Order Defects and Intermolecular Potentials

By Friedrich Kohler and J. Fischer

Institute of Physical Chemistry, University of Vienna, Austria

Received 16th January 1967

On the basis of a cell model, an explicit introduction of coordination defects is possible. In binary mixtures, consideration of coordination defects gives only a small correction to the thermodynamic excess properties of mixing. The excess free energy is lowered, and its concentration dependence is influenced in about the same way as by using the quasichemical approximation. Furthermore, the modified cell model has been used to calculate the thermodynamic properties of solid and liquid argon, employing a Kihara pair potential. Comparison is made with previous calculations using a Lennard-Jones pair potential. The parameters of the Kihara potential giving the best fit at high densities differ markedly from those giving the best fit for transport properties and second virial coefficients. The influence of the exact form of the pair potential on the thermodynamic properties is not very important.

The modified cell model [1, 2] combines some development of Kirkwood's variational method [3] with an explicit consideration of order defects. The latter are responsible for density fluctuations, by analogy with Kirkwood's [3] undetermined parameter for multiple occupancy of the cells. Therefore, we have carried out the development of Kirkwood's variational method for single occupancy of the cells, and then consider order defects.

In developing Kirkwood's variational method, we have had two aims: (i) to account for the distribution of the locations of the neighbouring molecules within their cells, (ii) to allow a certain correlation of the motion of the central molecule with the motion of the neighbouring molecules, at least near the edges of the cells. The first point has been considered by Mayer and Careri.[4] As we want to employ the Lennard-Jones 6:12 pair potential or the Kihara potential, we have used a square-well approximation for the probability density in the neighbouring cells rather than the Gaussian approximation used by Mayer and Careri. Like them, we have adjusted the size of the square well consistently to the free volume available in the central cell. The second point has been raised by Hirschfelder, Dahler, and Thacher,[5] who have pointed out that without such a correlation the cell model will always give too positive an energy and too small a free volume, especially at low densities. Whereas Kirkwood [3] has based his variational method on the assumption of independent motions of molecules in their cells, our method shows a certain degree of dependence upon these motions. Therefore, it is necessary to introduce the correlation function before minimizing the free energy. Our starting equation is

$$P(\mathbf{r}_1, \mathbf{r}_2, \ldots \mathbf{r}_N) = \prod_{i=1}^{N} \phi(\mathbf{r}_i) \prod_{i>k=1}^{k=N-1} [1 + \chi(r_{ik})] \tag{1}$$

Here $P(\mathbf{r}_1, \mathbf{r}_2 \ldots \mathbf{r}_N) d\mathbf{r}_1 d\mathbf{r}_2 \ldots d\mathbf{r}_N$ denotes the probability of finding the first particle a the dislocation $\mathbf{r}_1$ of the centre of the first cell, the second particle at the dislocation $\mathbf{r}_2$ of the centre of its cell, etc. $\phi(\mathbf{r}_1) d\mathbf{r}_1$ is the probability that a particle is at a distance **r** from the centre of its cell, provided that no correlation with the motion of neighbouring molecules is taking place. The effect of the correlation function $\chi(r_{ik})$, which is supposed to be a function only of the mutual distance of pairs of particles, is to overweigh pairwise configurations which are strongly attractive and to exclude pairwise configurations which are strongly repulsive. The correlation is limited to small mutual distances. For higher distances, the χ are set arbitrarily equal to zero. The limitation is made in such a way that the product $\Pi(1+\chi_{ik})$ can be developed into various sums, each containing factors with different subscripts only, analogous to the treatment of real gases at low densities:

$$\prod_{i>k}(1+\chi_{ik}) = 1+\sum\chi_{ik}+\sum\sum\chi_{ik}\chi_{lm}+\ldots \quad (2)$$

Inserting eqn. (1) and (2) into the expression for the free energy, and minimizing it with respect to each ϕ and χ, these functions can be calculated. We have approximated the probability density ϕ by a square well, and the correlation function χ by ($\chi = -1$) for small pairwise distances, and by ($\chi = 0$) for larger distances. By using the minimizing procedure a consistent size for the square well is established and a value of the pairwise distance where the step should occur is obtained.

An order defect is thought of as the removal of a nearest neighbour into the shell of next-nearest neighbours. In this process, the distance between the centres of neighbouring cells has been stretched from the nearest neighbour distance a to the distance $A = 2^{\frac{1}{2}}a$. Let F_a be the free energy for a nearest neighbour distance a according to the model above, without order defects. Let F_A be the same for a nearest neighbour distance A. Then the free energy for an assembly with nearest neighbour distance a, but with a fraction x of stretched contacts, is assumed to be given by

$$F = (1-x)F_a + xF_A - RT\ln g(x) \quad (3)$$

Here $[g(x)]^N$ denotes the number of possible arrangements due to order defects. The fraction x is again determined by a minimization process. For densities lower than the critical density, x becomes equal to about 0.5; $R \ln g(x)$ is then the communal entropy per mole of gas. Including a correction for the void of a face-centered cubic packing, $\ln g(x)$ has been written[1]:

$$\ln g(x) = -(z/2)\{x\ln x + (1-x)\ln(1-x) + 1{,}88x(1-x)\} \quad (4)$$

In eqn. (4), z denotes the coordination number.

BINARY MIXTURES

The model for the order defects may be combined with simpler (and poorer) approximations of the cell model than the one described in the introduction. We now investigate the effect of our coordination defects on the thermodynamic excess properties of mixing of simple liquids. For this, we use the cell model for single occupancy in the approximation given by Prigogine and coworkers[6, 7]. Again, a square well is assumed for the probability density, but the square well is arbitrarily extended to the distance $(a-D)/2$ from the centre of the cell (a being the diameter of the cell, and D being the mutual distance between two molecules where the pair potential passes through zero). Furthermore, the energy is calculated as if all molecules would be located at the centres of their cells.

In mixtures, a given molecule A is surrounded by both A and B molecules. Therefore, the energy parameter $\Lambda_{aa} = z\varepsilon^\circ_{aa}$ ($\varepsilon^\circ_{aa}\ldots$ minimum of pair potential between A molecules) applicable in the pure A liquid has to be changed to a parameter $\Lambda_a = \bar{x}\Lambda_{aa} + (1-\bar{x})\Lambda_{ab}$ in the mixture. In the same way, we have for cells occupied by a B molecule an energy parameter $\Lambda_b = \bar{x}\Lambda_{ab} + (1-\bar{x})\Lambda_{bb}$. Here $\bar{x}$ denotes the overall mole fraction of A, and random mixing is implied. For non-random mixing, the mole fraction applicable for the construction of Λ_a would differ somewhat from the mole fraction to be used in the expression for Λ_b. Introducing the concept of stretched contacts, we define the following quantities: x_a and x_b denote, for A-cells and B-cells respectively, the fraction of neighbouring molecules which have been removed into the shell of next-nearest neighbours (i.e., the fractions of stretched contacts). Starting from an A-cell, a fraction γ of the normal contracts, and a fraction $\bar{\gamma}$ of the stretched contacts will lead to other A-cells. Starting from a B-cell, the corresponding fractions are called ξ and $\bar{\xi}$. The various quantities are interrelated by the following relationships: (a) mass balance equations of the form,

$$\gamma(1-x_a) + \bar{\gamma}x_a = \bar{x}, \tag{5}$$

(b) identity between AB and BA contacts like

$$\bar{x}(1-x_a)(1-\gamma) = (1-\bar{x})(1-x_b)\xi, \tag{6}$$

(c) an assumption about the molecular distribution. We have tried as alternatives the statistical distribution,

$$\bar{N}_{ab}^2/(\bar{N}_{aa}\bar{N}_{bb}) = 4, \tag{7a}$$

and the quasichemical approximation [8]

$$\bar{N}_{ab}^2/(\bar{N}_{aa}\bar{N}_{bb}) = 4\eta. \tag{7b}$$

Here $\bar{N}_{ab}, \bar{N}_{aa}$, and $\bar{N}_{bb}$ denote the numbers of AB, AA, and BB normal contacts, respectively, and η stands for $\exp(2\Lambda_{ab} - \Lambda_{aa} - \Lambda_{bb})/(zkT)$.

The starting point is the equation for the free energy of the mixture:

$$F = -kT \ln \left[\Psi_a^{N_a(1-x_a)} \Omega_a^{N_a x_a} \Psi_b^{N_b(1-x_b)} \Omega_b^{N_b x_b} \right] + (N_a/2)[(1-x_a)\bar{E}_a + x_a \bar{\varepsilon}_a] +$$
$$(N_b/2)[(1-x_b)\bar{E}_b + x_b \bar{\varepsilon}_b] - kT \ln \left\{ [g(x_a)]^{N_a} [g(x_b)]^{N_b} \frac{(N_a+N_b)!}{N_a!N_b!} \right.$$
$$\left. \frac{\bar{N}_{aa}!(\bar{N}_{ab}/2)!(\bar{N}_{ab}/2)!\bar{N}_{bb}!}{\bar{\bar{N}}_{aa}!(\bar{\bar{N}}_{ab}/2)!(\bar{\bar{N}}_{ab}/2)!\bar{\bar{N}}_{bb}!} \right\} \tag{8}$$

N_a and N_b are the numbers of A and B molecules. Ψ_a and $\bar{E}_a$ denotes the translational partition function within the free volume and the energy of an A molecule in a cell of diameter a_a, Ω_a and $\bar{\varepsilon}_a$ stands for the same quantities in a cell of diameter $a_a 2^{\frac{1}{2}}$. The double bar means that the number of contacts corresponds to the statistical distribution.

The free energy is essentially a function of the size of A- and B-cells, and of the fraction of stretched contacts $F(a_a, a_b, x_a, x_b)$. In order to determine the parameters, F has to be minimized subject to the condition that the volume, which is a function of the same parameters, remains constant: $V(a_a, a_b, x_a, x_b) = \text{const.}$ This leads to equations of the type

$$\frac{\partial F}{\partial a_b} + \lambda \frac{\partial V}{\partial a_b} = 0, \tag{9}$$

where the Lagrange multiplier λ can be evaluated from one of these expressions, e.g.,

$$\lambda = -\frac{\partial F}{\partial a_a} \bigg/ \frac{\partial V}{\partial a_a}. \tag{10}$$

Then each of the partial differentials can be expressed by one of them, say, by $\partial F/\partial a_a$, and the equation of state can be written as

$$\partial F/\partial V = -P = -\lambda = (\partial F/\partial a_a)(\partial a_a/\partial V). \tag{11}$$

As long as P can be assumed to be practically zero, each partial derivative of the free energy with respect to the parameters vanishes, as the derivatives of V with respect to the parameters are all different from zero. Thus we get—by analogy with the treatment of Prigogine and Bellemans[6]—the conditions

$$\partial F/\partial a_a = \partial F/\partial a_b = \partial F/\partial x_a = \partial F/\partial x_b = 0. \tag{12}$$

The computation proceeds as follows. First, estimated values of x_a and x_b are used to calculate the values of $\gamma, \bar{\gamma}, \xi$ and $\bar{\xi}$. Then, with a first guess of a_b, values for a_a and x_a are determined in small iteration cycles. On the basis of these values, the same iteration cycles are used for the determination of a_b and x_b. Now a new set of the γ and ξ is calculated, and the whole procedure is repeated. The most sensitive parameters are x_a and x_b. In our example, about five cycles have been necessary to arrive at values constant to 0·001 %.

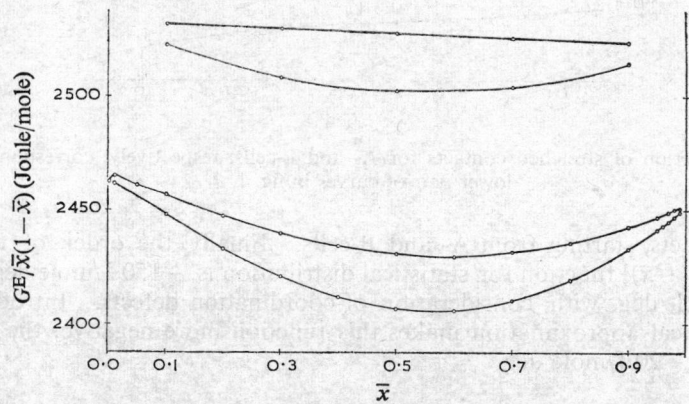

FIG. 1.—$G^E/[\bar{x}(1-\bar{x})]$ as calculated for 293·15°K with the parameters given in the text. Upper pair of curves: no coordination defects considered, statistical and strictly regular distribution, respectively. Lower pair of curves: the same with coordination defects.

The example presented here has been calculated with constants appropriate to the mixture 1,2,4-trichlorobenzene + n-hexane [9, 10] ($\Lambda_{aa} = 66231·5$; $\Lambda_{ab} = 53124·7$; $\Lambda_{bb} = 43425·7$ J/mole; R_{aa}° (the distance at the minimum of the pair potential of A molecules) $= 6·6666 \times 10^{-8}$; $R_{ab}^\circ = (R_{aa}^\circ + R_{bb}^\circ)/2$; $R_{bb}^\circ = 6·6782 \times 10^{-8}$ cm). The temperature variation of Λ_{aa}, caused by the dipole-dipole contribution, has been neglected. Fig. 1 shows the excess free energy of mixing G^E, divided by the product of the mole fractions. The upper pair of curves is calculated without coordination defects (i.e., $x_a = x_b = 0$), for statistical and strictly-regular distribution, respectively. The lower pair of curves show the results of the consideration of coordination defects. Their effect on the absolute value of G^E is not very marked, which is satisfying from the point of view of current theories of mixtures. The main effect of the coordination defect is the enhanced curvature of the $G^E/[\bar{x}(1-\bar{x})]$ function. For this detail, the consideration of coordination defects is at least as important as the effect of the quasichemical approximation. As the curvature of the $G^E/[\bar{x}(1-\bar{x}_2]$ function is related to the shape of consolute curves,[11] one might expect that the consideration of coordination defects will facilitate the explanation of the consolute curves found experimentally. On the other hand, our calculations—which are based on the assumption of central force fields of the molecules—have given no indication of an inversion of the curvature of the $G^E/[\bar{x}(1-\bar{x})]$ function at high $\bar{x}$ values, as has been found experimentally.[9] Fig. 2 gives the concentration dependence of the fractions of

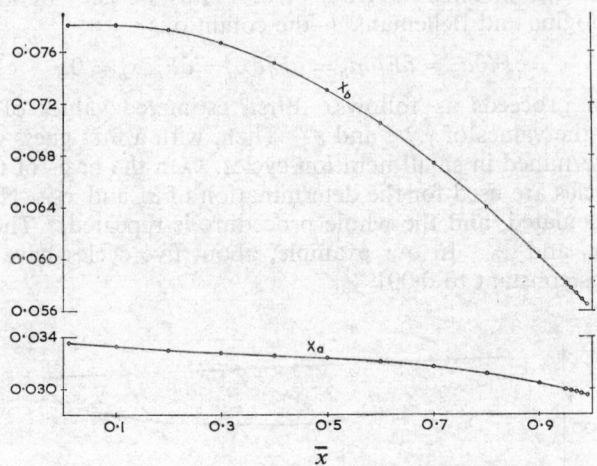

FIG. 2.—The fraction of stretched contacts for A- and B-cells, respectively, corresponding to the lower pair of curves in fig. 1.

stretched contacts, starting from A- and B-cells. Finally, the order of magnitude of the $TS^E/[\bar{x}(1-\bar{x})]$ function for statistical distribution is -150 J/mole deg without, and $+70$ J/mole deg. with, consideration of coordination defects. Introduction of the quasichemical approximation makes this function more negative, the value for $\bar{x} = 0.5$ being -20 J/mole deg.

COORDINATION IN DENSE SUPERCRITICAL VAPOURS

Another possible application of the model of coordination defects is based on the fact that volume expansion may be caused primarily either by diminishing the coordination or by extending the average distance to the nearest neighbours. Fig. 3 shows the result of calculations for argon at 0°C, which demonstrates that up to a volume, about twice that of the liquid at the boiling point, expansion is caused primarily by diminution of the coordination. The nearest neighbour distance increases only about 10 %. One might speculate and correlate this with the findings of Hensel and Franck [12] on the strong increase in conductance with pressure found in the dense, supercritical vapour of mercury. The assumption seems to be reasonable that electron transfer occurs only between atoms which are below a certain minimum distance. Fig. 3 shows that there might be a large range of volumes, where normal contacts are less than this minimum distance and stretched contacts are greater. Then the conductance would be determined by the number of interruptions which occur in a row of normal contacts. By interruption we mean that the row of normal contacts has either no continuation or the continuation would result in an opposing potential. Therefore, the last atom must be the starting point for nine stretched contacts at least. The specific resistance would be essentially proportional to the ninth power of the fraction of stretched contacts. In detail,

$$\frac{\kappa}{a}\bigg/\left(\frac{\kappa}{a}\right)_{l.d.} = \frac{1}{3x^9(1-x)(1+2x^2)}. \qquad (13)$$

Here κ is the specific conductivity, which is referred to the nearest neighbour distance

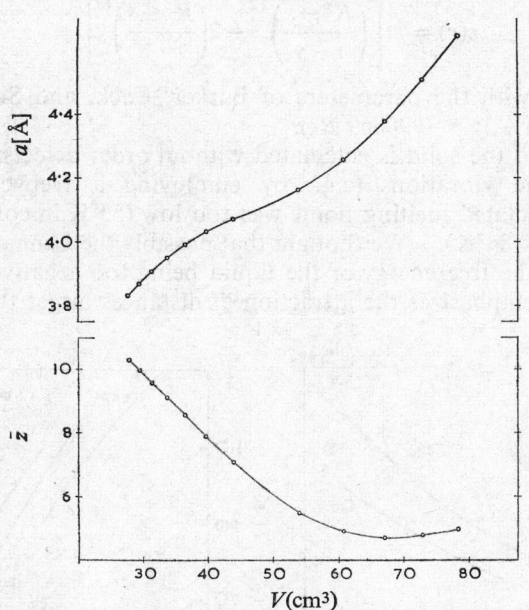

FIG. 3.—The nearest neighbour distance a and the mean coordination number $\bar{z}$, as calculated for argon at 273·15°K.

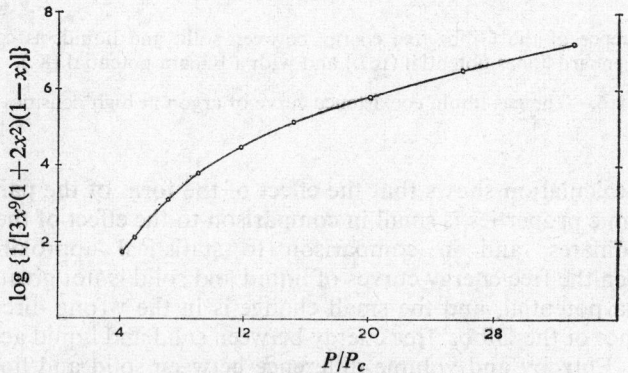

FIG. 4.—The r.h.s. of eqn. (13) for argon at 273·15°K.

a, and the subscript l.d. stands for "low density", where transferable electrons are absent. The quantity on the r.h.s. of eqn. (13) depends on the pressure according to fig. 4, where the calculated results of the 0°C-isotherm of argon are used. It is questionable to transfer the results from argon to mercury, although it demonstrates how important the distinction can be between volume expansion by coordination defects and volume expansion by increasing the nearest neighbour distance.

PAIR POTENTIAL AND THERMODYNAMIC PROPERTIES

In the previous paper,[2] the modified cell model has been applied to argon at higher densities, using a Lennard-Jones 6 : 12 pair potential with the minimum coordinates $\varepsilon^0 = 128\,k$, $R^\circ = 3\cdot83$ Å. In the present paper, a Kihara potential

$$\varepsilon(r) = \varepsilon^\circ\left[\left(\frac{R^\circ - s}{r - s}\right)^{12} - 2\left(\frac{R^\circ - s}{r - s}\right)^{6}\right] \qquad (14)$$

has been employed with the parameters of Barker, Fock, and Smith [13] (i.e., $\varepsilon^\circ = 142\cdot9\,k$, $R^\circ = 3\cdot7338$ Å, $s = 0\cdot90069\,R^\circ$).

The free energy of the solid is calculated without order defects, but by considering coupling of the vibrations (e.g., by employing a Debye approximation). Previously,[2] the calculated melting point was too low (55°K in comparison with the experimental value of 84°K). We thought that possibly the Lennard-Jones potential was responsible for the free energy of the liquid being too negative, as the Lennard-Jones potential overemphasizes the attraction at distances larger than R°.

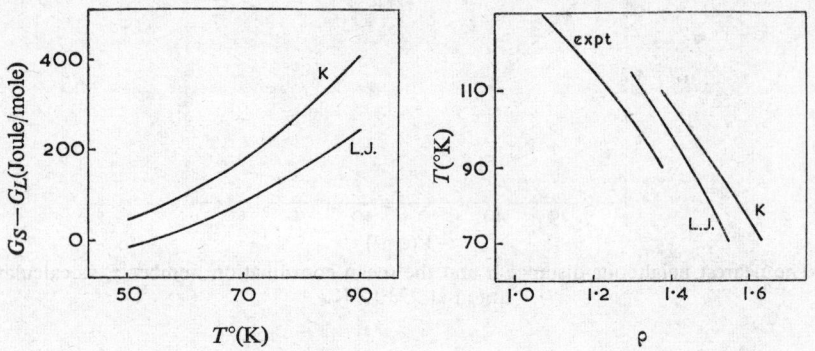

Fig. 5.—The difference of the Gibbs free energy between solid and liquid, as calculated with a Lennard-Jones potential (L.J.) and with a Kihara potential (K.).

Fig. 6.—The gas-liquid coexistence curve of argon at high densities.

The present calculation shows that the effect of the form of the pair potential on the thermodynamic properties is small in comparison to the effect of the choice of the minimum coordinates, and in comparison to statistical approximations. The difference between the free energy curves of liquid and solid is not greatly changed by using the Kihara potential, and the small change is in the wrong direction. Fig. 5 gives the difference of the Gibbs' free energy between solid and liquid according to the potential used. Entropy and volume difference between solid and liquid phase are about correct at the temperature of the experimental melting point. Furthermore, fig. 6 shows part of the coexistence curve between liquid and gas at high densities.

The parameters of the Lennard-Jones potential used correspond to a ratio $\varepsilon^\circ/R^\circ$, which is rather high compared to the values most frequently given. The parameters of the Kihara potential are supposed to fit the measurements of gas viscosities and second virial coefficients. Nevertheless the use of the Kihara potential gives a smaller volume and a larger energy of solid and liquid than the use of the Lennard-Jones potential.

Fig. 7 shows the entropy of the solid as function of the temperature. This function seems to be most seriously influenced by the square-well approximation for the probability density, which leads to characteristic temperatures rising with temperature. If a constant characteristic temperature $\Theta°$ is used (taken from the curvature of

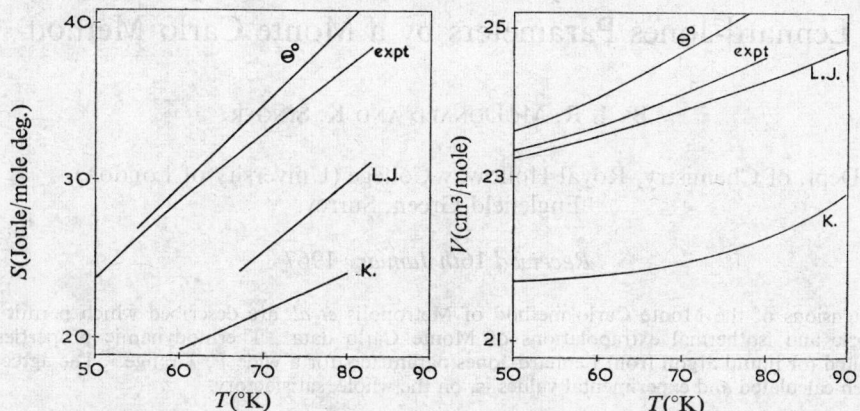

FIG. 7.—The entropy of solid argon; (L.J.) and (K.) calculated with a square-well approximation for the probability density in the cells, using a Lennard-Jones and Kihara potential, respectively; $\Theta°$ calculated with a characteristic temperature evaluated directly from the Lennard-Jones potential.

FIG. 8.—The volume of solid argon; descriptions of curves as in fig. 7.

the Lennard-Jones potential around the potential minimum), then too high an entropy is obtained. In the square-well approximation, the Kihara curve should differ from the Lennard-Jones potential around the potential minimum), then too great an entropy and this is the case. Finally fig. 8 shows the volume of the solid as function of the temperature. Qualitatively, the situation is the same as for the entropy, but the volume according to the Kihara potential is much too small.

[1] F. Kohler, *Ber. Bunsenges.*, 1966, **70**, 1068.
[2] F. Kohler and F. Weissenböck, submitted to *J. Chem. Physics*.
[3] J. G. Kirkwood, *J. Chem. Physics*, 1950, **18**, 380.
[4] J. E. Mayer and G. Careri, *J. Chem. Physics*, 1952, **20**, 1001.
[5] J. S. Dahler, J. O. Hirschfelder and H. C. Thacher, *J. Chem. Physics*, 1956, **25**, 249.
[6] e.g., I. Prigogine and A. Bellemans, *Disc. Faraday Soc.*, 1953, **15**, 80; I. Prigogine, *Molecular Theory of Solutions* (North Holland 1957).
[7] see also, F. Kohler, *Monatsh*, 1957 **88**, 857.
[8] E. A. Guggenheim, *Mixtures* (Oxford, 1952).
[9] R. J. Munn and F. Kohler, *Monatsh*, 1960, **91**, 381; A. Neckel and F. Kohler, *Monatsh*, 1956, **87**, 176.
[10] F. Kohler, *Chem. Technik*, 1966, **18**, 272.
[11] F. Kohler, *J. Chem. Physics*, 1955, **23**, 1398.
[12] F. Hensel and E. U. Franck, *Ber. Bunsenges.*, 1966, **70**, 1154; we are indebted to the authors for communicating their results prior to publication.
[13] cited from J. S. Rowlinson, *Disc. Faraday Soc.*, 1965, **40**, 19.

Calculation of Thermodynamic Properties of Liquid Argon from Lennard-Jones Parameters by a Monte Carlo Method

By I. R. McDonald and K. Singer

Dept. of Chemistry, Royal Holloway College (University of London),
Englefield Green, Surrey.

Received 16*th January* 1967

Extensions of the Monte Carlo method of Metropolis *et al.* are described which permit both isochoric and isothermal extrapolations of Monte Carlo data. Thermodynamic properties are calculated for liquid argon from Lennard-Jones parameters for a wide V, T-range. The agreement between calculated and experimental values is, on the whole, satisfactory.

The Monte Carlo (MC) method devised by Metropolis *et al.*[1] has been applied to the calculation of equilibrium properties of a variety of systems.[1-12] Of particular interest in the present context is the work of Wood *et al.* who calculated the radial distribution function, internal energy, pressure and specific heat of argon over a large range of densities [4] at 55°C, and for one density [5] of the liquid at −147°C from Lennard-Jones (LJ)—parameters.

This paper explores the possibility of calculating the principal thermodynamic functions of a simple classical liquid from a LJ-potential over an appreciable range of volume and temperature. The project has become practicable (*a*) because the greater power of computers now available permits the execution of computations of the type reported in ref. (4) without excessive cost in computer-time; and (*b*) because the MC method has been modified so that properties for a certain range of V, T-values can be obtained from MC data for one V, T-point. Argon is chosen for this work because reliable LJ-parameters [13] and excellent P-V-T data [14-16] covering the entire liquid range are available.

MONTE CARLO METHOD

The essential features of the method of ref. (1), which has been discussed,[1, 4, 17] are these. A fluid "sample" is represented by N coordinate triplets confined within a cube of volume v. The potential energy Φ, assumed to be a sum of pair energies, is calculated for the initial configuration. One of the N "particles" receives a random displacement and the resultant change $\Delta\Phi$ of the potential energy is determined. If $\Delta\Phi$ is negative, the new configuration is accepted; if it is positive, the move is accepted only with the probability $p = \exp(-\beta\Delta\Phi)$, $\beta \equiv 1/kT$. If the move is accepted, the new configuration and the new potential energy become the "current" properties; if it is rejected the system returns to the previous state. The sequence of configurations generated by repetition of this procedure has been shown to tend towards a Boltzmann-weighted ensemble. The mean value of any function of the $3N$ coordinates over a sufficiently long MC sequence is therefore an approximation to the ensemble average of this quantity. Periodic boundary conditions are imposed to minimize the error resulting from the small size of the sample, which, for reasons of economy, usually cannot exceed $N \sim 10^2$.

The mean potential energy $\langle \Phi \rangle$ so obtained determines the molar configurational internal energy $U^\dagger$; the mean virial,

$$\langle \Psi \rangle = \langle \sum_i \mathbf{r}_i \cdot \nabla_i \Phi \rangle$$

determines the pressure according to

$$PV = RT - (N_0/3N)\langle \Psi \rangle$$

Isothermal changes of the Helmholtz free energy can be calculated from $\langle \Psi \rangle$-values and isochoric changes of the configurational entropy from $\langle \Phi \rangle$-values by

$$\Delta A = -(N_0/N)\int_{v_1}^{v_2} P dv \text{ (1) and } \Delta S^\dagger = \int_{T_1}^{T_2} C_v^\dagger dT/T, \ C_v^\dagger = (N_0/N)(\partial \langle \Phi \rangle / \partial T)_v. \quad (2)$$

In these and subsequent formulae, N is the number and v the volume of the MC sample; molar quantities are denoted by N_0 and V; the dagger $\dagger$ means "configurational" and the angular brackets $\langle \rangle$ indicate ensemble averages.

The present extension of this method is designed to evaluate the classical configurational partition function in the form

$$Q^\dagger(N,v,T) = (v^N/N!)\int_{\Phi_{\min}}^{\Phi_{\max}} g(\Phi) \exp(-\beta\Phi) d\Phi,$$

where $g(\Phi)d\Phi$ is the fraction of all accessible configurations for which the potential energy has a value between Φ and $\Phi + d\Phi$. Boltzmann-weighted sequences of configurations and averages of Φ and Ψ are calculated as in ref. (4); but in addition, a histogram is accumulated of the numbers of configurations with potential energies within small specified ranges of width δ. The entry for the n-th interval is the number of configurations with potential energies between $\Phi_n - \delta/2$ and $\Phi_n + \delta/2$, denoted by

$$F_n \equiv F(\Phi_n - \delta/2, \Phi_n + \delta/2).$$

For sufficiently small δ, F_n is assumed to converge statistically to

$$K^{-1}f(\Phi_n), \quad f(\Phi_n) \equiv g(\Phi_n) \exp(-\beta\Phi_n), \quad (3)$$

where K depends on v but not on T. Since

$$Q^\dagger(N,v,T) \cong K\sum_n F_n(T)$$

the histogram determines the partition function apart from the normalizing constant K.

$Q^\dagger$ at another temperature, T' can be obtained by reweighting the histogram:

$$Q^\dagger(N,v,T') = K\sum_n F_n(T') = K\sum_n F_n(T) \exp[-(\beta'-\beta)\Phi_n], \quad (4)$$

where $\beta' \equiv 1/kT'$. In practice, the range of temperatures which can be reached by this procedure is limited by the width of the parent histogram.

Since K cannot be determined by the present method, isothermal changes of $Q^\dagger$ are calculated indirectly, by means of (1). To compute changes along a neighbouring isotherm T', a reweighting procedure is applied. Let $\{\alpha\}_n$ be the set of G_n configurations for which the potential energy lies between $\Phi_n - \delta/2$ and $\Phi_n + \delta/2$, $\Psi_{n,\alpha}$ the virial of one of these configurations, and $\overline{\Psi}_n$ the average for the set $\{\alpha\}_n$, i.e.,

$$\overline{\Psi}_n = (\sum_{\{\alpha\}_n} \Psi_{n,\alpha})/G_n. \quad (5)$$

The ensemble average of the virial at T is

$$\langle \Psi \rangle_T = \sum_n F_n(T)\bar{\Psi}_n / (\sum_n F_n(T)) \qquad (6)$$

and the value $\langle \Psi \rangle_{T'}$ is obtained by substituting $F_n(T') = F_n(T)\exp[-(\beta'-\beta)\Phi_n]$ for $F_n(T)$ in (6). Tables of $\bar{\Psi}_n$-values are calculated during the MC runs.

Another extension of the range of application of the MC method arises from the possibility of calculating from MC data obtained for the LJ-parameters (ε, σ) properties corresponding to different parameters (ε', σ'). This can be done if the differences between the "new" and the "old" parameters are small.

The LJ-potential is defined by

$$\phi(r) \equiv 4\varepsilon[(\sigma/r)^{12} - (\sigma/r)^6] \qquad (7)$$

modified by a hard core, i.e., $\phi(r) = \infty$ for $r < r_c$, introduced to increase the speed of computation. Since the potential function and the corresponding virial function, $\psi(r) = rd\phi/dr$, are linear combinations of r^{-12} and r^{-6}, the potential function $\phi'(r)$ and the virial function $\psi'(r)$ for the parameters (ε', σ') can be written as linear combinations of ϕ and ψ. The same relationships hold for the total potential energy $\Phi_{n,\alpha}$ and the total virial $\Psi_{n,\alpha}$ of any configuration α belonging to the set $\{\alpha\}_n$ calculated with different LJ-functions, i.e.,

$$\Phi'_n = a\Phi_{n,\alpha} + b\Psi_{n,\alpha}, \qquad (8)$$

$$\Psi'_{n,\alpha} = c\Phi_{n,\alpha} + d\Psi_{n,\alpha}, \qquad (9)$$

where

$$a = \tau(-\lambda^{12} + 2\lambda^6), \qquad b = \tau(-\lambda^{12} + \lambda^6)/6, \qquad (10a)$$

$$c = -72b, \qquad d = \tau(2\lambda^{12} - \lambda^6) \qquad (10b)$$

with $\tau = \varepsilon'/\varepsilon$ and $\lambda = \sigma'/\sigma$.

The ensemble average for the "new" potential energy is

$$\langle \Phi' \rangle = \{\sum_n \sum_{\{\alpha\}_n} (a\Phi_n + b\Psi_{n,\alpha}) \exp[-\beta(a\Phi_n + b\Psi_{n,\alpha})]\} / \{\sum_n \sum_{\{\alpha\}_n} \exp[-\beta(a\Phi_n + b\Psi_{n,\alpha})]\},$$

where $\Phi_{n,\alpha}$ is replaced by Φ_n since $\Phi_{n,\alpha} \cong \Phi_n$. The further substitutions

$$\Psi_{n,\alpha} \equiv \bar{\Psi}_n + \Delta_{n,\alpha}, \qquad a\Phi_n + b\bar{\Psi}_n \equiv \tilde{\Phi}_n,$$

lead to

$$\langle \Phi' \rangle = \{\sum_n \sum_{\{\alpha\}_n} (\tilde{\Phi}_n + b\Delta_{n,\alpha}) \exp[-\beta(\tilde{\Phi}_n + b\Delta_{n,\alpha})]\} / \{\sum_n \sum_{\{\alpha\}_n} \exp[-\beta(\tilde{\Phi}_n + b\Delta_{n,\alpha})]\}. \quad (12)$$

Eqn. (10a) shows that $b \ll 1$ if $|\sigma - \sigma'| \ll \sigma$; in this case $\exp(-\beta b \Delta_{n,\alpha})$ may be expanded and terms of higher than the second order in $\beta b \Delta_{n,\alpha}$ neglected. If the substitutions

$$\sum_{\{\alpha\}_n} \Delta^2_{n,\alpha} \equiv G_n \overline{\Delta^2_n} \quad \text{and} \quad G_n \exp(-\beta \tilde{\Phi}_n) \equiv \tilde{F}_n$$

are made in the resulting expressions, one obtains

$$\langle \Phi' \rangle = \{\sum_n \tilde{F}_n [\tilde{\Phi}_n(1 + \beta^2 b^2 \overline{\Delta^2_n}/2) - \beta b^2 \overline{\Delta^2_n}]\} / \{\sum_n \tilde{F}_n(1 + \beta^2 b^2 \overline{\Delta^2_n}/2)\} \qquad (13)$$

The analogous formula for the virial is

$$\langle \Psi' \rangle = \{\sum_n \tilde{F}_n [\tilde{\Psi}_n(1 + \beta^2 b^2 \overline{\Delta^2_n}/2) - \beta b d \overline{\Delta^2_n}]\} / \{\sum_n \tilde{F}_n(1 + \beta^2 b^2 \overline{\Delta^2_n}/2)\}, \qquad (14)$$

where $\tilde{\Psi}_n = c\Phi_n + d\bar{\Psi}_n$. Eqn. (13) and (14) are exact if the distributions of $\Delta_{n,\alpha}$ are

Gaussian. If $\beta^2 b^2 \overline{\Delta_n^2} \ll 1$ for all n, one may use the simpler expressions,

$$\langle \Phi' \rangle \cong (\sum_n \widetilde{F}_n \widetilde{\Phi}_n)/\sum_n \widetilde{F}_n \tag{15}$$

$$\langle \Psi' \rangle \cong (\sum_n \widetilde{F}_n [\widetilde{\Psi}_n - \beta b d \overline{\Delta_n^2}])/\sum_n \widetilde{F}_n. \tag{16}$$

The values of $\overline{\Delta_n^2}$ i.e., the variances of $\Psi_{n,\alpha} - \overline{\Psi}_n$ may be calculated during MC runs without loss of computing speed.

These formulae can be used (a) to investigate the effect of changes of the LJ-parameters on the equilibrium properties, and (b) to extrapolate data calculated for v, T to v', T'. Eqn. (13)-(16) are applicable to isothermal changes because substitution of the LJ-parameter σ by $\sigma' = \sigma/\lambda$ is equivalent to the scaling of all linear dimensions of a sample configuration by λ, i.e., $r_{ij} \to \lambda r_{ij}$ for all i, j and $v \to v' = \lambda^3 v$. Changes of ε to ε' are equivalent to changes of T and can be dealt with by the reweighting procedure according to (4) and (6). The isothermal extrapolation is limited to small changes of volume because, apart from the approximation made in the derivation of eqn. (13) and (14), the reweighting of the histogram F_n to $\widetilde{F}_n$ becomes inaccurate if the two histograms do not overlap sufficiently.

MC data for the calculation of thermodynamic properties may also be obtained by a method not based on ref. (1). In this, a sequence is generated by a random walk in $3N$-dimensional configuration space without Boltzmann-weighting. A move is rejected only if it raises the potential energy above a preset upper bound. The histogram $G(\Phi_n - \delta/2, \Phi_n + \delta/2) \equiv G_n$ so obtained is assumed to tend to $g(\Phi)$ in (3), and the partition function is calculated from

$$Q^\dagger(N, v, T) = K \sum_n G_n \exp(-\beta \Phi_n),$$

i.e., by Boltzmann-weighting of the histogram according to the temperature required. The limitation of this method of "unweighted configurations" arises from the very rapid increase of $g(\Phi)$ with Φ. A considerable number of MC runs with different upper energy bounds is therefore required to cover a Φ-range sufficient for the calculation of properties over a wide T-range. Isothermal changes and extrapolations can be dealt with as described above. The disadvantages of the "unweighted" method increase with density and with N; but they are not too serious in the gaseous range, even at high pressures. Results obtained by this method for gaseous argon over a wide P-V-T range will be reported elsewhere.[18] The two methods have not been compared systematically.

RESULTS AND DISCUSSION

Calculated values of selected thermodynamic properties of argon at five temperatures between the triple point (83·8°K) and the critical temperature (150·7°K) and a range of densities are shown in table 1. The experimental results for the same V, T-points are given where these are available; properties of the orthobaric liquid obtained by graphical interpolation are shown in table 2. Experimental P-V-T data at 86·3 and 97·0 °K are derived from the empirical equation of state given in ref. (15); those for 108·2, 136·0 and 148·2°K by interpolation of the data of ref. (16).

All calculations are based on samples with $N = 108$ and on the LJ-parameters $\varepsilon/k = 119·76°K$, $\sigma = 3·405$ Å,[13] with $r_c = 2·7$ Å (cf. eqn. (7)). Not less than 168,000 configurations were used to obtain the data for a given v, T-point. The mutual consistency, the broad agreement with experiment and the magnitude of the statistical fluctuations of the calculated mean values indicate that MC sequences of this length usually yield reliable statistical data. The standard deviations (calculated from sub-averages over 4000 configurations) are $\approx 0.3 \times 10^{-15}$ ergs for $\langle \Phi/N \rangle$ and ≈ 2 to 4×10^{-15} ergs for $\langle \Psi/N \rangle$. The relative error in the virial is therefore largest when

TABLE 1.—THERMODYNAMIC PROPERTIES OF ARGON

T °K	V cm³	$\langle \frac{-\Phi}{N} \rangle$ erg $\times 10^{14}$	$\langle \frac{\Psi}{N} \rangle$ erg $\times 10^{14}$	P dyne cm⁻² $\times 10^{-8}$ MC	expt.	$\frac{-U^\dagger}{RT}$ MC	expt.	$\frac{C_v^\dagger}{R}$ MC	expt.	$\frac{-1}{V}\left(\frac{\partial V}{\partial P}\right)_T$ cm² dyne⁻¹ $\times 10^{10}$ MC	expt.	$\left(\frac{\partial P}{\partial T}\right)_V = \left(\frac{\partial S}{\partial V}\right)_T$ dyne cm⁻² deg⁻¹ $\times 10^{-7}$ MC	expt.	$\frac{1}{V}\left(\frac{\partial V}{\partial T}\right)_P$ deg⁻¹ $\times 10^3$ MC	expt.
86.3	24.78	11.90	1.64	1.57		9.98		0.91		1.60		1.74		2.78	
	25.60	11.51	4.12	−0.43		9.66		0.96		1.66		1.82		3.02	
	26.44	11.15	6.68	−2.36		9.36		1.27		1.71		2.44		4.17	
	26.90	10.93	7.32	−2.79		9.17		1.23							
	27.50	10.56	6.36	−2.03		8.85		1.28							
	27.50	10.30	0.66	2.13	2.10	8.64*		1.35*		1.87	1.73	2.30	1.94	4.30	3.36
	28.03	10.12	2.51	0.76	0.92	8.49		1.03		2.17	1.91	1.73	2.07	2.75	3.95
	28.48	9.95	3.34	0.17	0.09	8.35		1.09		2.34	2.06	1.77	2.15	4.14	4.43
	28.95	9.76	4.18	−0.42	−0.67	8.19		1.02		2.50	2.19	1.72	2.22	4.30	4.86
	29.68	9.50	5.55	−1.34		7.97		0.85		2.76		1.40		3.86	
	30.92	9.14	7.58	−2.60				0.68		3.10		1.05		3.32	
97.0ᵃ	28.48	9.75	−0.14	2.93	2.16	7.28*		1.00*							
	29.68	9.36	2.91	0.81	0.35	6.99		0.91							
97.0ᵇ	27.50	10.14	−2.21	4.55	4.24	7.57*		0.88*		1.88	1.94	1.52	1.21	2.86	2.35
	28.03	9.97	0.01	2.87	3.01	7.44		0.93		2.18	2.14	1.47	1.39	3.20	2.97
	28.48	9.81	0.85	2.23	2.16	7.32		0.83		2.31	2.29	1.42	1.50	3.28	3.44
	28.95	9.62	1.60	1.68	1.39	7.18		0.91		2.45	2.43	1.50	1.59	3.68	3.86
	29.68	9.38	3.43	0.40	0.35	7.01		0.71		2.71	2.64	1.18	1.69	3.20	4.46
108.2ᶜ	28.48	9.59	−2.87	5.61		6.41*		1.13*							
	29.68	9.24	0.78	2.54	2.29	6.18		0.78							
136.0ᵈ	33.51	7.97	1.42	2.52	2.37	4.24	4.15	0.56	0.58	4.73	4.53	0.83	1.21	3.91	5.26
	36.58	7.33	4.20	0.79	0.95	3.90	3.82	0.47	0.57	6.70	8.30	0.60	0.97	4.03	8.08
	40.00	6.72	5.88	−0.12	0.28	3.58		0.46	0.58	17.31	23.50	0.56	0.61	9.76	14.29
148.2ᵃ	33.51	7.87	−0.35	3.89		3.85	3.75	0.61	0.61	2.89		0.88		2.55	
	35.00	7.58	1.68	2.49	2.79	3.69	3.60			4.27	4.72				
	36.58	7.25	2.80	1.93	2.01	3.54	3.46	0.50	0.57	6.50	6.58	0.64	0.89	4.16	5.86
	38.19	6.95	3.38	1.45	1.52	3.39	3.32			9.15	9.66				
	40.00	6.64	4.54	0.80	1.13	3.25	3.18	0.44	0.57	15.42	16.73	0.54	0.65	8.25	10.87

MC = present work; expt = experimental results; * see text.

ᵃ direct MC calculation; ᵇ reweighted from 86.3°K data; ᶜ reweighted from 97.0°K data; ᵈ reweighted from 148.2°K data.

$\langle \Psi/N \rangle$ is small, i.e., when $PV \approx RT$ and the relative error in P is largest when $P \approx 0$ ($\langle \Psi/N \rangle \approx 3kT$). Estimated probable statistical errors are: $\delta U^\dagger \approx 5$ cal/mole and $\delta P \approx 2 \times 10^7$ dyne cm⁻². The isochoric reweighting gives reliable results for variations of up to 15 % in T.

PRESSURE

The variation of PV/RT is shown in the figure; with the exception of one point (28.48 cm³, 97.0°K) the agreement with experiment may be regarded as satisfactory throughout the range of stability of the liquid. At 86.3°K the calculated pressures form distinct "solid" and "liquid" branches. Although the pressure calculated for $V = 27.50$ cm³ from an initial face-centred cubic arrangement remained much below that calculated from an initial disordered liquid-type configuration, the pressure of the "solid" is anomalous, being higher than that calculated for $V = 26.90$ cm³. This arises almost certainly from the presence of liquid-type configurations or regions in the MC sample, indicating a fluctuation between two phases.[4,10] At 148.2°K and $V = 40.00$ cm³ the calculated pressure falls well below the experimental value.

This is interpreted as the onset of a van der Waals' loop, a view supported by more extensive computations [18] in this region with $N = 32$. The values of P at 97·0°K obtained by isochoric reweighting of the 86·3°K-data are in particularly good agreement with experiment. The reason for the discrepancy between these results and

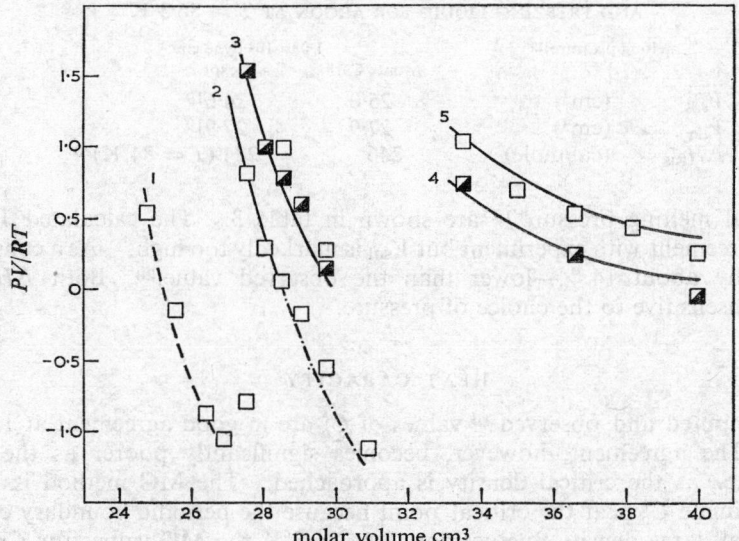

FIG. 1.—P-V isotherms for argon. □, data from direct MC calculation; ◪, data from isochoric reweighting. Full curves: expt. results; dashed curve: sketched through MC points. Curve 1: 86·3°K ("solid" branch); curve 2: 86·3°K ("liquid" branch, expt. equation of state extrapolated to negative pressures); curve 3: 97·0°K; curve 4: 136·0°K; curve 5: 148·2°K.

the value obtained directly from MC runs for 28·48 cm³ is not known. Inspection of the statistical data reveals signs of long-term fluctuations which suggests that substantially longer sequences than 170,000 configurations are occasionally required.

INTERNAL ENERGY AND LATENT HEATS

The agreement between observed [14] and calculated values of $U^{\dagger}$ at 148·2 and 136·0°K is good. Comparison with experimental data for the lower temperatures is made in table 2. The latent heat ΔH_{vap} of vaporization at 86·3°K can be

TABLE 2.—PROPERTIES OF ORTHOBARIC LIQUID ARGON

T °K	P dyne cm$^{-2}\times10^{-6}$	V cm³		$-U^{\dagger}/RT$		$C_v^{\dagger}/R$	
		calc.	expt.	calc.	expt.	calc.	expt.
86·3	0·92	28·62	28·52	8·34	8·19	1·07	0·85
97·0	2·59	29·91	29·95	6·97	6·86	0·65	0·78
108·2	5·97	31·13	31·71	5·92	5·69	0·35(?)	0·65

calc = graphical interpolation of MC data of table 1; expt = linear interpolation of experimental results.[21]

calculated from the experimental vapour pressure [20] (0.91×10^6 dyne cm^{-2}) and the MC data. This gives a value of 1543 cal/mole compared with the measured value [20] of 1564 at 85·7°K. The discontinuity of the pressure at 86·3°K and $V = 27.50$ cm³ indicates a phase transition in the MC model; in a real system the phase equilibrium is characterized by the equality of the Gibbs free energy and of P at different densities. Properties relating to the liquid-solid transition calculated from MC data and the

TABLE 3.—LATENT HEAT OF FUSION AND VOLUMES OF MELTING SOLID
AND FREEZING LIQUID FOR ARGON AT $T = 86\cdot3°$K

		melting pressure [19] Monte Carlo	$1\cdot03 \times 10^8$ dyne cm^{-2} expt.
V_{sol}	(cm^3)	25·0	24·6[19]
V_{liq}	(cm^3)	27·9	27·9[19]
ΔH_{fus}	(cal/mole)	246	284 ($T = 84°$K)[20]

experimental melting pressure [19] are shown in table 3. The calculated V_{liq} is in excellent agreement with experiment but V_{sol} is markedly too high. As a consequence ΔH_{fus} is—by about 14 %—lower than the observed value.[20] Both ΔH_{vap} and ΔH_{fus} are insensitive to the choice of pressure.

HEAT CAPACITY

The computed and observed [14] values of C_v^t are in good agreement at 136·0 and 148·2°K. The agreement, however, becomes significantly poorer as the volume increases, i.e., as the critical density is approached. The MC method is expected to underestimate C_v^t near the critical point because the periodic boundary condition suppresses all large density fluctuations. At 86·3°K the MC values for C_v^t/R show a clear maximum in the neighbourhood of the pressure discontinuity ($V = 27\cdot50$ cm^3). Experimental and calculated values for the orthobaric liquid are compared in table 2. Ref. (16) tabulates C_v as a function of P at 90, 100 and 110°K but the data show as much scatter as those given for 97·0 and 108·2°K in table 1 and interpolation is difficult. The values of C_v^t/R measured at 100°K between $P = 4 \times 10^6$ and 300×10^6 dyne cm^{-2} lie between 1·09 and 1·78, suggesting that the MC results are too low.

OTHER PROPERTIES

The compressibilities (column 10 of table 1) are calculated by least-squares fitting of a parabola to the MC P-V data for each temperature. The thermal pressure coefficients (column 11) are determined by isochoric reweighting (eqn. (6)), $\Delta T = 1°$K). The expansivity (column 12) is the negative product of the two quantities. The good agreement at 97·0°K is probably fortuitous. Elsewhere the agreement is mostly fair.

ISOTHERMAL EXTRAPOLATION

Values of $\overline{\Delta_n^2}$ have not yet been reliably determined over a range of densities. The results obtained for $V = 28\cdot03$ and $28\cdot95$ cm^3 from the MC data for $V = 28\cdot48$ cm^3 and $T = 86\cdot3°$K by means of eqn. (15) and (16) are shown in table 4. The differences between the extrapolated and the independently calculated values of $\langle \Phi/N \rangle$ and $\langle \Psi/N \rangle$ are smaller than the statistical error of the MC calculation. For moderately small extrapolations of $\langle \Phi/N \rangle$ ($\Delta V/V \sim 2$ %) values of $\overline{\Delta_n^2}$ are not required. This is also true for small extrapolations of $\langle \Psi/N \rangle$ ($\Delta V/V \sim 0\cdot5$ %) when the second term in eqn. (16) can be neglected. Extrapolation from 28·48 to 28·38 cm^3 yielded a compressibility of $2\cdot24 \times 10^{-10}$ cm^2 dyne^{-1} compared with $2\cdot34 \times 10^{-10}$ cm^2 dyne^{-1} obtained from the MC isotherm. These results are regarded as encouraging.

TABLE 4.—ISOTHERMAL EXPRAPOLATION OF MONTE CARLO DATA FOR
$V = 28\cdot48$ cm^3, $T = 86\cdot3°$K

	direct calculation		extrapolation	
V	$\langle\frac{\Phi}{N}\rangle$	$\langle\frac{\Psi}{N}\rangle$	$\langle\frac{\Phi}{N}\rangle$	$\langle\frac{\Psi}{N}\rangle$
(cm^3)	(erg $\times 10^{15}$)		(erg $\times 10^{15}$)	
28·03	$-10\cdot12$	2·51	$-10\cdot08$	2·64
28·95	$-9\cdot76$	4·18	$-9\cdot81$	4·34

CONCLUSIONS

Calculations based on an MC method and an LJ-potential have been shown to yield quantitatively significant values of thermodynamic properties of a simple liquid (argon) over a considerable V,T range, including phase transitions. Satisfactory results have been obtained for the internal energy. For the pressure, the agreement with experimental values is less good but still, on the whole, satisfactory. For the derivatives of $U^\dagger$ and P the agreement with experiment is better than qualitative.

In a number of cases the discrepancies between calculated and experimental results are larger than the statistical sampling errors inherent in the MC method. It is hoped that future work will show to what extent the discrepancies are due to the approximations of the MC method, e.g., small sample size and the periodic boundary condition, or to inadequacy of the potential function.

By calculating not merely the mean values but also the frequency distributions for the potential energy and the virial, it has been possible greatly to extend the T-range covered by a given number of MC calculations. Further economies in computation become possible by means of an isothermal extrapolation procedure for which only limited results have so far been obtained. This method will also permit the systematic investigation of the effects of changes of the LJ-parameters on the thermodynamic properties.

The computing time required to obtain results of the type reported in this paper is large but not prohibitive. MC calculations for more complex systems, e.g., mixtures of simple fluids or systems governed by non-central forces, need no longer be regarded as impractical.

APPENDIX

APPROXIMATIONS

EFFECT OF DISTANT PARTICLES. To reduce computing labour the sum of all pair energies is replaced by one in which the potential due to a uniform density is substituted for the effect of the distant particles,[4] i.e.,

$$\Phi = \sum_{r_{ij} < r_m} \phi(r_{ij}) + (N/2v)\int_{r_m}^\infty \phi(r)4\pi r^2 dr \equiv \Phi^*(r_m).$$

In this work $r_m = 6\cdot5$ Å. MC runs yield ensemble averages of the "effective" potential energy $\langle\Phi^*(r_m = 6\cdot5\text{ Å})\rangle$. These values are further corrected by computing the values of $\Phi^*(r_m = 6\cdot5\text{ Å})$ and $\Phi^*(r_m = 8\cdot4\text{ Å})$ for a small number of configurations at each density and adding the mean difference of $\{\Phi^*(r_m = 8\cdot4\text{ Å}) - \Phi^*(r_m = 6\cdot5\text{ Å})\}$ to $\langle\Phi^*(r_m = 6\cdot5\text{ Å})\rangle$ in all cases. The same procedure is applied to the virials. For the potential energy the "effective" long-range potential amounts to 15-20 % of the total; for the virial, the long-range contribution is of opposite sign and of the same order of magnitude as the exactly calculated short range contribution. The "effective" long range contributions and their corrections vary smoothly with density. It is estimated that the error resulting from this procedure does not exceed 0·5 % for Φ and 5 % for Ψ.

THE SAMPLE SIZE. In all calculations $N = 108$. The mean values of all macroscopic equilibrium properties are assumed to be determined by the mean values of the MC sample. This involves errors because the periodic boundary condition excludes configurations which in reality occur, and because density fluctuations are suppressed. Density fluctuations in small volume elements can be calculated from the isothermal compressibility. For $N = 108$ such fluctuations would not contribute significantly to the macroscopic entropy if the microscopic subsystems are treated as independent. This assumption is, however, unjustified because adjacent subsystems share a large number of pair interactions which must be expected to lead to a correlation of their fluctuations. No analysis of these errors has been carried out so far. Properties calculated for some v,T-points with samples of size $N = 32$ and $N = 108$ are in good agreement.[18]

THE COMPUTER PROGRAMME

A large part of the computation is done by means of integer arithmetic (i.e., 24-bit words). This reduces the execution times of transfers, additions and subtractions and makes an extensive use of tables possible. The sample cube has the length $L = 1000$; the 3×108 coordinates are integers between 0 and 999. At the prevailing densities a hard core radius $r_c = 2·7$ Å corresponds to >100 units. No serious distortions are likely to result from the discreteness of the variables. Changes of volume are taken into account by scaling of the LJ parameters. The periodic boundary condition requires that in the calculation of a pair distance r_{ij}^2, the components x_{ij}, y_{ij}, z_{ij} must be "modified", i.e., if $x_i - x_j > L/2$, it is replaced by $x_i + L - x_j$, etc. To determine the interaction potential between particles i and j, the computer calculates $x_i - x_j$, $y_i - y_j$, $z_i - z_j$ from the listed particle coordinates; it then obtains the squares of the "modified" differences from a table, adds these and looks up the values of the potential and of the virial functions for the r_{ij}^2 from tables. Lists are kept of all coordinates, of all pair potentials in the "present" configuration (W_{ij}) and of the contribution of each particle i to the "present" value of Φ ($A_i = \frac{1}{2}\sum_{j \neq i} W_{ij}$, $\sum_i A_i = \Phi$). When a move is attempted by a displacement of particle k, a list is formed of the provisionally altered pair potentials (V_{kj}, all $j \neq k$), and the provisional new contribution of k to Φ ($A = \sum_{j \neq k} V_{kj}$). The provisional new Φ is accepted or rejected according to the criterion of ref. (1) (the exponential functions required for $\exp(-\beta \Delta \Phi)$ are tabulated). If the move is accepted, the lists of coordinates, pair interactions, particle contributions and the value of Φ are updated (e.g., $V_{kj} \to W_{kj}$, $A \to A_k$) and an entry corresponding to the new value of Φ is made in the histogram. If the move is rejected an entry corresponding to the "present" value of Φ is made (again) in the histogram. The treatment of the virials by means of tables is analogous.

The programme generates about 3000 configurations per minute on the Mark 1 Atlas computer of the University of London. Calculations for a v,T-point were based on not less than six ten-minute runs (168,000 configurations) of which the first one was discarded to allow for "equilibration". The formation of tables for the potential and the virial functions at the beginning of each run does not add significantly to the computing time; calculations with any other type of pair potential instead of the LJ-potential would not present any problem (though eqn. (13)-(16) for the isothermal extrapolation would not be applicable).

We thank the Institute of Computer Science (University of London) for the allocation of sufficient computer time, Mr. K. R. Knight for his contribution to the computer programme, and the Science Research Council for financial support. We are grateful to Prof. J. S. Rowlinson for bringing to our attention some important experimental data.

[1] N. Metropolis, A. W. Rosenbluth, M. N. Rosenbluth, A. H. Teller, and E. Teller, *J. Chem. Physics*, 1953, **21**, 1087.
[2] M. N. Rosenbluth and A. W. Rosenbluth, *J. Chem. Physics*, 1954, **22**, 881.
[3] W. W. Wood and J. D. Jacobson, *J. Chem. Physics*, 1957, **27**, 1207.
[4] W. W. Wood and F. R. Parker, *J. Chem. Physics*, 1957, **27**, 720.
[5] W. W. Wood, F. R. Parker and J. D. Jacobson, *Nuovo Cimento*, supp. 1, vol. 9, series X, 1958, 133.
[6] Z. L. Salsburg, J. D. Jacobson, W. Fickett and W. W. Wood, *J. Chem. Physics*, 1959, **30**, 65.
[7] E. B. Smith and K. R. Lea, *Trans. Faraady Soc.*, 1963, **59**, 153.
[8] A. Rotenberg, *J. Chem. Physics*, 1965, **43**, 1198.
[9] A. Rotenberg, *J. Chem. Physics*, 1965, **43**, 4377.
[10] B. J. Alder, *Physic. Rev. Letters*, 1966, **16**, 88.
[11] A. A. Barker, *Austral. J. Physics*, 1965, **18**, 119.
[12] S. G. Brush, H. L. Sahlin and E. Teller, *J. Chem. Physics*, 1966, **45**, 2102.
[13] A. Michels, Hub. Wijker and Hk. Wijker, *Physica*, 1949, **15**, 627.
[14] A. Michels, J. M. Levelt and G. J. Wolkers, *Physica*, 1958, **24**, 769.
[15] A. van Itterbeek and O. Verbeke, *Physica*, 1960, **26**, 931.
[16] A. van Itterbeek, O. Verbeke and K. Staes, *Physica*, 1963, **29**, 742.
[17] W. W. Wood and J. D. Jacobson, *Proc. Western Joint Computer Conference*, (San Francisco, 1959), 261.
[18] I. R. McDonald and K. Singer, to be published.
[19] F. Din, *Thermodynamic Functions of Gases*, vol. 2, (Butterworths, London, 1956), p. 146-201.
[20] P. Flubacher, A. J. Leadbetter and J. A. Morrison, *Proc. Physic. Soc.*, 1961, **78**, 1449.
[21] J. S. Rowlinson, *Liquids and Liquid Mixtures*, (Butterworths, London, 1959), p. 64.

GENERAL DISCUSSION

Dr. J. A. Barker and **Dr. D. Henderson** * (*C.S.I.R.O., Melbourne*) said: At present, reliable values for the radial distribution function and the equation of state are available only for the hard-sphere fluid. Thus, a promising method for dealing with systems of molecules with attractive forces is to consider the attractive potential as a perturbation on the hard-sphere potential. We have recently used perturbation theory to calculate the equation of state of a fluid of molecules interacting according to the square-well potential. This is a particularly good potential because the effect of the attractive forces is not complicated by the "softness" of the repulsive part of the potential. In addition, Monte Carlo [1] and molecular dynamics [2] calculations have provided quasi-experimental data with which our calculations can be compared without the uncertainty due to presence of three-body forces and the lack of knowledge of the intermolecular potential which is inevitable in applications to real fluids.

We divide the intermolecular potential into the "unperturbed" hard-sphere potential $u_0(R)$ and the "perturbation" $u_1(R)$. In our calculations, $u_1(R) = -\varepsilon$ for $\sigma < R < 1\cdot5\sigma$ and is zero otherwise. If N_1 is the number of intermolecular distances in the interval $\sigma < R < 1\cdot5\sigma$, then the Helmholtz free energy can be written:

$$\frac{F-F_0}{kT} = -\left(\frac{\varepsilon}{kT}\right)\langle N_1 \rangle - \frac{1}{2}\left(\frac{\varepsilon}{kT}\right)^2 [\langle N_1^2 \rangle - \langle N_1 \rangle^2] + O(T^{-3}), \qquad (1)$$

where F_0 is the free energy of the unperturbed system and the angular brackets mean "average over the configurations of the unperturbed system".

The average $\langle N_1 \rangle$ is given by an integral over the radial distribution function of the unperturbed system, $g_0(R)$. Thus, the first-order term is identical with that given by Zwanzig.[3] The second-order term is equivalent to that given by Zwanzig but is simpler and more suggestive. For example, it is intuitively plausible that the deviations of N_1 from its mean value should be least important at high densities so that the perturbation expansion (1) converges best at high densities. Also N_1 can be regarded as representing the number of molecules in a spherical shell surrounding a central molecule. If this shell were a large macroscopic volume, then

$$\langle N_1^2 \rangle - \langle N_1 \rangle^2 = \langle N_1 \rangle kT(\partial\rho/\partial p), \qquad (2)$$

where $(\partial\rho/\partial p)$ is the macroscopic compressibility. An even better approximation is obtained if we use the *local* compressibility instead of the macroscopic compressibility, i.e., if we replace $(\partial\rho/\partial p)_0 g_0(R)$ by $(\partial/\partial p)[\rho g(R)]_0$. Our results are based on this local compressibility approximation. However, similar results are obtained if the macroscopic compressibility approximation is used. We are presently making Monte Carlo calculations of $\langle N_1^2 \rangle$ and $\langle N_1 \rangle$ which will eventually supersede (2). At present we have only a few scattered results. However, these results do indicate that (2) is a reasonable approximation.

---

* permanent address: University of Waterloo, Canada.
[1] A. Rotenberg, *J. Chem. Physics*, 1965, **43**, 1148.
[2] B. J. Alder, unpublished results.
[3] R. W. Zwanzig, *J. Chem. Physics*, 1954, **22**, 1420.

Using (2), the free energy is

$$\frac{F-F_0}{NkT} = -2\pi\rho\left(\frac{\varepsilon}{kT}\right)\int_\sigma^{1\cdot 5\sigma} R^2 g_0(R)\mathrm{d}R -$$

$$\pi\rho\left(\frac{\varepsilon}{kT}\right)^2 \frac{(1-\eta)^4}{1+4\eta+4\eta^2} \frac{\partial}{\partial\rho}\left[\rho\int_\sigma^{1\cdot 5\sigma} R^2 g_0(R)\mathrm{d}R\right], \quad (3)$$

where $\eta = \pi\rho\sigma^3/6$. In obtaining (3) we have used the Percus–Yevick (PY) compressibility isotherm [1] to obtain $(\partial\rho/\partial p)_0$. In evaluating F we used the PY expression for $g_0(R)$. To order T^{-2}, (3) gives the exact second virial coefficient.

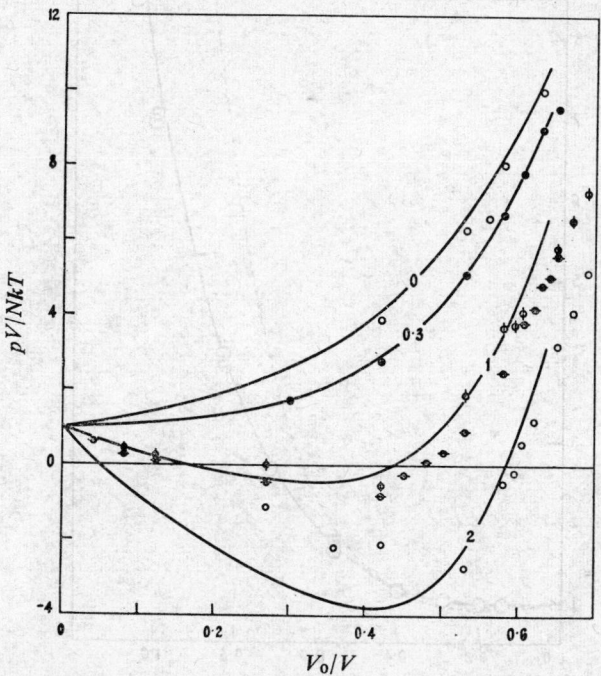

FIG. 1.—Equation of state for the square-well potential. The points are the Monte Carlo values of Rotenberg and the curves are isotherms calculated from eqn. (3). The points given by ○ ●, ⌽ and ⊙ were calculated using 256 molecules at $\varepsilon/kT = 0, 0\cdot 3, 1$ and 2, respectively, while the points given by ⊖ were calculated using 864 molecules at $\varepsilon/kT = 1$.

In fig. 1 we have compared the equation of state which results from numerical differentiation of (3) with the Monte Carlo calculations of Rotenberg.[2] The agreement is good—even at the lowest temperature, $kT/\varepsilon = 0\cdot 5$, which is far below the critical temperature. The agreement with Alder's [3] molecular dynamics calculations is even better.

We have generalized this procedure to include potentials with a soft core such as the 6 : 12 potential. For an arbitrary potential $u(R)$ we define a modified potential

[1] M. S. Wertheim, *Physic. Rev. Letters*, 1963, **10**, 321 ; *J. Math. Physics*, 1964, **5**, 643. E. Thiele, *J. Chem. Physics*, 1963, **39**, 474.
[2] A. Rotenberg, *J. Chem. Physics*, 1965, **43**, 1148.
[3] B. J. Alder, unpublished results.

by the equations,

$$v(\alpha, \gamma, d, \sigma; R) = u\left(d + \frac{R-d}{\alpha}\right), \quad d + \frac{R-d}{\alpha} < \sigma,$$

$$= 0, \quad \sigma < d + \frac{R-d}{\alpha} < d + \frac{\sigma-d}{\alpha},$$

$$= \gamma u(R), \quad R > \sigma. \tag{4}$$

When $\alpha = \gamma = 0$, v becomes the hard-sphere potential with diameter d, while for $\alpha = \gamma = 1$ the original potential $u(R)$ is recovered; α is an inverse steepness parameter

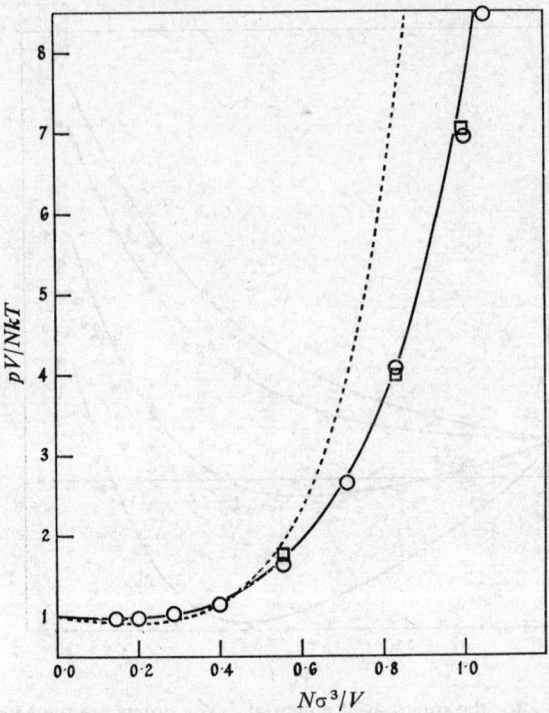

FIG. 2.—Equation of state for the 6:12 potential, $kT/\varepsilon = 2.74$. The solid line gives the results obtained from eqn. (5) and the broken line gives the results of McQuarrie and Katz. The points given by ○ and □ were calculated by Wood and Parker for 32 and 108 molecules, respectively.

for the repulsive region and γ a depth parameter for the attractive region. By a method based on the ideas of Rowlinson [1] and Zwanzig [2] the first derivatives of the configuration integral with respect to α and γ can be calculated in the limit $\alpha, \gamma \to 0$. Thus, we find for the Helmholtz free energy

$$\frac{F}{NkT} = \frac{F_0}{NkT} - \frac{2\pi N d^2 \alpha}{V} g_0\left(\frac{Nd^3}{V}, 1\right)\left[\int_0^\sigma \exp\left(-u(R)/kT\right)dR - (\sigma-d)\right] +$$

$$\frac{2\pi N \gamma}{V} \int_\sigma^\infty g_0\left(\frac{Nd^3}{V}, \frac{R}{d}\right)\frac{u(R)}{kT} R^2 dR + \text{higher order terms}, \tag{5}$$

[2] J. S. Rowlinson, *Mol. Physics*, 1964, **7**, 349; 1964, **8**, 107.
[1] R. W. Zwanzig, *J. Chem. Physics*, 1954, **22**, 1420.

where F_0 and g_0 are the free energy and radial distribution function respectively for the hard-sphere system. For $\alpha = \gamma = 1$ we obtain an expression for the free energy corresponding to the potential $u(R)$. We choose σ so that $u(\sigma) = 0$ and determine d so that the second term in (5) is zero. These choices should minimize the contribution of the higher-order terms and are a generalization of Rowlinson's procedure.[1] In addition, these choices ensure that (5) reduces to (3) if the square-well potential is used. Thus, d is an effective core diameter which may depend on temperature but not on density. Pressures calculated by differentiation of (5), using the Percus–Yevick radial distribution function, the 6:12 potential, and neglecting the higher-order terms, are compared with the Monte Carlo results of Wood and Parker[2] for $kT/\varepsilon = 2.74$ in fig. 2. The contribution of the term in γ^2 calculated by our "local compressibility" approximation is very small at this temperature. Also shown are results given by the equation of McQuarrie and Katz.[3] The results given by eqn. (5) appear to be satisfactory.

Dr. P. Hutchinson (*A.E.R.E., Harwell*) said: I report the results of some calculations in which the Percus–Yevick (P.Y.) and hypernetted chain (H.N.C.) approximations are tested against the molecular dynamics calculations of Rahman[4] at densities corresponding to the liquid phase of argon.

The procedure is that suggested by Johnson, Hutchinson and March.[5] From the pair correlation function $h(r)$, computed by Rahman, the direct correlation function $C(r)$ was calculated. It is then possible from the P.Y. and H.N.C. equations to calculate the potentials $\phi_{\text{P.Y.}}$ and $\phi_{\text{H.N.C.}}$ which would give such forms of $C(r)$ and $h(r)$ in these approximations. These can then be compared with the potential $\phi(r)$ which was the starting point of Rahman's calculation. This is a 6-exp Buckingham potential truncated at $7.65\,\text{Å}$; the temperature was $T = 85.5°\text{K}$, and the density was 0.02103 atm/Å^3 (equivalent to an argon density of 1.407 g/cm^3). The temperature is thus significantly below the critical temperature for argon.

The numerical procedure is to calculate $C(r)$ via a double Fourier transform. Fourier transformation of the Ornstein Zernike equation gives

$$\tilde{C}(k) = \tilde{h}(k)/(1+\rho\tilde{h}(k)), \tag{1}$$

where

$$\tilde{h}(k) = \int \exp(-i\boldsymbol{k}\cdot\boldsymbol{r})h(r)\mathrm{d}^3r. \tag{1a}$$

Hence to calculate $C(r)$ we first evaluate $\tilde{h}(k)$ by Fourier transformation. From this we may obtain $\tilde{C}(k)$ from (1), and $\tilde{C}(k)$ may be transformed to obtain $C(r)$. Great care is necessary to obtain accurate results from a numerical Fourier transforms method. The overall accuracy of the method may be assessed by evaluating

$$h_1(r) = \frac{1}{(2\pi)^3}\int \exp(i\boldsymbol{k}\cdot\boldsymbol{r})\tilde{h}(k)\mathrm{d}^3k.$$

Formally, $h_1(r) \equiv h(r)$, so that the difference between the two functions is an indication of the error in the method. Comparison of these two functions showed that the differences were about 1 % except at the origin where they may rise to ~ 5 %. However, errors near the origin are unimportant as this region contributes little to the

---

[1] J. S. Rowlinson, *Mol. Physics*, 1964, **7**, 349; 1964, **8**, 107.
[2] W. W. Wood and F. R. Parker, *J. Chem. Physics*, 1957, **27**, 720.
[3] D. A. McQuarrie and J. L. Katz, *J. Chem. Physics*, 1966, **44**, 2393.
[4] A. Rahman, *Physic. Rev. Letters*, 1964, **12**, 575.
[5] M. D. Johnson, P. Hutchinson and N. H. March, *Proc. Roy. Soc. A*, 1964, **282**, 283.

transformation (1a). An additional check is available by direct solution of the Ornstein Zernike equation for $C(r)$. Given $h(r)$ the O–Z equation is simply an inhomogeneous linear integral equation which may be solved by direct inversion. While this last method is subject to greater numerical error it produces the same general result for $C(r)$ as that described below.

The results of the Fourier transform method are shown in fig. 1 where $C(r)$ is plotted with $h(r)$ and $-\phi(r)/kT$. The values for $C(r)$ are reliable for $r \leqslant 6$ Å, in that the values obtained there are insensitive to the truncation point of $h(r)$ and the choice

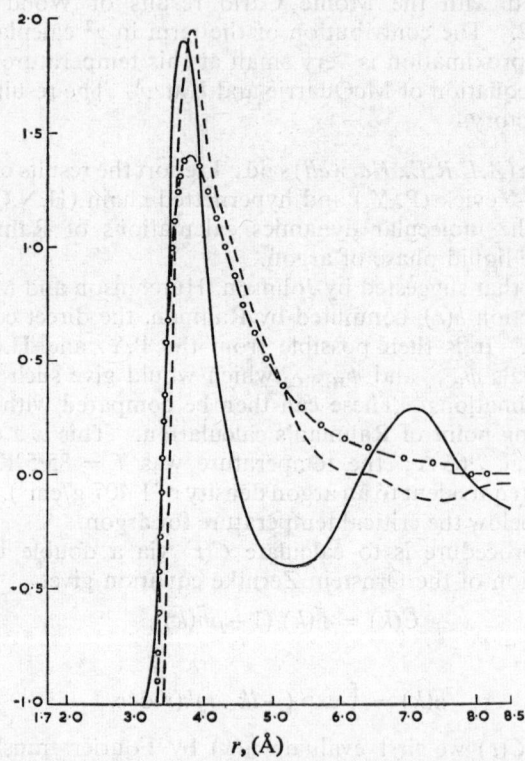

Fig. 1.—Comparison of the direct and total correlation functions and the potential.
———, $h(r)$; – – –, $C(r)$; ○, $\varphi(r)/kT$.

of mesh for the integral over k. Beyond 6 Å the results are strongly sensitive to the above variations and decrease in magnitude when $\tilde{C}(k)$ is smoothed. This indicates that the last part of the curve is due to cancellation error (noise) and that $C(r)$ is vanishingly small in this region. The most notable feature of $C(r)$ is that it has the same general shape as the potential but dies away rather more rapidly. This is contrary to the expectation of both the P.Y. and H.N.C. approximations that $C(r) \sim -\phi(r)/kT$ for r large. In fig. 2 are shown the two approximate potentials $\phi_{\text{P.Y.}}(r)$ and $\phi_{\text{H.N.C.}}(r)$ in comparison with $\phi(r)$, given in dimensionless units. The fit obtained by $\phi_{\text{H.N.C.}}(r)$ is much the better of the two. The well depth of $\phi_{\text{P.Y.}}(r)$ is much too large and displaced too far to the right. The comparison between well depths is

$$\phi_{\text{P.Y.}}(4 \cdot 6)/kT = -4 \cdot 01, \qquad \phi_{\text{H.N.C.}}(4 \cdot 0)/kT = -1 \cdot 28, \qquad \phi(3 \cdot 8)/kT = -1 \cdot 40.$$

It has been shown by Gaskell [1] that when the compressibility is small the H.N.C. approximation gives values of the pressure which are several orders of magnitude too large the virial equation is used. This situation would hold here as calculation gives

$$kT(\partial \rho/\partial p)_T \simeq 0.05.$$

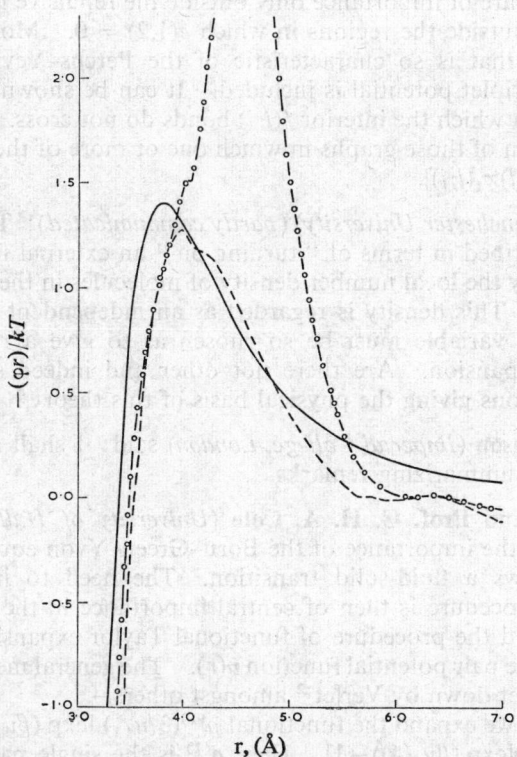

FIG. 2.—Comparison of exact and approximate potentials.
———, $-\varphi(r)/kT$; – – –, $-\varphi_{\text{HNC}}(r)/kT$; O, $-\varphi_{\text{P.Y.}}(r)/kT$

The virial equation is

$$P = \rho kT - \frac{2\pi}{3}\rho^2 \int_0^\infty r^3 \phi'(r) g(r) dr.$$

This minimum value of $\phi_{\text{H.N.C.}}(r)$ is shifted just far enough to bring the large positive values of $-\phi'(r)$ into coincidence with the peak in $g(r)$, and this produces the gross over-estimate of the pressure. The virial equation is thus a very sensitive test of any theory in the low-pressure, high-density state of a liquid. Finally we may conclude that despite the poor results obtained from the virial equation the H.N.C. approximation is superior to the P.Y. equation for a liquid well below its critical temperature. Grateful thanks are due to Dr. A. Rahman for making his results available for this calculation.

Prof. J. S. Rowlinson (*Imperial College, London*) said: In his lecture Rushbrooke mentioned that he and Silbert [2] have been able to show that the inclusion of a triplet

[1] T. Gaskell, *Proc. Physic. Soc.*, 1966, **89**, 231.
[2] G. S. Rushbrooke and M. Silbert, *Mol. Physics*, 1967, **12**, 505.

potential in the hyper-netted chain theory is "particularly simple" since it leads only to the introduction of a new elementary graph, $x_1(1,2)$ in his notation, which is of lower order in the density than those arising from the two-body potential. There is an analogous result for the Percus–Yevick theory.[1] The new graph is here always of the form $[e(1,2)x_1(1,2)]$, which leads at once to the physically reasonable result that the triplet forces are of importance only outside the repulsive regions of the two-body potential, i.e., outside the regions in which $e(1,2) = 0$. Moreover, the simple graphical expansion that is so characteristic of the Percus–Yevick theory is still preserved when the triplet potential is included. It can be shown that $g(1,2)$ is still a sum of all graphs in which the interior $f(i,j)$ bonds do not cross. The only change needed is the inclusion of those graphs in which one or more of the peripheral bonds are not $f(i,j)$, but $[e(i,j)x_1(i,j)]$.

Dr. S. Levine (*Manchester University*) (*partly communicated*): The Percus–Yevick theory has been described in terms of "turning on" an external field which enables one to vary arbitrarily the local number density of molecules in the fluid in the grand canonical ensemble. This density is regarded as an independent variable and then a suitable dependent variable must be so chosen as to give a rapidly convergent functional Taylor expansion. Are there not other and indeed simpler and more meaningful explanations giving the physical basis of this theory?

Prof. J. S. Rowlinson (*Imperial College, London*) said: I shall attempt to answer this question in my summarizing remarks.

Mr. A. Moreton and **Prof. G. H. A. Cole** (*University of Hull*) (*communicated*): We too would stress the importance of the Born–Green–Yvon equation as an exact equation which shows a fluid-solid transition. The need to improve upon the Kirkwood closure procedure is then of central importance in the theory of liquids. We have recently used the procedure of functional Taylor expansion to express $g^{(3)}$ in terms of $g^{(2)}$ and the pair potential function $u(r)$. The general method of functional expansion has been set down by Verlet [2] amongst others.

For our purposes we expand the functional $\rho^{(1)}(3/u_{12})\,[\exp(\beta u_1(3))-1]$ as a series in terms of $\rho^{(1)}(4/u_1)[\exp(\beta u_1(4))-1]$. Here $\rho^{(1)}$ is the single particle distribution, u_{12} is an external potential due to the presence of two extra particles at positions r_1 and r_2. The expansion is made about the condition $u_1 = 0$; $u_{12} = u_1 + u_2$ reduces to $u_{12} = u_{21}$ in this limit. Taken to the linear term, our expansion gives the Kirkwood superposition statement, which is (1) of the Rice–Young paper but with $\tau = 0$. The inclusion of the quadratic term in the expansion gives

$$g^{(3)}(1,2,3) = g^{(2)}(1,2)g^{(2)}(1,3)g^{(2)}(2,3)\left[1+\rho\int dr_4 y(1,4)f(1,4)\times \left\{\frac{g^{(3)}(2,3,4)}{g^{(2)}(2,3)}-g^{(2)}(2,4)-g^{(2)}(3,4)+1\right\}\right]. \quad (1)$$

Here we use

$$y(r) = g^{(2)}(r)\exp\beta u(r),$$
$$f(r) = \exp(-\beta u(r))-1.$$

In the low-density limit the various functions in (1) can be expressed as a simple density expansion using an iterative method and (1) is then exact up to the linear term

---

[1] J. S. Rowlinson, *Mol. Physics*, 1967, **12**, 513.
[2] L. Verlet, *Physica*, 1966, **32**, 304.

in the density. When used in conjunction with the Born–Green–Yvon equation, (1) then provides as an exact expression for the fourth virial coefficient. The triplet term in the functional Taylor expansion has also been obtained. Although it is too lengthy an expression to set down here we have found that, in the low density limit, it leads to an exact expression for $g^{(3)}$ up to the quadratic density term, and so gives an exact expression for the fifth virial coefficient.

For higher densities than those where $g^{(2)}$ can be expressed as a simple density expansion, the above expansion procedure is still applicable and the expression (1) for $g^{(3)}$ can be used as a closure expression for the Born–Green–Yvon equation. The solution of this more general situation, for given $u(r)$, could apply to higher fluid densities. We are at present calculating $g^{(2)}$ by using (1) and the Born–Green–Yvon equation, for a function u of the Lennard–Jones type but with a hard core at vanishing interparticle separation. Our method could be extended to include correlations higher than the triplet. In this way it can be considered with the method of Fisher.[1]

Prof. Stuart A. Rice and **Dr. David A. Young** (*University of Chicago*) said: The mediocre quality of the thermodynamic functions which are obtained from the solutions of the Yvon–Born–Green equation seem to exclude this equation as a useful tool in the study of fluids. However, by modifying the YBG equation we may obtain useful and interesting results. The YBG equation arises from the introduction of the Kirkwood superposition approximation into the second member of an infinite sequence of integral equations. This latter equation, which involves the three-particle distribution $g(123)$, is *exact*, and we may construct increasingly good approximations to this exact equation by multiplying the superposition product by a series of triplet correlation terms. By introducing the first two correlation terms, we get good results for rigid spheres and discs, and for 6-12 and square-well potentials. We may even expect good results from the simple YBG equation for long-range potentials of the Coulomb type.[2]

The exact meaning of the singularity in the YBG equation is unclear. However, Kirkwood has shown [3] that periodic, solid-like solutions may exist at densities above this singular point. Also, by introducing an approximation to the long-range behaviour of $g(123)$ into the modified equations we may be able to correlate the YBG singularity with the fluid-solid phase transitions predicted by molecular dynamics. Despite the limitations imposed by the speed of present-day computers, we hope that these studies will add a little to our understanding of the statistical theory of fluids and phase transitions.

Prof. J. Walkley and **Dr. Wing Y. Ng** (*Simon Fraser University*) said: In two papers use has been made of the Lennard-Jones 12-6 potential. In each case an agreement between theory and experiment is found, despite the inadequacy of this potential function to express the two-body second virial coefficient behaviour. In an N-body situation the total potential experienced by any one particle cannot be regarded as the simple pair-additive sum of the interaction with all other particles. For the 3-body case the perturbation of the pair-additive sum coming from the mutual disposition of the three particles has been calculated for the dispersion r^{-6} attraction term.[4] The use of the 12 : 6 pair potential in a strictly pair-additive manner appears to generate an (apparently) acceptable N-body potential. In calculations pertaining

[1] I. Z. Fisher, *Statistical Theory of Liquids* (Univ. of Chicago Press, 1964), p. 152.
[2] C. W. Hirt, *Physics Fluids*, 1967, **10**, 565.
[3] J. G. Kirkwood and E. Monroe, *J. Chem. Physics*, 1941, **9**, 514.
[4] R. J. Bell and A. E. Kingston, *Proc. Physic. Soc.*, 1966, **88**, 901.

to the solid phase of the inert gases, it was similarly observed that the simple bi-reciprocal 12 : 6 potential allowed theoretical volume-temperature and heat capacity-temperature data are in good agreement.[1] For a range of two parameter m : 6 potentials (viz., $\phi(r_{ij}) = \varepsilon f(r_{ij}/\sigma)$, with usual rotation) the characteristic parameters ε and σ can be obtained by fitting the theory (a harmonic Einstein theory) to certain properties extrapolated to °K. The total lattice energy U_0 and the molar volume V_0 were originally used. The "best" set of parameters were then obtained by a plot of the theoretical reduced zero-point energy (λ_0^*) and the reduced "experimental" zero-point energy ($9R\theta_\infty/8N\varepsilon$, with θ_∞ the limiting Debye frequency) simultaneously as functions of the de Boer parameter ($\Lambda = h/(m\varepsilon)^{\frac{1}{2}}\sigma$). The intersection of the two curves give the "best" value of ε and σ without specifying the "best" potential function. However, this set of values allowed both second virial and viscosity data for the inert gases to be reduced to a corresponding states pattern of behaviour.[2]

TABLE 1.—$m : n$ KIHARA CORE POTENTIAL PARAMETERS FOR ARGON

$m:n$	ε/k(°K)	σ(Å)	β	ν	λ_0 (cal mole^{-1})
9 : 6	123·2	3·3932	0·157	0	187
10 : 6	123·0	3·3948	0·1056	0	187
11 : 6	122·0	3·3960	0·0567	0	187
12 : 6	120·5	3·3987	0·0098	0	187

Experimental data: $U_0 = -1846$ cal mole^{-1}; $R_0 = 3.7549$ (Å); $K_T = 0.375$ cm dyne$^{-2} \times 10^{10}$; $\lambda_0 == (9/8\theta_\infty) = 187$ cal mole^{-1}.

TABLE 2.—$m : n$ KIHARA CORE POTENTIAL PARAMETERS FOR XENON

$m:n$	ε/k(°K)	σ(Å)	β	ν	λ_0 (cal mole^{-1})
9 : 6	240	3·9483	0·157	0	133
10 : 6	238	3·9510	0·106	0	133
11 : 6	236	3·9521	0·0567	0	133
12 : 6	234	3·9599	0·0098	0	133

Experimental data: $U_0 = -3856$ cal mole^{-1}; $R_0 = 4.3356$ (Å); $K_T = 0.28$ cm dyne$^{-2} \times 10^{10}$; $\lambda_0 = (9/8\theta_\infty) = 123$ cal mole^{-1}.

We have extended these calculations to include a non-additivity term in the static lattice potential sum. In keeping with theory we consider only the largest term coming from the 3-body interaction and written as $A\nu/a_{ij}^9$, where A is the appropriate lattice constant, a_{ij} the nearest neighbour distance and ν an unknown non-additive coefficient. Calculations were also made more flexible by considering a series of $m : 6$ Kihara core pair potentials, viz.,

$$\phi(r) = K\varepsilon\left[\left(\frac{1-\delta}{r-\delta}\right)^m - \left(\frac{1-\delta}{r-\delta}\right)^6\right]$$

where $r = r_{ij}/\sigma$ tc. The calculation involves four unknown coefficients, the reduction parameters ε and σ, the coefficient ν and the reduced hard-core cut off δ. Four zero-point properties are required for their evaluation, and besides the three used above, U_0, V_0 and λ_0, an accurate value of the zero-point isothermal compressibility K_T could be used for both argon and xenon. The parameters obtained by fitting the theoretical model (again a harmonic Einstein model) to this data are given in tables 1 and 2.

[1] I. H. Hillier and J. Walkley, *J. Chem. Physics*, 1965, **43**, 3713.
[2] J. Walkley, *J. Chem. Physics*, 1966, **44**, 2417.

From these tables the following observations may be made: (i) for all $m:6$ potentials examined the non-additivity coefficient is effectively zero; (ii) for both argon and zenon, for the same value of m the resulting value of δ is identical, intimating an essentially corresponding states behaviour pattern, and (iii) for both argon and zenon each of the $m:6$ Kihara potentials gives, through the different δ values, curves which are virtually identical and which are exceedingly close to that of a $12:6$ Lennard-Jones potential. The calculations are, then, consistent with the accepted use of the Lennard-Jones 12-6 potential as an acceptable " many body " potential.

Prof. U. v. Weber (*Rostock University*) said: We studied the deviations from ideality of vapours by an isochoric method to get the second virial coefficients and by means of them the intermolecular potentials. Density was varied to take care of higher coefficients. To make the adjustment of parameters and powers in r unambigously, the range of temperature must be as large as possible. The best fitting powers of attraction obtained by the method of Buckingham are r^{-9} for benzene and n-octane and r^{-10} for hexane and n-octane with reasonable diameters. I restrict myself to quasispherical molecules.

Only r^{-6} is theoretically justified and is indeed a fair potential for rare gases, but not satisfying for large molecules. In our Institute, W. Lichtenstein investigated various potential models. Kihara allows for extension to hard cores, but his assumption of effect only between the two nearest points is not justified. Laeuger considered r^{-6} potentials between the corners of two cubes. Hoover and Rocco regarded spherical shell potentials with centres of attraction and repulsion on the shell, but they integrated only numerically. Lichtenstein considers two spherical models: attraction in -6 power between every volume element of the first particle to every volume element of the second and between every surface element of the first particle to the second. Repulsion was assumed in either model between the two centres in powers -24, to obtain an analytically integrable expression. The shell model fitted better. The argon, tetrachlormethane and benzene data were fitted as well as desirable by this potential with reasonable diameters. To avoid singularity in the case of contact, recession of the points of attraction up to a distinct amount was supposed. This seems to me a reasonable step towards a dynamic model. The potential well is much deeper and more narrow than for a Lennard–Jones potential, a fact which might be taken into account in the more complicated theory of liquids.

Random Close-Packed Hard-Sphere Model

I. Effect of Introducing Holes

By J. D. Bernal and S. V. King

Birkbeck College, University of London, Malet Street,
London, W.C.1.

Received 19*th December*, 1966

The structures have been examined of lower density random models, obtained by removing atoms from the close-packed, random-model built here. Radial distribution functions and coordination distributions for models containing different proportions of holes have been calculated.

Radial distribution functions calculated from X-ray or neutron diffraction patterns of liquids show that the effect of temperature is less to increase the interatomic distances between atoms than to reduce the number of neighbours of each atom. That is, the position of the first peak in the radial distribution function changes little but the total area of the peak which is proportional to the number of first neighbours decreases.

In the random close-packed sphere model of a liquid the increase in volume corresponding to increase in temperature [1] could be effected in two ways. First, the proportions of the basic polyhedra could be changed, i.e., there would be an increase in the proportions of the larger polyhedra so that there would be more archimedean antiprisms and tetragonal dodecahedra and fewer of the smaller polyhedra, the octahedra and tetrahedra. Secondly, atomic-sized holes could be introduced into the body of the liquid.

By using the first method alone it is only possible to achieve a maximum increase in volume of about 17 %. It is of interest therefore to investigate the effects of introducing atomic sized holes at random into the hard sphere model (or rather to remove atoms at random from the model).

Atoms were removed randomly from the model. Initially, the removal of atoms was restricted so that no two holes could be neighbours, a " neighbour " being defined to be within $\sqrt{2}$ diameters of another atom. There will be a limit to the number of holes which can be introduced in this way. A preliminary calculation was carried out to ascertain the maximum possible number of holes which could be removed from the model so that no two holes were neighbours.

This was done as follows: the central atom in the mass was removed, then, looking at the atoms in order of their distance from the centre of the mass, each atom was tested if it was a neighbour of a previously chosen hole. The atom remained in the assembly if it was not a neighbour of any previously chosen hole; then it was removed from the assembly. This process continued until all atoms in the assembly had been visited. The maximum number of holes which could be introduced in this way was 18·6 % (a neighbour being defined as within 1·414), roughly corresponding to an increase in volume of 18·6 %. If a neighbour was defined as being within 1·1 atomic diameters (position of potential = 0 for Lennard-Jones potential) the number of holes which could be introduced was 26 %. For a neighbour defined as within 1·05 diameters the number of holes which could be introduced was 28·3 %.

Two sets of calculations were carried out on introducing holes at random into the hard sphere assembly: (A) atoms were removed only if they were not neighbours of

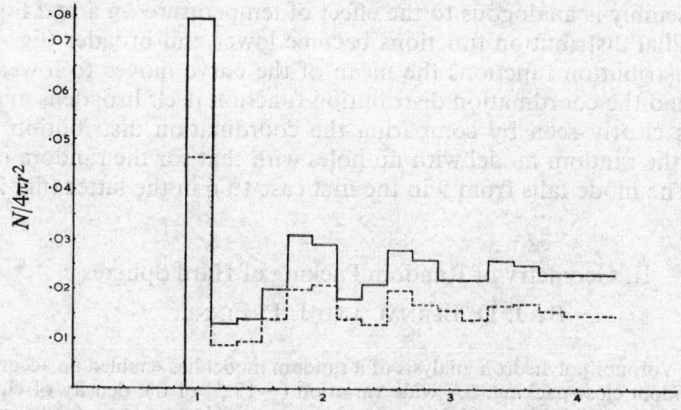

FIG. 1.—Radial distribution functions. Random model with no holes and 35 % holes.

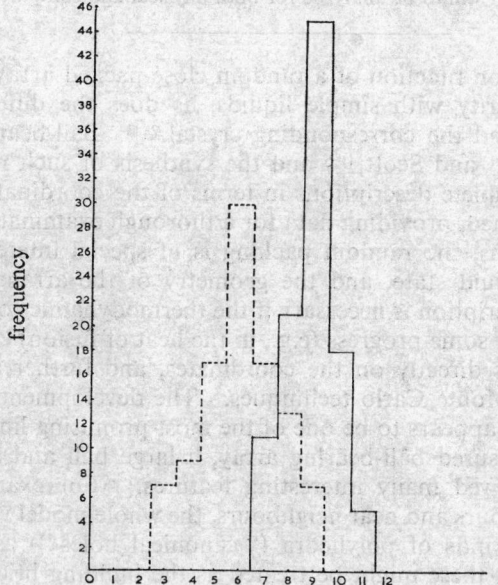

FIG. 2.—Coordination distribution functions. Random model with no holes and 35% holes.

holes already introduced (i.e., within 1·414); (B) atoms were removed at random, holes could be neighbours. In the first (A) set of calculations after about 16·6 % of holes had been introduced it was impossible to introduce any further holes unless holes were allowed to be neighbours.

In both sets of calculations, holes were introduced in increasing proportions of 5 %. First 5 % holes were introduced then 10, 15, 20, 25, 30, 35, 40 and finally 45, %

this being well above the critical volume. In the first (A) set of calculations after the saturation point of 16·6 % had been reached all further holes were allowed to be neighbours. For each of these new assemblies the radial distribution function and coordination distribution function was calculated.

In general outline, the effect of introducing holes into a random close-packed hard-sphere assembly is analogous to the effect of temperature on a real liquid. The peaks of the radial distribution functions become lower and broader (fig. 1). In the coordination distribution functions the mean of the curve moves to lower values of coordination, and the coordination distribution function itself broadens and becomes lower. This is clearly seen by comparing the coordination distribution histogram obtained from the random model with no holes with that for the random model with 35 % holes. The mode falls from 9 in the first case to 6 in the latter (fig. 2).

II. Geometry of Random Packing of Hard Spheres

By J. D. Bernal and J. L. Finney

A preliminary Voronoi polyhedron analysis of a random model has enabled an accurate fixing of the density of random close-packing. A wide variation (∼15 % of the density of closest regular packing) in local density is found, correlated with various topological types of polyhedra. The suspected predominance of 5-sided faces is verified, while the average number of faces per polyhedron, and the average number of sides per face, are a few per cent greater than the theoretical predictions of Coxeter. Much data remain still to be analyzed for both physical and computer models.

The radial distribution function of a random close-packed array of hard spheres shows a striking similarity with simple liquids, as does the difference in density between this packing and the corresponding crystal.[2,3] Ball-bearing models have been studied by Bernal[1] and Scott,[4,5] and the synthesis of such models attempted using computers. Complete descriptions in terms of the coordinates of the packed centres have been obtained, providing data for a thorough examination of the arrays.

Among other reasons, the random packing is of special interest because of its similarities with the liquid state, and the geometry of the arrangement itself. A manageable overall description is necessary if the thermodynamics of such an array is to be computed, though some progress (e.g., in the heat of fusion) can be made using computer computations directly on the coordinates, and further advances may be possible by exploring Monte Carlo techniques. The development of some kind of " statistical geometry " appears to be one of the most promising lines of attack.

From our first measured ball-bearing array, a large ball and spoke model was constructed. This showed many interesting features.[1] For example, considering vectors between neighbours and near neighbours, the whole model was seen to consist of only five different kinds of polyhedra (" canonical holes ") as the basic units, suggesting that perhaps these might be treated as the building bricks of a statistical geometry. Our present work, however, concentrates on describing the model as a network of Voronoi polyhedra. If we take an array of points, and perpendicularly bisect the vectors between them, we obtain a large number of intersecting planes. To define the Voronoi polyhedron of a point, we select the smallest polyhedron so formed about that point, ensuring no further possible planes can cut this chosen set. This polyhedron contains all those points closer to the chosen centre than to any other : hence, a network of such polyhedra completely fills space. The construction of the two dimensional " Voronoi polygon " is shown in fig. 3. Now each polyhedron contains information sufficient to describe completely the neighbourhood of a point :

we are trying to develop some statistical theory to describe an extended random model in these terms.

In a pilot experiment,[1] a number of plasticene spheres were compressed together, and the distribution of faces on each resulting polyhedron recorded. More recently, we have developed a computer programme to elucidate the polyhedra exactly using the coordinates of a measured hard-sphere array. Before we could use the data of Scott,[5, 6] it was necessary to correct the coordinates of a few centres apparently separated by much less than a sphere diameter. This was done by building a large scale ball-and-spoke model—which incidentally exhibited the same structural features of our original model; no rigorous structural analysis on the basis of the five canonical holes has, however, been attempted. All the errors thus found were simply ones of transcription. This large model also proved a help in choosing those centres whose Voronoi polyhedra would not intersect the outer boundary: in this way 407 of the 1006 centres were chosen.

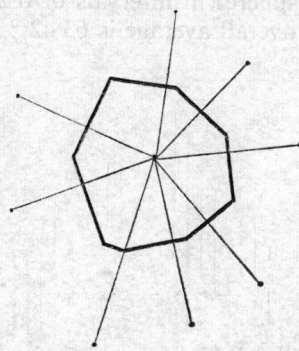

Fig. 3.—The construction of a Voronoi polygon.

The Voronoi computer programme starts by calculating the vertices of each polyhedron. As every vertex is equidistant from four centres, this basically reduces to solving four simultaneous equations. All possible combinations of four centres within a restricting combination radius r_c are taken, and the resulting solution accepted as a vertex if no other centre is closer than the initial four. The value of r_c was fixed at 1·6 diameters by trial runs on a limited number of polyhedra: if this proved insufficient for any particular polyhedron (as it did in two cases where r_c was consequently increased to $1·61d$) an inconsistency would arise in the form of a missing vertex. The reference numbers of the four centres associated with each vertex are stored: this provides sufficient data for the second half of the programme to sort out the topology. Each polyhedron takes about two seconds on the University of London's Atlas computer.

The programme produces the following data for each polyhedron: (1) the centre number and its coordinates; (2) the coordinates of the vertices, with their associated centres; (3) for each face: (a) the number of edges, (b) the area of the face, (c) the volume subtended by each face at the centre (d) the centre-face perpendicular distance, (e) the number of the centre with which the face is shared; (4) the total number of faces, total area, total volume, and percentage density; (5) the number of faces with 3, 4, ... etc. edges. e.g., 03651000 denotes three quadrangular, six pentagonal, five hexagonal, and one septagonal faces.

Cumulative histograms are output of: (1) the number of M-sided faces; (2) the number of N-faced polyhedra; (3) polyhedron density.

All these data are stored on tape, and are easily accessible for further computation if required.

SURVEY OF INITIAL RESULTS

DENSITY OF RANDOM PACKING

Scott [4] has measured the density directly, allowing for surface effects by extrapolation. We have previously attempted a measurement by calculating the *actual volume of material* within spheres of increasing radius from the centre of the array: this also involved extrapolation as the oscillations had not quite died out when the sphere cut the mass boundary.

In contrast, the Voronoi polyhedron provides, within the limits of the data, an exact measurement of average density, as well as the local variations. The results for 407 polyhedra are shown in fig. 4, which is a histogram of polyhedron density (percentage occupied by the sphere) in intervals of 0·25 %: the large spread from 57 to 70 % is obvious. The overall average is 63·42 %, which occurs at a *minimum*

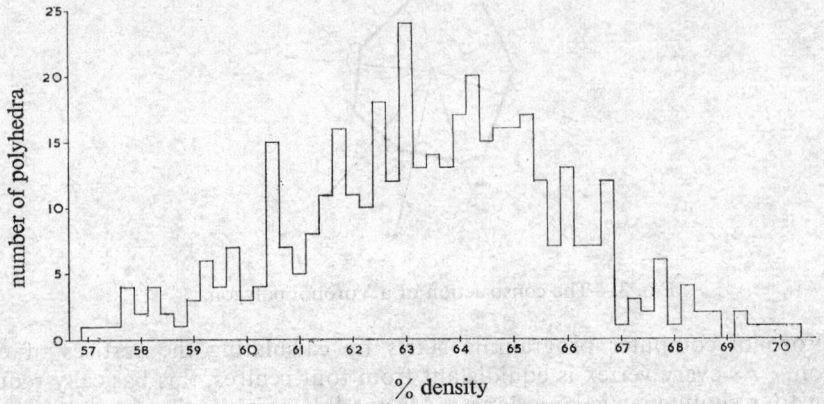

FIG. 4.—Polyhedron densities.

in the histogram. If we plot separate histograms for polyhedra with the same number N of faces ($N = 12, 13, \ldots, 19$), we find, as expected, that the mean density $\bar{\rho}$ increases as the number of faces N falls, with considerable overlap between them. The results of these separate histograms are plotted in fig. 5. The lengths of the ordinates indicate standard deviations from the mean (except for polyhedra with 18 and 19 faces), and the figure by each point is the number of such N-faced polyhedra. The average for the whole 407 centres is also plotted for comparison.

Not only the average density, but the peaks also appear to have no obvious structural significance (e.g., in terms of polyhedron type). The first implication is that the average density is a purely statistical figure. But this does not invalidate the possibility of there being a statistical upper limit to the overall density of random packing, as we cannot consider the array solely in terms of *isolated* polyhedra. For example, although some very high density polyhedra occur, we cannot necessarily increase the proportion of these at the expense of those of lower density, as the geometry of the packing may not allow this. Thus, although there may be local regions of density greater than the average they may occur only in conjunction with balancing polyhedra of lower density such as to keep the average density below a maximum value. A study of the packing of polyhedra around a central polyhedron is an obvious next step. We are also planning to examine the changing local density pattern in packings of different average densities, and see how the distribution of

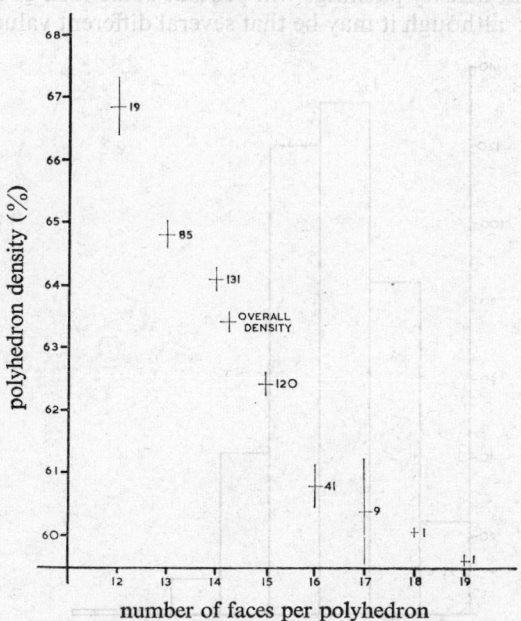

FIG. 5.—Polyhedron density against number of faces.

polyhedron types, as well as their sizes, changes. A detailed comparison of our results with the density curve of Kiang,[7] obtained from a *completely random* fragmentation of space, may also be useful, although our system is much more restricted.

FACES AND EDGES OF POLYHEDRA

Both the average number $\bar{N}$ of faces per polyhedron, and the average number $\bar{M}$ of edges per face may be important in the overall statistical picture. The distribution of M and N are shown in figs. 6 and 7, which are histograms of number of polyhedra with a given number N of faces, and number of faces with a given number M of edges respectively. The mean $\bar{N}$ of 14·28 is considerably higher than the 13·6 obtained from the plasticene spheres [1] and the 13·56 from Coxeter's theoretical model.[8] The histogram of the number M of edges per face verifies the predominance of five-fold, and shows traces of eight-, nine-, and even ten-fold faces. $\bar{M}$ is 5·160, higher than Coxeter's 5·115.[8,9]

These higher values immediately suggest two points. (a) In the plasticene model, very small faces are likely to be difficult to observe. Taking a sphere diameter about $\frac{3}{4}''$, and faces less than 1 mm² in area to be unobserved, the Voronoi analysis of the Scott model shows that about 130 faces come below this limit. $\bar{N}$ for the plasticene model is thus increased to about 13·9. This factor does nothing to remove the discrepancy with Coxeter's theoretical model. (b) If the packing density were lower than the maximum limit, $\bar{N}$ would be greater than the $\bar{N}_{\min}$ expected at that limit. Moreover, as fig. 5 suggests, a decrease in the spread of the density histogram keeping the same average would decrease $\bar{N}$, and a change in polyhedron distribution of a more general nature could have a similar effect. However, with regard to changes in distribution, we must bear in mind the possible restrictions imposed by the geometry of the packing, as discussed above.

Analysis of different density packings will provide some idea of how $\overline{N}$ (and hence $\overline{M}$) vary with density: although it may be that several different values of $\overline{N}$ may occur

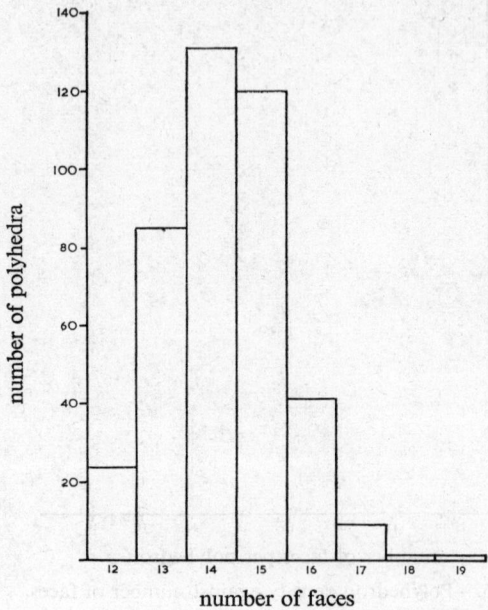

Fig. 6.—Histogram of number of faces per polyhedron.

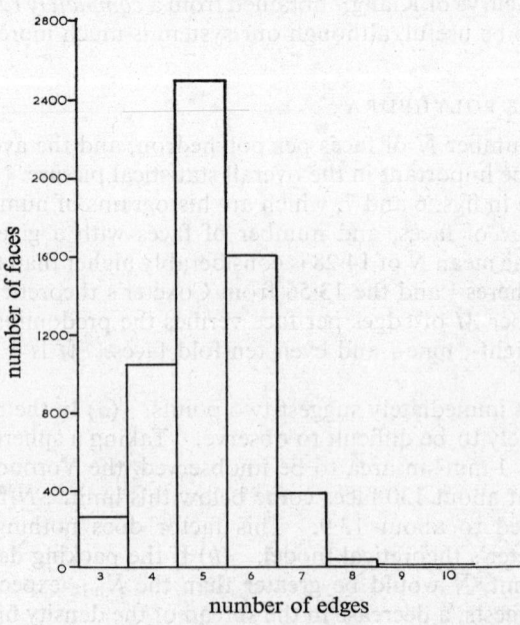

Fig. 7.—Histogram showing distribution of number of edges per face.

for the same density, it may be possible to deduce a relationship between overall density and $\bar{N}$. As the values of $\bar{N}$ and density for the Scott model fit reasonably well on the N against density curve of fig. 5, an investigation of local regions of different densities may be of interest in this connection.

TOPOLOGICAL CHARACTERISTICS

If the examination of some characteristics of a set of polyhedra showed the occurrence of certain " types ", in the simplest case an array could be described in terms of the frequency of occurrence n_i of type A_i. This system, however, gives us no information about how different polyhedra are spatially arranged: an extension therefore is to formulate a matrix showing the frequency of occurrence n_{ij} of type A_i next to type A_j:

$$\begin{array}{cccccc} & A_1 & A_2 & \ldots & A_i & \ldots \\ A_1 & n_{11} & n_{21} & \ldots & n_{i1} & \ldots \\ A_2 & n_{12} & n_{22} & \ldots & n_{i2} & \ldots \\ \cdot & \cdot & \cdot & & \cdot & \\ \cdot & \cdot & \cdot & & \cdot & \equiv (n_{ij}) \\ \cdot & \cdot & \cdot & & \cdot & \\ A_j & n_{ij} & n_{2j} & \ldots & n_{ij} & \ldots \\ \cdot & \cdot & \cdot & & \cdot & \\ \cdot & \cdot & \cdot & & \cdot & \end{array}$$

A further extension adds a third dimension to the matrix, showing the type of face B_k by which A_i and A_j are joined. The general case occurs when all polyhedra are of different types, so that $n_{ijk} = 0$ or 1.

One possible characteristic by which similarity between polyhedra can be assessed is the topology. In this connection, it might be worth elucidating all the possible topologically different types of polyhedra with N faces, and see whether any of these types are specifically excluded or frequently occurring in a Voronoi network. This type elucidation has been done for $N = 4$ to 12 inclusive, after which the task of further extension for large N becomes unmanageable. If interesting results come out of comparing our 24 twelve-faced polyhedra with the possible 77 types, it may be worth considering further work along these lines.

PRELIMINARY TOPOLOGICAL RESULTS

A predominance of certain types is evident. Table 1 shows those polyhedron types with five or more examples present, together with the full plasticene sphere analysis for comparison. 255 of the 407 polyhedra (63 %) are thus accounted for: the total number of plasticene polyhedra was 65. The number of *exact* correspondences between the two models, especially in the six and eight pentagonal face groups, is worth noting. And there are other near correspondences between polyhedra differing only slightly, e.g., 04460 and 13451, where one quadrangular face has become triangular, and one hexagonal has become septagonal; similarly with 13532 and 04541.

What this representation fails to do is to allow for the differences in relative arrangements of faces; for example, there are five distinct polyhedra of type 03630 (the 6 referring to the pentagonal faces). However, we now have a programme to sort out these sub-types. So far we have found that even where two polyhedra have deintical arrangements of the same types of faces, they are not quantitatively similar. A case in point is polyhedra 1 and 322 in table 2, which have only four faces (1, 9, 10, 13) corresponding vaguely in size and distance from the centre. Can two such

TABLE 1

A (Scott model)	B (plasticene)	A	B
1		**3**	
	14150(1)		05331(1)
4		**5**	
	04420(1)	13532(6)	
	04440(1)		04541(2)
04450(7)	04450(1)		04531(1)
04460(11)	04460(1)		12530(1)
04470(5)			
	13431(1)		
	13441(2)		
13451(10)	13451(3)		
	13461(2)		
6		**7**	
	03620(1)		03721(3)
03630(7)	03630(5)		03731(1)
03640(30)	03640(5)	03741(8)	
03650(17)	03650(3)	12722(7)	
03660(17)	03660(5)	12732(11)	
12641(5)			
	04642(1)		
8		**9**	
	02810(2)		10930(1)
02820(6)	02820(3)		02951(1)
02830(13)	02830(3)		
02840(15)	02840(4)		
02850(10)			
	02860(1)		
11831(8)			
10		**12**	
01″10″20(16)	01″10″20(4)		00″12″00(1)
01″10″30(11)			00″12″20(1)
	01″10″40(2)		
	01″12″00(5)		

polyhedra be considered to be similar for the purposes of our required geometrical description, and if not, how can the differences be represented? Much remains to be studied merely with respect to this one analysis, which may throw further light on problems such as these.

FUTURE WORK

The polyhedron analysis of this and other models will be pursued, as variously mentioned above, using in addition auxiliary tools such as computer programmes to produce stereographic projections and stereoscopic pictures of the polyhedra. We intend to measure a large (~3000 centres) random close-packed model on our coordinate measuring machine, which will give a much greater accuracy of measurement than anything at present available: the increased size will give greater flexibility and statistical reliability, and more scope for investigating local density fluctuations. Analyses of models of different densities may give some indication of how to deal with

TABLE 2

face no.	no. of edges	face area		distance between centre and face	
		1	322	1	322
1	7	5·8	5·7	1·58	1·61
2	5	4·6	2·7	1·63	1·92
3	4	0·3	2·7	2·13	1·89
4	5	4·3	3·3	1·66	1·78
5	5	3·6	1·7	1·68	2·05
6	6	5·0	5·8	1·60	1·59
7	6	4·9	5·6	1·59	1·62
8	4	0·9	2·3	2·05	1·92
9	6	5·0	4·8	1·59	1·60
10	4	0·5	0·2	2·17	2·28
11	5	3·7	2·7	1·60	1·78
12	5	4·2	5·1	1·60	1·59
13	5	4·2	4·2	1·64	1·59
14	5	0·5	2·8	2·18	1·81

temperature variations (such as by polyhedron dilatations or a change in the distribution of types). The use of the Voronoi polyhedron as a basis for thermodynamic calculations is to be investigated, and we are also intending an approach to the thermodynamics via Monte Carlo computer techniques. Along these lines we see the development of further consequences of a random-packed liquid, and thus hope to provide more points for experimental comparison.

[1] J. D. Bernal, *Proc. Roy. Soc. A*, 1964, **280**, 299.
[2] J. D. Bernal, *Nature*, 1960, **185**, 68.
[3] J. D. Bernal and J. Mason, *Nature*, 1960, **188**, 910.
[4] G. D. Scott, *Nature*, 1960, **188**, 908.
[5] G. D. Scott, *Nature*, 1962, **194**, 956.
[6] J. D. Bernal, J. Mason and K. R. Knight, *Nature*, 1962, **194**, 958.
[7] T. Kiang, *Z. Astrophysik*, 1966, **64**, 433.
[8] H. S. M. Coxeter, *Introduction to Geometry*, (John Wiley, 1961), p. 411.
[9] J. D. Bernal, in *Liquids; Structure, Properties, Solid Interactions*, ed. T. J. Hughel. (Elsevier Pub. Co. Amsterdam, 1965), p. 25.

Hidden Variables in the Critical Region*

By Marshall Fixman

Chemistry Dept., Yale University, New Haven, Connecticut, U.S.A.

Received 19th December, 1966

A gas in the one-phase region near the critical point exhibits unusually large fluctuations of density in volume elements much larger in linear dimension than are molecular diameters. These fluctuations in density give rise to forces and energy fluxes which may be treated by essentially macroscopic equations of thermodynamics and hydrodynamics, because the dominant wavelengths are so large in a Fourier decomposition of the density fluctuation. The anomalous thermal conductivity and shear viscosity of a gas near the critical point have been calculated, and compared with experiments on CO_2. The comparison of thermal conductivities is satisfactory, but the comparison of shear viscosities is inconclusive, because of the smallness of the predicted effect and the difficulty of its measurement.

1. INTRODUCTION

In a variety of relaxation problems, an unexpected dissipation of energy is explained through the existence of an uncontrolled or "hidden" variable, such as an intramolecular mode of energy, whose probability distribution is unable to remain in equilibrium with the varying hydrodynamic variables. The anomalous ultrasonic absorption of gases near the critical point has been explained on this basis,[1,2] with the hidden variables taken to be the spectrum of long-wave-length density fluctuations. The density fluctuations appear in an anomalous contribution to the entropy, from which a complex, dynamic heat capacity was derived and used to calculate the sound absorption. In the previous work the anomalous entropy varied in time because of a uniformly varying temperature, but here we consider a non-uniform variation of temperature and from the variation in entropy derive a formula for the anomalous heat flux. The anomalous shear viscosity of the gas is also calculated, by techniques mathematically similar to those used for the shear viscosity of the binary mixture in the critical region [3] (although the physical bases are different). The thermal conductivity calculation may significantly be compared with experiment, but the anomalous gas viscosity is calculated to be so small, and the discrepancies between different experiments are so large, that no useful comparison can be made.

Zwanzig and Mountain [4] have also calculated the anomalous thermal conductivity and shear viscosity of a gas. Apparently, their results for the thermal conductivity are qualitatively similar to ours, but they predict no anomaly in the viscosity. Their method of calculation differs from ours in two respects. First, they calculated the transport coefficients from correlation function expressions (as did Kawasaki,[5] in his calculations on binary mixtures). Secondly, they retained explicitly in their equations of motion an intermolecular potential. The use of correlation functions makes unnecessary any search for a coupling between the motion of the fluid and the driving force for shear flow or thermal conduction. We have thought it worthwhile to find this coupling, as something interesting in itself and also to provide an insight

* supported in part by the Public Health Service, GM 13556, and the Alfred P. Sloan Foundation.

into non-linear transport processes. Regarding the intermolecular potential, Zwanzig and Mountain used a long-range potential to justify some of the manipulations. We use an alternative justification which consist in the restriction of density variations to those describable by long-wave-length Fourier components. The potential itself is presumed to be short range and to manifest itself only implicitly in the various thermodynamic derivatives that are present. The quasi-thermodynamic forms of our equation facilitates a numerical comparison with experimental results. Only one parameter occurs which is microscopic in nature,[6] the short-range correlation length l. In principle, l may be determined from light scattering, but in practice l is here determined for CO_2 from a previous comparison [1] of heat capacity predictions with experiment.

The following remarks are essentially a summary of methods and results, the details of which must be published elsewhere for lack of space here.

2. EQUATIONS OF MOTION

We assume that at each point a specific energy and specific entropy are known, and that the specific entropy is a function of the local density and temperature, while the specific energy contains one ordinary part, a function of the specific entropy and mass density, and another part proportional to the square of the density gradient. Thus

$$E = \int e(\mathbf{r},t)\rho(\mathbf{r},t)d\mathbf{r}, \tag{2.1}$$

$$S = \int s(\mathbf{r},t)\rho(\mathbf{r},t)d\mathbf{r}, \tag{2.2}$$

$$e = e_L + e_I, \tag{2.3}$$

$$e_I = \alpha |\nabla \rho|^2. \tag{2.4}$$

e_L is the ordinary specific energy, while e_I becomes significant in the critical region, not because α is supposed to become large, but because the second deriivtive of e_L at constant s becomes small near the critical point, and vanishes as the reciprocal compressibility.

For a given state of density fluctuation, the force acting on any unit element of mass is presumed to be given by

$$d\mathbf{u}/dt = \rho^{-1}\nabla \cdot \boldsymbol{\sigma}_0 + \mathbf{F}, \tag{2.5}$$

where

$$\boldsymbol{\sigma}_0 = 2\eta_0(\nabla \mathbf{u})^{sym} \tag{2.6}$$

and η_0 is a hypothetical shear viscosity which the fluid would have if density fluctuations were not allowed. The force which arises because of the density fluctuations is designated $\mathbf{F}$ in eqn. (2.5).

The force $\mathbf{F}$ is calculated on the basis of a mechanical variational principle. The position $\mathbf{r}_0$ of any element of mass is taken to be a function of time and the position $\mathbf{w}$ of the element in an initial reference configuration. The positions $\mathbf{w}$ are taken to be stochastic variables, and an implicit average over their possible values is required when macroscopic quantities are calculated:[7]

$$\mathbf{r}_0 = \mathbf{r}_0^\dagger(\mathbf{w},t) \tag{2.7}$$

The mechanical variational principle is that

$$\delta E = -\int \mathbf{F} \cdot \delta \mathbf{r}_0 dm,$$
$$dm = \rho(\mathbf{r},t)d\mathbf{r}, \tag{2.8}$$

where $\delta \mathbf{r}_0$ is the variation in the path of a mass element, the variation being at a constant value of the entropy of the mass element. A straightforward calculation yields

$$\rho \mathbf{F} = \nabla \cdot \boldsymbol{\sigma}_\rho, \tag{2.9}$$
$$\boldsymbol{\sigma}_\rho = -p\mathbf{1} + 2\alpha[\rho|\nabla\rho|^2 + \rho^2\nabla^2\rho]\mathbf{1} - 2\alpha\rho(\nabla\rho)(\nabla\rho). \tag{2.10}$$

The last term on the right-hand side of eqn. (2.10) is of utmost significance at two points in the analysis. First, with the consistent neglect of third-order fluctuations, and the consistent interpretation of ρ as an average over a small volume element (with dimensions much larger than the range of the intermolecular potential, but much smaller than the range of correlation in the critical region), an ensemble average of eqn. (2.5) gives

$$\sigma^{xz} = \dot{\varepsilon}\eta_0(\mathbf{e}_x\mathbf{e}_z + \mathbf{e}_z\mathbf{e}_x) + 2\alpha\rho^3 \lim_{r \to 0} \partial^2 G^{(1)}(r)/\partial x \partial z. \tag{2.11}$$

In this equation, $\dot{\varepsilon}$ is at the rate of shear of the fluid in laminar flow, $G^{(1)}(r)$ is the perturbation in the radial correlation function evaluated to first order in $\dot{\varepsilon}$. The limiting process in eqn. (2.11) is not taken towards a mathematical zero, but to a value of r much smaller than the range of the correlation. The second point where the last term in eqn. (2.10) plays a major role is in a thermal conduction experiment, where this term provides the coupling between the uniform temperature gradient and the density fluctuations. We derive below an expression for the anomalous thermal conductivity.

3. HEAT CONDUCTION

For the anomalous specific entropy, Botch and Fixman [1] derived an expression equivalent to

$$\langle \delta s \rangle = (\tfrac{1}{2})s_{vv}^\circ \rho_0^{-4} \langle (\delta \rho)^2 \rangle \tag{3.1}$$

where the subscripts on the right-hand side designate the second derivative of the specific entropy with respect to the specific volume. Interpretation of ρ as an average over a small volume element led to a transformation of the right-hand side to an integral over the long wave-length components of the radial correlation function. Then, a differential equation for the radial correlation function, the one introduced below, allowed a dynamic heat capacity to be calculated. However, there is another way in which the anomalous specific entropy can vary with time, and that is by heat conduction. In the absence of heat sources, an anomalous heat flux can be related to $\langle \delta s \rangle$ by

$$\rho_0 T_0 \partial \langle \delta s \rangle / \partial t = -\nabla \cdot \mathbf{q}', \tag{3.2}$$

and eqn. (3.1) and (3.2) together give

$$\mathbf{q}' = T_0 s_{vv}^\circ \rho_0^{-1} \lim_{r \to 0} \mathbf{u}(r), \tag{3.3}$$

where $\mathbf{u}(r)$ is the mean fluid velocity at a point r due to the combined effects of a molecule fixed in location at the origin, and the presence of a temperature gradient.

We have calculated $\mathbf{u}(\mathbf{r})$ for a fluid in the critical region, subject to a uniform temperature gradient independent of time. This velocity must be determined from the modified Navier-Stokes equation, eqn. (2.5) together with eqn. (2.9) and (2.10) for the forces. The linearized equation of mass conservation shows that the divergence of $\mathbf{u}$ must vanish in the steady state; that is, $\mathbf{u}$ can be written as the curl of a vector potential. Therefore any part of eqn. (2.5) which can be written as the gradient of a scalar potential will not contribute to the desired solution. The rejection of such terms gives

$$\eta_0 \nabla^2 \mathbf{u} = 2\rho_0^2 \alpha (\partial p/\partial T)_p (\nabla T) \nabla^2 G^\circ(r), \tag{3.4}$$

$$G^\circ(r) = a\, e^{-\kappa r}/r, \tag{3.5}$$

where G° is the equilibrium radial correlation function and κ is related to the thermodynamic parameters by

$$\kappa^2 = -p_v/(2\alpha \rho_0^4), \tag{3.6}$$

or, at the critical density, by Debye's relation,

$$\kappa^2 = 6(T-T_c)/l^2 T_c.$$

Eqn. (3.4) still includes some scalar potential contributions to $\mathbf{u}$, but these may be rejected and a thermal conductivity determined from eqn. (3.3). The result for the anomalous conductivity λ' is

$$\lambda' = -(\tfrac{2}{3}) T_0 a \eta_0^{-1} (\partial p/\partial T)_\rho (\partial^2 p/\partial T \partial \ln v) \kappa^{-1}. \tag{3.7}$$

4. SHEAR VISCOSITY

The fluctuation formula for the radial correlation function,

$$\langle \delta\rho(\mathbf{r}_1) \delta\rho(\mathbf{r}_2) \rangle = \rho_0^2 G(\mathbf{r}_1, \mathbf{r}_2) \tag{4.1}$$

and eqn. (2.5) linearized in the density fluctuations, together with the ordinary thermal conduction equation gives a result, previously derived by Botch and Fixman,

$$h \mathrm{d}G(\mathbf{r})/\mathrm{d}t = h\{\partial G/\partial t + [\mathbf{u}(\mathbf{r}) - \mathbf{u}(0)] \cdot \nabla G\} = \nabla^2[\kappa^2 G - {}^2\nabla G], \tag{4.2}$$

$$h = T_0 p_T s_v^\circ / [4\alpha \lambda_0 \rho_0^3], \tag{4.3}$$

where λ_0 is, like η_0, a hypothetical quantity, the thermal conductivity in the absence of long wavelength density fluctuations. Like η_0, λ_0 must be determined by extrapolation from outside the critical region. The previous expression for h was too large by a factor of two, due to the neglect of the fact that two time-dependent density fluctuations enter the formula (4.1) for G. A first-order solution of eqn. (4.2) for the perturbation induced by simple shear flow is straightforward, and gives on substitution into eqn. (2.11) a formula for the anomalous part of the shear viscosity:

$$\eta' = aT_0 p_T^2 / (40 \lambda_0 \kappa). \tag{4.4}$$

A virtually identical formula, with different interpretation of the coefficients, has been derived for the shear viscosity of a binary liquid mixture by several workers.[5, 8, 9] The present method may also be used to reproduce the previous results.

5. COMPARISON WITH EXPERIMENT

For CO_2 in the critical region all of the thermodynamic and transport coefficients required in eqn. (3.7) and (4.4) are available. The value of l was previously [1] estimated to be 4·5 Å, and this value has been used here. The numerical predictions are, at the critical density:

$$\eta' = 38(T-T_c)^{-\frac{1}{2}} \text{ micropoise,} \tag{5.1}$$

$$\lambda' = 2\cdot6 \times 10^{-4}(T-T_c)^{-\frac{1}{2}} \text{ cal/deg. cm sec.} \tag{5.2}$$

The predicted η' is some five times smaller than indicated by the data of Michels et al.,[10] measured in a capillary viscometer, and some five times larger than indicated by the data of Kestin et al.,[11] measured in a rotating disc viscometer. The latter experimental anomalies were increased by factors of about three in sample corrections for density gradients.

Eqn. (5.2) has been compared with Sengers' data,[12] the total conductivity being taken to be $\lambda = \lambda_0 + \lambda'$, with $\lambda_0 = 10^{-4}$ cal/deg. cm sec. Over a 40°C interval above T_c, the calculated and observed conductivities agree within 10 %, although the observed results show a slightly sharper dependence on T than given by eqn. (5.2).

[1] W. Botch and M. Fixman, *J. Chem. Physics*, 1965, **42**, 196.
[2] W. Botch and M. Fixman, *J. Chem. Physics*, 1965, **42**, 199.
[3] M. Fixman, *Adv. Chem. Physics*, 1963, **6**, 175.
[4] R. Zwanzig and R. D. Mountain, private communication.
[5] K. Kawasaki, *Physic. Rev.*, 1966, **150**, 291.
[6] In principle even this parameter may be determined from macroscopic observations on inhomogeneous systems.
[7] The explicit computation of averages proceeds in terms of correlation functions which are the solutions of differential equations.
[8] M. Fixman, *J. Chem. Physics*, 1962, **36**, 310.
[9] J. M. Deutsch and R. Zwanzig, preprint.
[10] A. Michels, A. Botzen and W. Schuurman, *Physica*, 1957, **23**, 95.
[11] J. Kestin, J. H. Whitelaw and T. F. Zien, *Physica*, 1964, **30**, 161.
[12] J. V. Sengers, *Thesis* (University of Amsterdam, 1962).

GENERAL DISCUSSION

Mr. G. Mason (*University of Bristol*) said: I should like to report some work on random sphere packings using a computer to generate the co-ordinates of the sphere centres. This work is directed more towards a model of porous materials than to the problem of liquid structure, but the results are of interest in both fields. The method of generating the packing was first developed in two dimensions, packing circles on a plane, and a short film has been made to illustrate this.* Three-dimensional packings have also been obtained, although these are as yet only of 100 and 200 spheres.

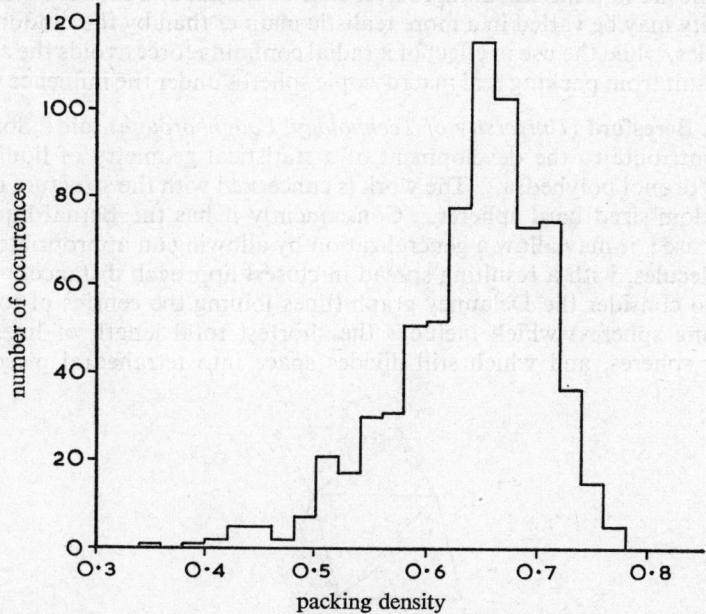

FIG. 1.—Tetrahedron densities.
bulk packing density = 0·63(4); number of spheres in packing = 200; total number of tetrahedra = 727.

Initially a number of points are generated at random in a " box " in space. These points are then considered to be small spheres of a chosen radius. If two spheres overlap, they are moved apart along the line of centres until they are just touching. The computer continues moving spheres apart until none overlap. The spheres are then increased in size by a chosen increment and the process repeated. Spheres are free to move out of the " box " during the process. The method may be regarded as a means of creating a random distribution of spheres in space, and bringing them together toward a point in the centre of the packing as if under the influence of a radial gravitational field. Packings of even these small numbers of spheres reach a limiting packing density of 0·63-0·64 [1] which is close to the density of experimentally produced

---

* This film was shown during the discussion.
[1] G. D. Scott, *Nature*, 1960, **188**, 908.

packings. The value cannot yet be determined precisely because of the small number of spheres in the packings.

The packings have been analyzed in terms of tetrahedral sub-units rather than Voronoi polyhedra. There are several reasons for choosing tetrahedral sub-units. The analysis is simpler; there are more tetrahedra than Voronoi polyhedra in a packing of given size, so that the results are statistically more significant; and it is easier to correct for edge effects. Radial distribution functions have been calculated over a wide range of packing density and detailed analyses of the tetrahedra in the denser packings obtained. The packing density of each tetrahedron in one particular packing was determined and fig. 1 is a histogram of the results. As would be expected, the histogram is spread over a wider range of packing density than the polyhedra of Bernal and Finney. It is hoped with more machine time to pack as many as 1000 spheres and to vary their " hardness ".

The present method has advantages over that of Bernal and his co-workers. The packing density may be varied in a more realistic manner than by the random creation of discrete holes, while the use in effect of a radial confining force avoids the asymmetry which may result from packing real macroscopic spheres under the influence of gravity.

Mr. R. H. Beresford (*University of Technology, Loughborough*) said: Some of our work may contribute to the development of a statistical geometry of liquids and to the study of Voronoi polyhedra. The work is concerned with the structure of random heaps of random-sized hard spheres. Consequently it has the Bernal liquid model as a limiting case; it may allow a generalization by allowing an appropriate variation in size of molecules, with a resulting spread in closest approach distance. The basic approach is to consider the Delauney graph (lines joining the centres of touching or nearly touching spheres) which includes the shortest total length of lines between non-touching spheres, and which still divides space into tetrahedral pieces. Lines

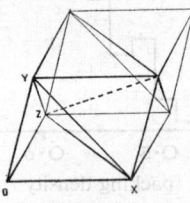

Fig. 1.

corresponding to contact points are " edges ", and the others are " diagonals ". Each edge represents a constraint—that the sphere centre separation equals the sum of the radii—and so the number of edges can be related to the number of degrees of freedom of the system. An attempt has been made to overcome boundary effects, and to tie up with crystal structures, by considering a heap as the limiting case of a repeating primitive lattice. As the number of random spheres in this lattice approaches a completely random heap.

A 3-dimensional repeating lattice (fig. 1) can be divided into 6 tetrahedra per cell by 7 lines per cell (12 cell edges, each shared by 4 cells; 6 face diagonals, each shared by 2 cells; one body diagonal. The other two body diagonals are redundant). There is one lattice point per cell, and if a sphere is centred on this point, the number of spheres per cell ($= m$) is 1. This system has 6 degrees of freedom, for if the sphere radius is taken as unity, the **X** vector has a 1 degree of freedom, the **Y** vector 2 and the **Z** vector 3. Any additional spheres in this lattice are either " random "—with centres falling within an existing tetrahedron, or " ordered ", falling on a tetrahedron boundary. Ignoring the ordered case, an additional random sphere can be joined by four lines to the four vertices of its surrounding tetrahedron (fig. 2). This adds

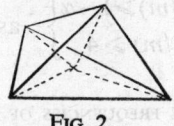

FIG. 2.

3 tetrahedra to the system by creating 4 new ones whilst destroying the original one. Each sphere will have $(3+\alpha)$ degrees of freedom, where the 3 corresponds to the three co-ordinates, and α is the number of degrees of freedom associated with the particle shape. If monosized spheres are employed $\alpha = 0$. If any size of sphere is permissible, $\alpha = 1$. Then for a total of m spheres:

$$\text{no. of tetrahedra} = T = 3m+3$$
$$\text{no. of lines} = L = 4m+3$$
$$\text{no. of degrees of freedom} = N_{df} = 6+(m+1)(3+\alpha)$$

(The constants are obtained by reference to the case where $m = 1$.)

This analysis gives the minimum number of lines needed to divide the cell into tetrahedra. It appears likely that the shortest set of lines can be obtained by an exchange system which replaces one long line by one or more shorter ones. For instance, consider two spheres which have n equatorial neighbours, and are joined by a " polar " line (fig. 3). The resulting n tetrahedra can be replaced by $(2n-4)$

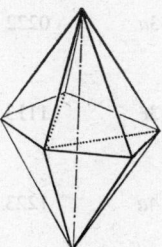

FIG 3.—($n = 5$), ... equatorial; —·—·—· polar.

tetrahedra if $(n-3)$ equatorial lines replace the polar line. This increases both the number of tetrahedra and the number of lines by $(n-4)$. The original construction ensures that $n \geqslant 4$, and a later analysis shows $n \to 4\frac{1}{2}$ as $m \to \infty$. The net effect therefore appears to be an increase in the number of lines. Let the shortest set of lines be $L' \geqslant L = 4m+3$; as $E \leqslant N_{df}$,

$$D = L'-E \geqslant 4m+3-6-(m-1)(3+\alpha).$$
$$\therefore \quad D \geqslant m-\alpha(m-1) = (1-\alpha)m+\alpha,$$

and a large random assembly of equal spheres must have an average of at least one diagonal per sphere. For $m = 1$, this reduces to $E \leqslant 6$, $D \geqslant 1$; and the equalities hold for crystalline close packing, which cannot have more than $12(= 2E)$ contacts per sphere.

Consideration of a bounded cluster of spheres gives the approximation:

$$L' \quad 4m - 6(m^{\frac{1}{3}} - 1)^2; \qquad D \quad (1-\alpha)m - 6(m^{\frac{1}{3}} - 1)^2.$$

As both approaches give

$$\left.\begin{array}{l} \text{limit } (D/m) \geqslant 1 - \alpha \\ \text{limit } (L'/m) \geqslant 4 \end{array}\right\} \quad \text{as} \quad m \to \infty,$$

FIG. 4.—RELATIVE FREQUENCIES OF TETRAHEDRAL TYPES

structures	number	face name	frequency	frequency if $L=4, D=1$.
	0	0000	$\dfrac{(L-D)^6}{L^6}$	$\dfrac{729}{4096}$
	1	0011	$\dfrac{6(L-D)^5 D}{L^6}$	$\dfrac{1458}{4096}$
	2a	0112	$\dfrac{12(L-D)^4 D^2}{L^6}$	$\dfrac{972}{4096}$
	2o	1111	$\dfrac{3(L-D)^4 D^2}{L^6}$	$\dfrac{243}{4096}$
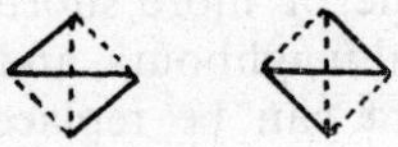	3o	1122	$\dfrac{12(L-D)^3 D^3}{L^6}$	$\dfrac{324}{4096}$
	3a	0222	$\dfrac{4(L-D)^3 D^3}{L^6}$	$\dfrac{108}{4096}$
	3c	1113	$\dfrac{4(L-D)^3 D^3}{L^6}$	$\dfrac{108}{4096}$
	4a	1223	$\dfrac{12(L-D)^2 D^4}{L^6}$	$\dfrac{108}{4096}$
	4o	2222	$\dfrac{3(L-D)^2 D^4}{L^6}$	$\dfrac{27}{4096}$
	5	2233	$\dfrac{6(L-D) D^5}{L^6}$	$\dfrac{18}{4096}$
	6	3333	$\dfrac{D^6}{L^6}$	$\dfrac{1}{4096}$

face types	0 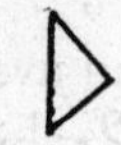	1 	2 	3 
frequency	$\dfrac{27}{64}$	$\dfrac{27}{64}$	$\dfrac{9}{64}$	$\dfrac{1}{64}$

it would appear to be a useful hypothesis that a large random close-packed assembly of equal spheres has 3 contacts and one near contact per sphere. This only applies to spheres with an infinite range of sizes. Probably for equal spheres, $L'/m \rightarrow 7$, $D \rightarrow 4$, the chances are 4/7 and 3/7, and there are tetrahedra round each line. A second hypothesis is that the elements of the Delaunay graph of such an assembly have a chance $\frac{1}{4}$ of being a diagonal and $\frac{3}{4}$ of being an edge. This allows estimates of the frequency of occurrence of closed tetrahedra in such an assembly, together with the 10 other types of tetrahedra which can have two types of edge. These are given in fig. 4. Further statistical results should arise from the consideration of the surface patterns on each sphere (fig. 4). One such result is that there are $4\frac{1}{2}$ tetrahedra round each edge. This arises because the average number of points on each sphere ($ = 2L$) is $P = 8$ and so the average number of triangles is $T_r = 2P-4 = 12$. Thus there are 36 apices round 8 points. These correspond physically to tetrahedra round lines, and so the average must be $36/8 = 4\frac{1}{2}$ tetrahedra round each line.

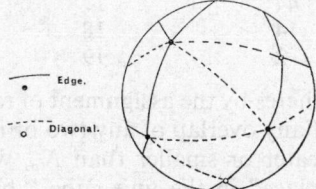

FIG. 5.

Although there is a large number of possible surface patterns, the frequency of occurrence of those with a high density of diagonals must be low. Also the number of possible patterns with a high density of edges is reduced by the geometrical requirements for monosize spheres, and so it is hoped that enumeration of the likely patterns will be of value. The relationship of these patterns to Voronoi polyhedra has yet to be investigated. The number of redundant diagonals adjacent to an included diagonal can be evaluated for each section of a surface pattern; the total number of diagonals and edges will be related to the number of faces on the Voronoi polyhedron. Adjacent Voronoi polyhedra will result in mirror image patterns round the line joining two spheres, and will also set conditions for the surrounding polyhedra. This may be relevant to the study of packing density. Finally, it is hoped that the cases where $D > m$ will shed light on less dense assemblies, and that the total length of diagonals will be related to the separation of spheres, as discussed by Kohler and Springer (this Discussion).

Prof. J. Walkley (*Simon Fraser University*) and **Dr. I. H. Hillier** (*University of Manchester*) said: Many of the problems associated with the prediction of the thermodynamic properties of a system at fluid densities arises from the conceptual difficulty of describing a fluid. Bernal's work [1] lays particular emphasis on the structural identity in a liquid. The concept of a "coherent structure" existing in the high density fluid region agrees well with the molecular dynamics studies of hard sphere systems.[2] We have made computer studies at the other end of the liquid density range where it might be expected that the coherent structure gives way to a completely random structure.

[1] J. D. Bernal, *Nature*, 1960, **185**, 68.
[2] B. J. Alder and T. E. Wainwright, *J. Chem. Physics*, 1960, **33**, 1439.

The generation of random configurations of hard-sphere molecules at a liquid density presents its own problems. By adding spheres to a " box " in a consecutive manner in random positions (as simulated by the choice of random coordinates on a computer) leads to maximum densities that are unexpectedly low. Any process involving the " swelling " of spheres already in the box at random positions has the disadvantage that high densities can only be achieved at the expense of having only a few sample spheres in the box. A method of generating random configurations at the required density is as follows.

TABLE 1.—DISTRIBUTION OF FINAL PACKING DENSITY; $N_p = 32$, $N_i = 80$; PERIODIC BOUNDARY CONDITION

number of boxes	number of remaining N_j
2	13
18	14
50	15
70	16
44	17
14	18
2	19

The box is packed with N_i spheres by the assignment of random, x, y, z coordinates to each molecule, irrespective of any overlap of any two or more spheres. The initial packing number N_i may be greater or smaller than N_p, where N_p is the maximum number of spheres able to be placed in the unit cube " box " on a primitive cubic lattice. This defines the hard-sphere diameter. The coordinates of the centres of each sphere allows the scalar distance between centres to be found and by comparison

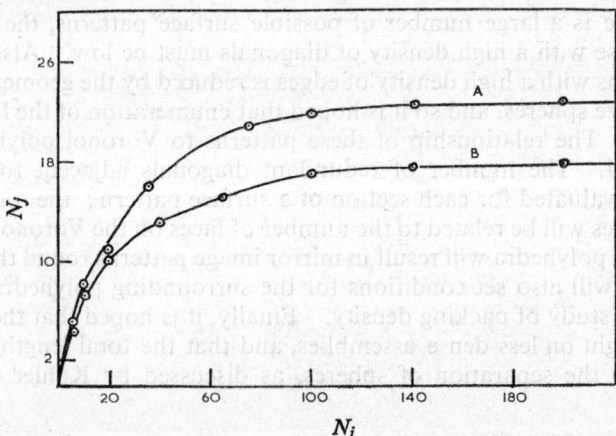

FIG. 1.—Peak value of the N_j distribution for $N_p = 32$; curve A, without periodic boundary conditions; curve B, with periodic boundary conditions.

to the molecular diameter the number of spheres N_k which overlap the M_ith sphere may be determined. Spheres are now removed from the box such that the sphere M_q which incurs the greatest number of overlaps is removed. If spheres M_r, M_s and M_t each have the same (maximum) number of overlaps then a random choice between these is made to determine the one to be rejected. A re-evaluation of N_k for each of the remaining ($N_i - 1$) spheres is now made and again the one incurring the greatest overlap is removed. This procedure is repeated until there is no overlap between any two of the remaining N_j spheres in the box.

This process was carried out for N_i as small as 5 to values as large as 300 for a typical box where $N_p = 64$. In general, any " run ", i.e., the generation of a series of randomly packed boxes from a given N_i value, was continued until 200 sample boxes were obtained. The distribution of the final N_j population for any initial N_i values was always narrow. A typical result for a " box " for which $N_p = 32$ and for $N_i = 80$ is given in table 1.

In fig. 1 the peak value of the N_j distribution for any given N_i value is plotted against N_i. Curves are given for a " box " with a torroidal (periodic) boundary condition and for a " box " without such a condition. In each case the random packing density approaches a maximum value, independent, of N_i. For a box size, $N_p = 32$, this limiting random density is $N_j = 18$ if periodic boundary conditions are imposed and $N_j = 22$ is they are not.

The tentative result is that the random distribution of spheres can only occur to a limiting density. Bernal in an earlier paper comments upon the liquid-gas transition and the implication of a λ-point in the constant-pressure heat-capacity curve. The density limit observed in the present study agrees well with the limit suggested by Bernal for the break up of the liquid " coherent structure " and the inherent implication in the heat-capacity curve.

Mr. R. Collins (*University of Salford*) said: Bernal and King (I) and Bernal and Finney (II) use the term " polyhedron " in two different contexts, which perhaps ought to be distinguished. Polyhedron in II means Voronoi polyhedron (VP), but polyhedron in I does not. The lattice of polyhedra in I is a subset of the lattice of tetrahedra topologically *inverse* to the lattice of VP's. The definition of neighbour in II is much more precise than the $\sqrt{2}$ criterion in I. If the II definition of neighbour is adopted, then the average number of neighbours of a given atom in a real liquid *increases* with decreasing density since it is 14 for (slightly perturbed) close-packing, 14·28 at the intermediate density described in II and for vanishingly small densities approaches the random distribution (perfect gas) figure of $2 + 48\pi^2/35 = 15·54$.[1]

The basic problems in using a realistic " soft " potential $\phi(l)$ appropriate to an interatomic distance l are to calculate the energy and the entropy of any irregular configuration. Both are easier to express in terms of the lattice of tetrahedra inverse to that of the Voronoi polyhedra rather than the VP lattice itself. In this connection the work described by Beresford also breaks the structure down into tetrahedra only.

In addition to the entropy contribution arising from the local atomic co-ordination numbers θ_r discussed by Everett, there is also the contribution arising from the probability function $\psi(l)$ of the neighbour distances l. We have estimated this using information theory arguments, and even if the entropy contribution from the θ_r is completely neglected, there results an equation of state for a general $\phi(l)$ which gives reasonable qualitative agreement with experiment.[2] Contrary to a widely held view, the geometric theory *is* capable of yielding thermodynamic results for a realistic $\phi(l)$.

The histogram of what are effectively atomic co-ordination numbers θ_r in fig. 6 of II is valuable since it provides a starting point for evaluating the corresponding entropy contribution, which has so far proved an intractable analytic problem. Real progress would become possible in this direction if fig. 6 could be repeated for various densities, and extended to cover configuration generated by a soft (e.g., Lennard-Jones) potential. I would expect that the other statistics (such as illustrated in fig. 7) will prove of much less thermodynamic importance, although of some theoretical interest.

[1] J. L. Meijering, *Philips Res. Rep.*, 1953, **8**, 270.
[2] R. Collins, *Proc. Physic. Soc.*, 1965, **86**, 199. D. C. S. Allison and R. Collins, to be published.

In an attempt to develop a realistic physical formalism, I would suggest that in the first instance it is easier to consider initially a two-dimensional liquid. Here the topology is much easier; the Voronoi polygons have an inverse lattice which consists of triangles only, and the mean co-ordination number $\bar{N}$ is a strict topological constant equal to 6 at all densities. Also, one can see directly how the long-range order appears in the crystalline state on freezing.[1] If an adequate mathematical formalism could be developed on this basis, it would not have the defect, inherent to the lattice-gas model of a liquid, that a long-range ordered lattice of sites is used to describe an essentially disordered physical state. If the problem cannot be solved in two-dimensions, there seems little hope of a three-dimensional solution.

Prof. D. H. Everett (*University of Bristol*) said: Although work on the random packing of spheres gives a valuable insight into the structural properties of liquids, it is not immediately apparent how the results of such studies can be applied to the calculation of thermodynamic properties. In introducing these papers, Finney has mentioned that the results can be used successfully to calculate the energy of a liquid and hence the heat of fusion: but it is also necessary to be able to use the model to calculate the entropy. An approximate approach to this problem seems possible along the following lines.

Simple cell theories of liquids predict too low an entropy for the liquid state. One feature of these theories which makes a major contribution to this discrepancy is the assumption that each molecule can be regarded as moving in the mean field of its neighbours (the *average potential model*): the energy of a captive molecule at the centre of its cell is the same for all cells. A more realistic model—which might be called the *heterogeneous cell model*—would taken account of the fact that at any instant a molecule finds itself in a field determined by a particular arrangement of neighbours. We might therefore regard the liquid as divided into cells, each of which determines a characteristic potential energy controlling the motion of the captive molecule. The depth of the potential energy minimum in a cell will differ from cell to cell, and through time a given molecule will sample cells of all kinds with a probability proportional to the frequency with which each type of cell occurs in the liquid. We could use this consideration to justify an intuitive evaluation of the configurational entropy. A rigorous calculation of the configurational entropy arising from the different arrangements of these heterogeneous cells would, however, presumably need a detailed knowledge of the number of ways of dividing space into cells. Studies of the statistical geometry of sphere packing, such as those described by Bernal and his co-workers, are, however, based on an analysis of only one (or a very few) specific random packings. Thus, only one particular division of space is examined, from which, when some arbitrary method of distinguishing cells of different kinds has been chosen, enables us to evaluate the number of cells of different kinds in the random packing. If a large enough number of spheres is considered, then the distribution function derived for one particular random packing will approximate to the mean distribution function derived from a large number of different packings. It seems reasonable to suppose that an approximation to the configurational entropy can be derived by equating the number of ways of dividing space to the number of ways of arranging the cells of a given packing among themselves. It may be argued that not all arrangements will completely fill space. The error so introduced will depend on the precision with which we define a " kind " of cell. If we were to specify the precise shape of each cell, then the error would be larger than if we specified, for

[1] R. Collins, *Proc. Battelle Coll. Phase Changes in Metals* (Geneva-Villars, March 1966), to be published by McGraw-Hill.

example, the potential energy of a molecule at the centre of the cell: minor changes in cell shape needed to fit a cell into its surroundings can be made without seriously affecting the energy. For the purposes of a preliminary estimate of the configurational entropy corresponding to a random packing of spheres, we may classify cells according to the number of nearest neighbours which define the cell without specifying the precise geometry of the cell. If a fraction θ_i of the cells are formed from i nearest neighbours, then the configurational entropy is simply $-R\sum_i \theta_i \ln \theta_i$. The intuitive argument mentioned above would lead to the same result. The histogram given by Bernal and King for close-packed spheres leads to a value of 2·77 cal deg.$^{-1}$ mole^{-1}. This is certainly of the correct order of magnitude for the configurational entropy of melting of a substance with freely rotating spherical molecules (e.g., CH_4, 2·5; CCl_4, 2·4). Other contributions to the entropy of fusion will arise from the loosening of the vibrational degrees of freedom in cells with smaller numbers of nearest neighbours; and from the fact that Bernal's analysis refers to spheres in closest random packing, to which liquids will tend only at the lowest temperatures. At the melting point of most substances the liquid will probably have a significantly less dense structure so that we shall expect the figure of 2·77 cal deg.$^{-1}$ mole^{-1} to represent a minimum value for the entropy of fusion: in fact, only metals have substantially lower values, while the noble gases (e.g., Ar, 3·4) have rather higher values.

It will be of considerable interest to see how the configurational entropy of random sphere packs varies with the density. However, we should not expect the method of reducing the density by random removal of single spheres used by Bernal and King to be realistic: random sphere packs containing discrete holes of " molecular " size are highly improbable distributions and calculations based on them are unlikely to be reliable. The method employed by Mason in which a continuous series of random packings of varying density is generated should (provided that surface effects can be eliminated) lead to much more realistic values.

To carry the theory further it would be necessary to show how the density varied with temperature: this is clearly a more complex problem and is not easily soluble without a much more detailed analysis requiring the introduction of an assumed intermolecular force law between pairs of spheres. The real value of Bernal's model is that it brings out clearly what is implied by the term randomness as applied to the structure of liquids, and emphasizes the fundamental geometrical distinction between solids and liquids.

Dr. J. Finney, *Birkbeck College, London,* (*communicated*). The advantages of a tetrahedral description of a random packing have been stressed by Beresford, Collins and Mason. Beresford and Mason are particularly interested in porosity and hence this approach is of greater use than polyhedra, while Collins' approach via neighbour distances implies the convenience of a tetrahedral lattice. We are interested in the geometry of the array and the packing problem itself and therefore the Voronoi polyhedron is the obvious unit as it defines *completely unambiguously* a region of space associated with one point only. The polyhedron shapes may be complex, but they do give us information which could be used to elucidate the thermodynamics.

For instance, Everett's use of the co-ordination polyhedra to estimate the configurational entropy shows an approach which could yield fruitful results, although use of the Voronoi geometrical co-ordination might be more realistic. To justify such an approach to configurational entropy, we must establish a relationship between the particular histogram (here the coordination number) and the " site energy " of a centre. Further work on this has shown the site energy to be effectively unrelated to geometrical coordination, but suggests a remarkably high correlation of 0·83-0·90 between the Voronoi *volume* and the centre energy. The physical reason for this is obscure—it may be connected to the packing restrictions—but the existence of such a high correlation shows promise for evaluating an improved approximation to the entropy and facilitates the use of a large number of *small* samples to this end, where realistic energy calculations could not normally be made.

The general problem of calculating the entropy of a random array is fraught with uncertainties. The approach of Collins and Allison via information theory entails the difficulty of sorting out what information is relevant, and how much is needed to give an unambiguous *minimum* description of the system. In this connection the use of either coordination number or geometric neighbour histograms is an insufficient description, for the information contained about each site is incomplete in energy terms.

Regarding the use of soft potentials suggested by Collins, we have in fact carried out analyses on some high density Monte Carlo runs kindly made available to us by Dr. Singer and Dr. Mcdonald of Royal Holloway College, in an attempt to compare a random packing with the structure of a " liquid like " arrangement generated in the computer. Initial results show a remarkable similarity between fig. 6 for the hard sphere model and the total histogram for several configurations at different times in the same Monte Carlo run. Moreover, there are interesting variations between the different configurations, suggesting complete inadequacy of single samples of about 100 centres for approaching the problem via geometrical neighbours.

As for the two-dimensional liquid, we think it is essentially different in kind from the three-dimensional system. For example, $\bar{N} = 6$ exactly in two dimensions, while $\bar{N}$ is a function of density in three; moreover, the generation programme of Mason crystallizes in two dimensions but not in three, suggesting differences in the basic natures of the two problems.

Beresford's attempts to develop a statistical geometry in terms of a tetrahedral description are interesting, but entail an ambiguity in the choice of " diagonals ", or near contacts. This ambiguity could be removed simply by defining tetrahedra directly from the Voronoi set—i.e. by choosing the inter-centre links to be the Voronoi face normals. With each Voronoi vertex are associated four centres, thus defining uniquely a set of tetrahedra completely filling space. After removing this ambiguity, it would be interesting to see what this approach to the statistical geometry yielded.

Mason's random model generation programme could be a step forward in producing data for analysis on a large scale as similar programmes constructed previously have not converged to a limiting density. We cannot see a theoretical argument to show that Mason's programme would converge. Moreover, it is not certain what the characteristics of the packing are, how they depend upon the exact mechanisms written into the programme, and how they compare with physically built models. For example, the final result may depend on exactly *how* we remove an overlap, and what system we use for picking out centres during the search for overlaps. The construction of a random model under a central gravitational field is an improvement over the physical models, but out present inability to describe the essential characteristics of a random model make it difficult to compare explicitly the results of the two modes of construction.

One of the features of such a generating programme is that it gives random packing with a large density variation up to the maximum of a random close packing and could give the data necessary for investigating thermodynamic properties with temperature variation. There are serious difficulties, however, in the long machine times necessary even for 200 spheres, and the rate of increase of time with sample size seems to prohibit the generation of much larger ones. Thus physical models still have an important place. However, if the thermodynamic significance of the Voronoi volume can be firmly established, a large number of smaller packings will be invaluable.

Prof. C. Domb (*King's College, London*) said: I wish to speak about the behaviour of the specific heat of a fluid in the critical region, and more particularly about comparing experimental results with the predictions of the lattice gas model. Following the accurate experimental work of Voronel [1] and his collaborators, various analyses were attempted to establish the experimental values of the critical indices for this specific heat. There were differences of opinion as to whether the data could best be

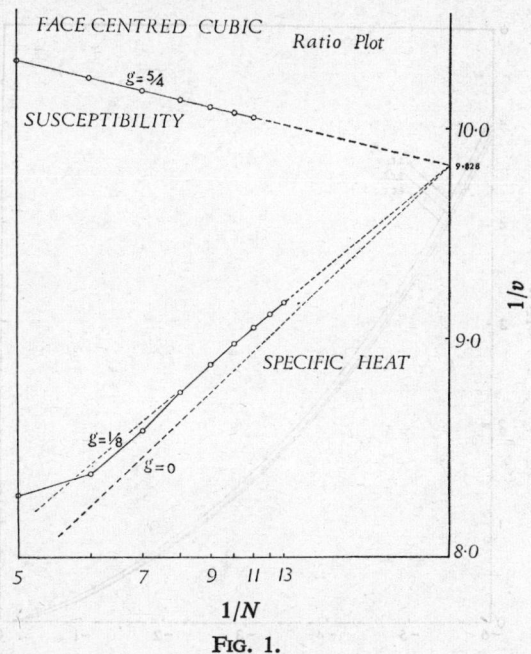

FIG. 1.

fitted by a logarithm or a power law.[2] Since the data cover a limited range with appreciable experimental errors, a formula of the type

$$\frac{A_\pm}{\alpha_\pm}\left[\left(\frac{T}{T_c}\right)^{\pm 1}-1\right]^{\alpha_\pm}+B_\pm$$

involving several disposable parameters was used, and it is not surprising that the data could be fitted by a range of values of α. (The $\pm$ in the formula refers to the region just above and just below the critical point, and the value $\alpha = 0$ corresponds to a logarithm.) In fact, for a theoretical model there are no disposable parameters, and to test the validity of the model, its predictions should be compared directly with experimental results. This has not been possible previously because of the lack of sufficiently precise theoretical information on the three-dimensional lattice gas model.

[1] A. V. Voronel, V. G. Gorbunova, Yu. R. Chashkin and V. V. Schekochikhina, *Soviet Physics JETP*, 1966, **23**, 597. A. V. Voronel, Yu. R. Chashkin, V. A. Popov and V. G. Simkin, *Soviet Physics JETP*, 1964, **18**, 568. M. I. Bagatskii, A. V. Voronel and V. G. Gusak, *Soviet Physics JETP*, 1963, **16**, 517.
[2] M. E. Fisher, *Physic. Rev.* 1964, **126**, 1599.

Recent calculations by members of the theoretical research group at King's College however, greatly improved the accuracy of the theoretical calculations.

By a remarkable co-ordination of techniques, Sykes [1] and his collaborators have succeeded in adding four new terms to the high temperature series expansion for the specific heat. This means, that series are available as far as $1/T^{13}$. (The term $1/T^{14}$ should be available shortly.) The result of plotting the ratio of successive coefficients [2] as a function of $1/N$ is shown in fig. 1; the upper points refer to the susceptibility and the lower points to the specific heat. The critical index is determined by the limiting slope of this ratio for large N and the evidence is convincing that the specific heat index is $\frac{1}{8}$. It is then possible with so many exact terms and

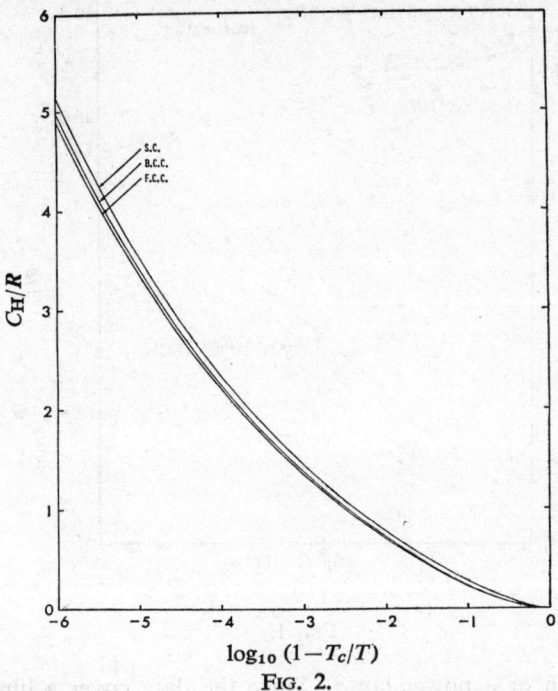

FIG. 2.

a limiting asymptotic form to calculate the specific heat accurately, and the result of such calculations for a number of three-dimensional lattices is presented in fig. 2. It will be seen that the specific heat depends little on crystal structure. At low temperatures, the position is much less satisfactory since the series behave less regularly. However, Gaunt [3] has examined other critical indices and has thereby produced indirect evidence that the critical index has the same value of $\frac{1}{8}$. For the diamond lattice, the low-temperature series are all positive, and Gaunt has made an estimate of the specific heat.

When we compare with experiment, we follow the approach of Fisher,[4] remembering at the same time that a lattice gas is a crude model and we should not expect too much. In fact, we wish to determine how adequate it is in accounting for critical

[1] M. F. Sykes, J. L. Martin and D. L. Hunter, *Proc. Physic. Soc.*, in press.
[2] C. Domb and M. F. Sykes, *J. Math. Physics*, 1961, **2**, 63.
[3] D. S. Gaunt, *Proc. Physic. Soc.*, in press.
[4] M. E. Fisher, *Physic. Rev.* 1964, **126**, 1599.

behaviour. Fig. 3 (prepared by D. L. Hunter) shows such a comparison; it will be seen that, when the critical point is closely approached, the experimental results show small but definite deviations from the theoretical calculations. The low-temperature comparison is shown in Fig. 4. Gaunt points out that in the range shown

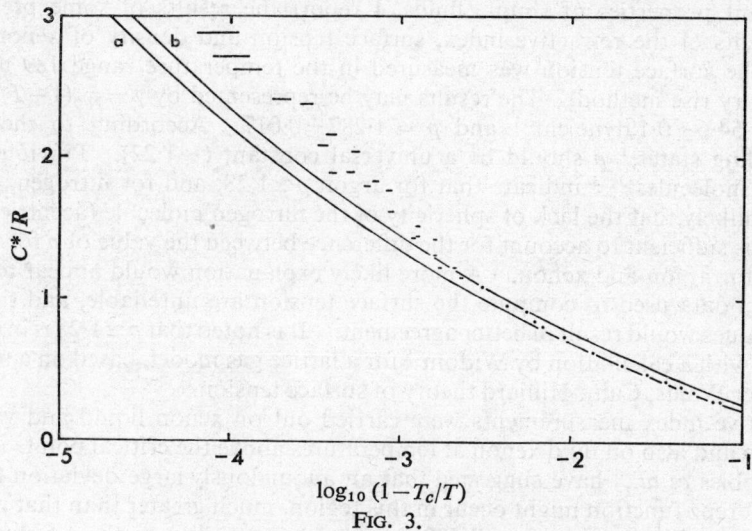

FIG. 3.
Points: Date for N_2 (Voronel et al.)
Curves: Ising model (a: F.C.C.; b: S.C.)

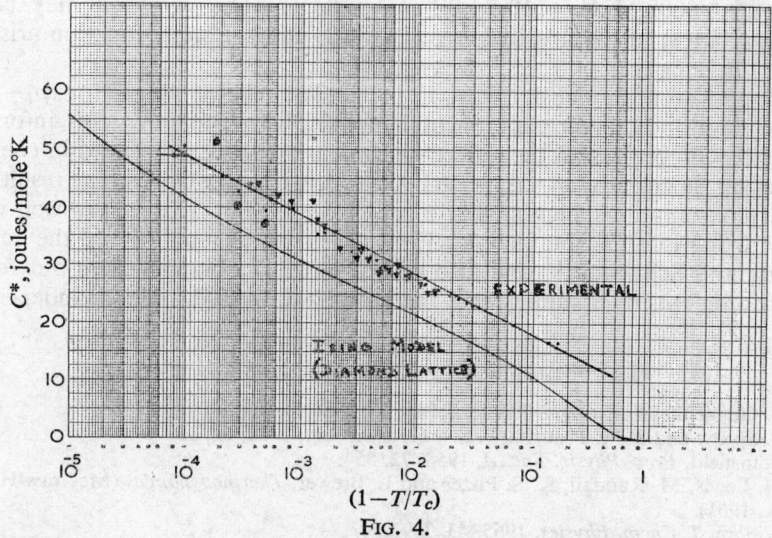

FIG. 4.

the theoretical curve could easily be mistaken for a logarithm since it is almost linear on the logarithmic scale. The disagreement between experiment and theory is more marked than on the high-temperature side; this was already noted by Fisher [1] who regarded it as a serious defect of the model. We may conclude that, although the

[1] M. E. Fisher, *Physic. Rev.* 1964, **126**, 1699.

lattice gas model has considerable success in accounting for critical behaviour, there is room for improvement which could perhaps be obtained by relaxing the rigidity of the model and allowing holes of different shapes and sizes.

Dr. B. L. Smith (*University of Sussex*) (*communicated*): In connection with the critical point properties of simple fluids, I report the results of some preliminary measurements of the refractive index, surface tension and density of xenon in this region. The surface tension was measured in the temperature range 189 to 286°K by a capillary rise method. The results may be represented by $\gamma = \gamma_0(1 - T/289.74)^p$ with $\gamma_0 = 54.6 \pm 0.1$ dyne cm^{-1} and $p = 1.287 \pm 0.017$. According to the law of corresponding states,[1] p should be a universal constant (~ 1.22). Previous results for simple molecules [2, 3] indicate that for argon $p \simeq 1.28$, and for nitrogen, $p \simeq 1.24$. It seems unlikely that the lack of sphericity of the nitrogen molecule (acentric factor [4] $\omega = 0.04$) is sufficient to account for the difference between the value of p for nitrogen and those for argon and xenon. A more likely explanation would appear to be that the ($\rho_l - \rho_g$) data used to compute the surface tension are unreliable, and that more accurate values would result in better agreement. It is noted that $p \simeq 1.28$ is in excellent agreement with a calculation by Widom [5] for a lattice gas model, based on a reformulated van der Waals, Cahn-Hilliard theory of surface tension.

Refractive index measurements were carried out on xenon liquid and vapour in coexistence and also on fluid xenon at temperatures above the critical point. Studies, e.g., by Abbiss *et al.*,[6] have suggested that an anomalously large deviation from the Lorentz-Lorenz function might occur in this region, much greater than that predicted by theory.[7, 8] The results of over 500 measurements lead us to the conclusion that the Lorentz-Lorenz function $(n^2-1)/(n^2+2)\rho$ remains constant to within $\pm 3\%$ over the whole range studied (0·002-0·024 mole cm^{-3}) and that at the critical point $n_c = 1.1383 \pm 0.0008$, L.L. $= 10.5 \pm 0.1$ cm^3 mole^{-1}. The variation may be much smaller, since most of the possible error in the Lorentz-Lorenz function arises from uncertainty in density.

The lack of accurate density data, in particular, reliable values for ($\rho_l - \rho_g$), has lead us to develop a direct experimental method [9] for obtaining this information. According to Guggenheim,[1] the difference in density between a liquid in coexistence with its vapour is given by $\rho_l - \rho_g = A(1 - T/T_c)^\beta$, where $\beta \simeq 0.33$. The results of our preliminary observations suggest that $\beta = 0.343 \pm 0.010$. This agrees well with the value $\beta = 0.345 \pm 0.015$ obtained by Fisher [10] from an analysis of the results of Weinberger and Schneider,[11] and also with $\beta = 0.341$ obtained from our refractive index measurements by assuming that the Lorentz-Lorenz function is independent of density, i.e.,

$$[(n^2-1)/(n^2+2)\rho]_l - [(n^2-1)/(n^2+2)\rho]_g = K(1-T/T_c)^\beta.$$

[1] E. A. Guggenheim, *J. Chem. Physics*, 1945, **13**, 253.
[2] F. B. Sprow and J. M. Prausitz, *Trans. Faraday Soc.*, 1966, **62**, 1097.
[3] D. Stansfield, *Proc. Physic. Soc. A*, 1958, **72**, 854.
[4] G. N. Lewis, M. Randall, K. S. Pitzer and L. Brewer, *Thermodynamics* (McGraw-Hill, New York, 1961).
[5] B. Widom, *J. Chem. Physics*, 1965, **43**, 3892.
[6] C. P. Abiss, C. M. Knobler, R. K. Teague and C. J. Pings, *J. Chem. Physics*, 1965, **42**, 4145.
[7] L. S. Taylor, *J. Math. Physics*, 1963, **4**, 824.
[8] S. Y. Larsen, R. D. Mountain and R. Zwanzig, *J. Chem. Physics*, 1965, **42**, 2187.
[9] B. L. Smith, *J. Sci. Instr.*, 1966, **43**, 958.
[10] M. E. Fisher, *J. Math. Physics*, 1964, **5**, 944.
[11] M. A. Weinberger and W. G. Schneider, *Can. J. Chem.*, 1952, **30**, 422.

Structure of Liquids

Part 7.—Determination of Intermolecular Potential Functions and Correlation Functions in Fluid Argon by X-Ray Diffraction Techniques *

By C. J. Pings

Division of Chemistry and Chemical Engineering
California Institute of Technology, Pasadena, California

Received 16th January, 1967

Methods of obtaining the radial distribution function and the direct correlation function for simple liquids from X-ray diffraction data are reviewed. A new theoretical analysis demonstrates that certain of the cluster integrals appearing in the density expansion of the radial distribution function can be evaluated directly from Fourier transforms of appropriate powers of the X-ray scattering function. These results are used to develop expressions which permit determination of the intermolecular potential function from moderately dense fluids using essentially only X-ray diffraction data. Non-additivity effects may also be treated. Experimental data available are inadequate for conclusive determination of the potential function; however, experimental results from one state of argon give plausible values for the lowest-order cluster integral.

The direct determination of the radial distribution function of a fluid from X-ray diffraction data is generally well understood. This paper will briefly review the pertinent equations relating the structure of the fluid to the X-ray measurements, and will summarize some current results for argon from the author's laboratory. We further call attention to the possibility of exploiting the diffraction data to obtain other quantities, viz., the direct correlation function and certain of the Mayer cluster integrals. Used in proper combination, the Fourier transforms of several different functions of the X-ray scattering data then lead to an expression in closed form for the intermolecular potential function.

RADIAL DISTRIBUTION AND DIRECT CORRELATION FUNCTION

For simple systems, the conventional radial distribution function is computed from the Fourier transform of the X-ray scattering function

$$G(r) = g(r) - 1 = (2\pi^2 r \rho)^{-1} \int_0^\infty s i(s) \sin rs \, ds = I_1(r). \tag{1}$$

In this expression, $g(r)$ is the radial distribution function, $G(r)$ is the net radial distribution function, ρ is the density, $s = 4\pi\lambda^{-1} \sin \theta$ is the scattering variable where 2θ is the angle between the incident and scattered beam, and λ is the wavelength of the monochromatic incident radiation. The scattering function, $i(s)$, for X-rays is defined as

$$i(s) = I(s)/f^2(s) - 1, \tag{2}$$

where $I(s)$ is the intensity of coherently scattered radiation, fully corrected for polarization absorption, etc.; $f(s)$ is the atomic scattering factor. The derivations [1] of these

---

*Work supported by the Directorate of Chemical Sciences, U.S. Air Force Office of Scientific Research, under Contract AF 49(638)-1273.

formulae for monatomic substances and extensive discussion of problems of normalization, pretruncation of the integral, etc., are available.[2, 3] Review articles by Gingrich,[4] Furukawa,[5] and Kruh[6] summarize results of measurements on many liquid systems. Although the number of substances studied has been large, the range of states has usually been limited to ambient temperature and pressure, or in some cases to states along the vapour pressure curve. The classic study for a simple system was reported in 1940 by Eisenstein and Gingrich.[7] That work included X-ray scattering patte ns for 26 states of confined argon specimens; six of these were Fourier analyzed to prrovide values of radial distribution function. Recently, the author's laboratory[8] has reported diffraction experiments on liquid argon at 13 states on a systematic grid in temperature and density. A sample of the final radial distribution functions from this latter study is shown in fig. 1 and fig. 2. The latter is a comparison with the

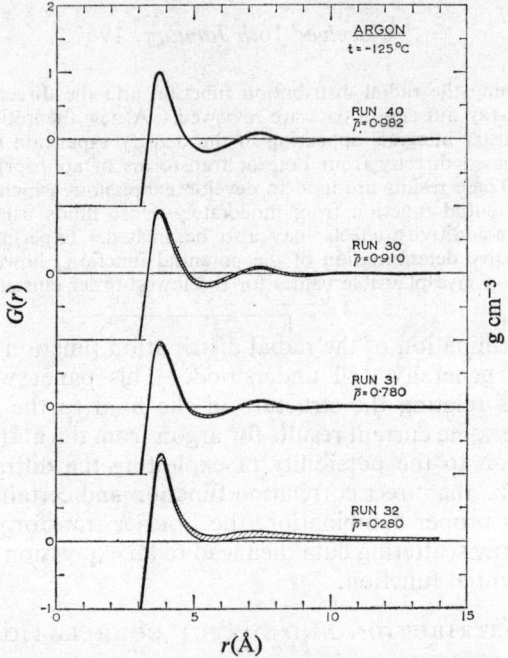

FIG. 1.—Net radial distribution function[8] of liquid and gaseous argon along the isotherm $t = -125°C$. Runs 31 and 32 correspond, respectively, to essentially saturated liquid and saturated gas.

earlier data from the Eisenstein-Gingrich study. In spite of the more modern detection systems and more sophisticated data-handling techniques, the recent experiments still reveal considerable uncertainty due both to experimental error and also to seemingly inevitable aberrations introduced in the numerical approximations to the Fourier integral. These uncertainties are reflected in fig. 1 by the shaded areas on each of the four radial distribution curves.

The direct correlation function, $C(r)$, as introduced by Ornstein and Zernike[9] has played a central role in theory of optical scattering near the critical state and also has figured in the development of several integral equations describing the general behaviour of fluids. This direct correlation function is defined formally in terms of the net radial distribution function by the following equation

$$C(r_{12}) = G(r_{12}) - \rho \int C(r_{13}) G(r_{23}) \mathrm{d}\mathbf{r}_3. \tag{3}$$

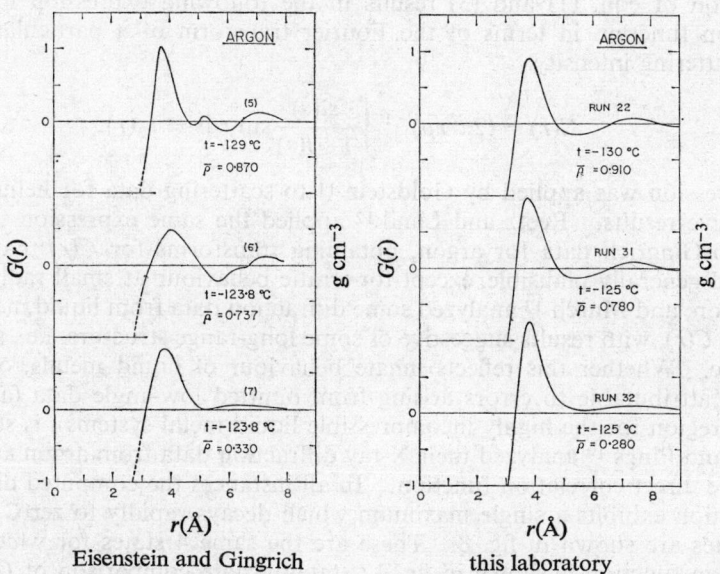

FIG. 2.—Comparison of radial distribution function determinations from two laboratories. Particularly note that the subsidiary feature at about 5·0 Å in the top state is absent in the second work.

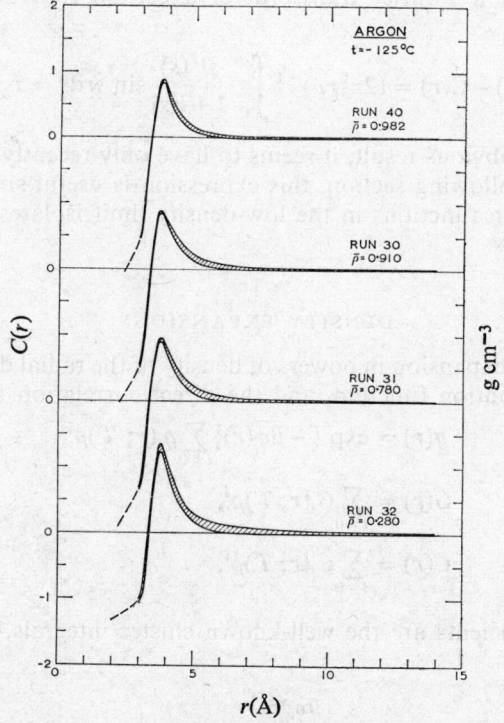

FIG. 3.—Direct correlation function [14] for liquid and gaseous argon along the isotherm $t = -125°C$. These curves might be compared state-by-state with the net radial distribution function in fig. 1.

Solution of eqn. (1) and (3) results in the following expression for the direct correlation function in terms of the Fourier transform of a particular function [10] of the scattering intensity.

$$C(r) = (2\pi^2 r\rho)^{-1} \int \frac{si(s)}{1+i(s)} \sin rs\, ds = I_2(r). \qquad (4)$$

This expression was applied by Goldstein [11] to scattering data for helium, but with inconclusive results. Reetz and Lund [12] applied the same expression to the earlier Eisenstein-Gingrich data for argon, obtaining transforms for $C(r)$ that were short range and generally plausible, except for erratic behaviour at small radii. Johnson, Hutchinson, and March [13] analyzed some diffraction data from liquid metals in order to obtain $C(r)$, with results suggestive of some long-range structure, i.e., second-order peaks, etc. Whether this reflects innate behaviour of liquid metals, or whether it might be attributable to errors arising from omitted low-angle data (a particularly sensitive region for the highly incompressible liquid metal systems), is still not clear. Mikolaj and Pings [14] analyzed their X-ray diffraction data from argon at 13 states to obtain the direct correlation function. In all instances the computed direct correlation function exhibits a single maximum which decays rapidly to zero. The results for 4 states are shown in fig. 3. These are the same 4 states for which the radial distribution function is shown in fig. 1; state-by-state comparison of $G(r)$ and $C(r)$ is informative.

Direct subtraction of eqn. (1) and (4) results in the following expression for the difference between the net radial distribution function and the direct correlation function in terms of a Fourier transform of a certain function of the scattering intensity.

$$G(r) - C(r) = (2\pi^2 r\rho)^{-1} \int_0^\infty \frac{si^2(s)}{1+i(s)} \sin srds = I_3(r). \qquad (5)$$

Although this is an obvious result, it seems to have only recently been pointed out.[15] As developed in a following section, this expression is useful since the difference of these two distribution functions in the low-density limit isolates certain of the low-order cluster integrals.

DENSITY EXPANSIONS

We represent the expansion in powers of density of the radial distribution function, the net radial distribution function, and the direct correlation function as follows;

$$g(r) = \exp\{-\beta\phi(r)\} \sum_{i=0} g_i(r;T)\rho^i, \qquad (6)$$

$$G(r) = \sum_{i=0} G_i(r;T)\rho^i, \qquad (7)$$

$$C(r) = \sum_{i=0} C_i(r;T)\rho^i. \qquad (8)$$

The expansion coefficients are the well-known cluster integrals,[16, 17] some of which are listed below

$$g_0 = 1 \qquad (9)$$

$$g_1 = \triangle \qquad (10)$$

$$g_2 = \tfrac{1}{2}\,[\text{diagram}] + [\text{diagram}] + 2\,[\text{diagram}] + \tfrac{1}{2}\,[\text{diagram}] \tag{11}$$

$$C_0 = [\text{diagram}] \tag{12}$$

$$C_1 = [\text{diagram}] \tag{13}$$

$$C_2 = \tfrac{1}{2}\,[\text{diagram}] + [\text{diagram}] + 2\,[\text{diagram}] + \tfrac{1}{2}\,[\text{diagram}] + \tfrac{1}{2}\,[\text{diagram}] + \tfrac{1}{2}\,[\text{diagram}] \tag{14}$$

$$G_0 = [\text{diagram}] \tag{15}$$

$$G_1 = [\text{diagram}] + g_1(r) \tag{16}$$

$$G_2 = \tfrac{1}{2}\,[\text{diagram}] + [\text{diagram}] + \tfrac{1}{2}\,[\text{diagram}] + [\text{diagram}] + g_2(r) \tag{17}$$

Eqn. (6) has been used [18] as a means of computing a theoretical $g(r)$ as a function of temperature and density using some assumed form of the intermolecular potential function. The equation also offers the prospect of reverse usage, viz., computation of the intermolecular function from an experimentally determined radial distribution function. In the limit of zero density, the intermolecular potential function would be exactly $-kT \ln g(r)$. Such a direct determination would hold considerable attraction since there is no model or parameterization involved. However, in this simple form the computation is unrealizable since it is impossible to take meaningful diffraction data at extremely low densities for the simple reason that the diffracted intensity above background is proportional to the density of the sample. Mikolaj and Pings [19] did demonstrate that plausible values of the intermolecular potential function could be obtained by applying an extended form of eqn. (6) to diffraction data taken on argon at about half the critical density. However, their procedure involved iteration techniques in order to evaluate the $g_1(r)$ term, and some question of convergence did arise.

We show here that the term $\rho g_1(r)$ and all but one of cluster integrals represented in the ρ^2 term in the expansion of $g(r)$ can be rigorously expressed as Fourier transforms of certain functions of the scattering data. Eqn. (7) and (8) are used to obtain the density series expansion of the difference between $G(r)$ and $C(r)$, and that difference is then equated to the integral of eqn. (5), yielding the following

$$I_3(r) = \rho\,[\text{diagram}] + \rho^2\left[\,[\text{diagram}] + 2\,[\text{diagram}]\,\right] + O(\rho^3). \tag{18}$$

One other of the cluster integrals in eqn. (6) can be related to an experimentally accessible integral.

$$\rho^2\,[\text{diagram}] = \rho^2\,[\text{diagram}] = \left[\rho\,[\text{diagram}]\right]^2 = [I_3(r)]^2 + O(\rho^3). \tag{19}$$

Before assembling the preceding expressions into a final expression, one further effect may be included, viz., possible non-additivity of the intermolecular forces.[20-22] We will concern ourselves here only with corrections to $g_1(r)$ which, in the presence of non-additivity effects, can be represented as follows:

$$g_1(r) = [\text{diagram}] + g_1^{(\text{NA})}(r), \tag{20}$$

where
$$g_1^{(NA)}(r) = \int \exp\{-\beta[\phi(r_{23})+\phi(r_{13})]\}[\exp\{-\beta\Delta\}-1]dr_3, \qquad (21)$$
where
$$\Delta = U(\mathbf{r}_1,\mathbf{r}_2,\mathbf{r}_3) - \sum_{pairs}\phi(\mathbf{r}_{ij}) \qquad (22)$$

By combining these preceding results, the following final expression then is obtained from eqn. (6)
$$g(r) = I_1(r)+1 = \exp\{-\beta\phi(r)\}[1+I_3(r)+\tfrac{1}{2}[I_3(r)]^2+\tfrac{1}{2}\rho^2 \bowtie + \rho g_1^{(NA)}(r) + O(\rho^3)]. \qquad (23)$$

Unfortunately, there seems to be no simple representation of the five-bonded cluster integral in the ρ^2 term, and this is carried into the analysis in the final form. If the expression is being used as a means of determining the intermolecular potential function, presumably an iteration would be possible since the cluster integral has a

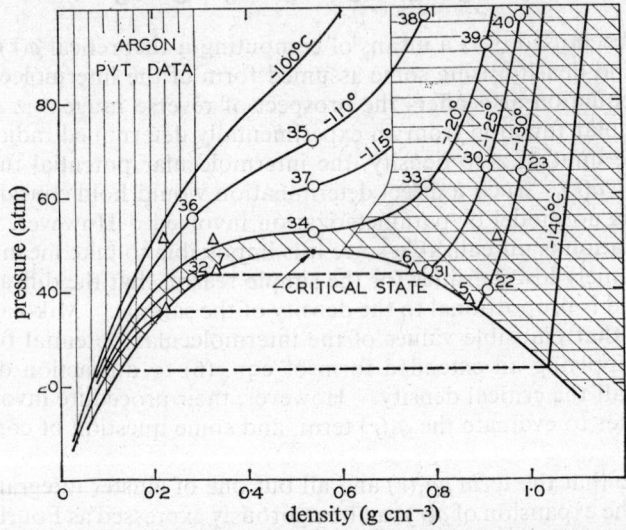

FIG. 4.—Thermodynamic plane for argon showing our estimates of region of applicability of equations developed in this paper for obtaining the intermolecular potential function from experimental diffraction data. The triangles represent states studied by X-ray by Eisenstein and Gingrich, the circles the states of Mikolaj and Pings. The shaded area to the right is precluded because of increasing contribution from $g_3(r)$ and higher terms; the shaded area to the left is essentially precluded because of too low bulk scattering from the low-density specimen; temperatures below $-120°C$ are unfavourable because of increasing contribution from the five-bonded double-rooted cluster integral.

known dependence on $\phi(r)$. However, fortunately this five-bounded cluster integral is the smallest term in $g_2(r)$; in particular for temperatures greater than approximately $1.2\,T_c$ the contribution is almost negligible. Therefore, a perfectly acceptable procedure is to use the above expression along with theoretical evaluations of this one remaining cluster integral, which has already been evaluated by Henderson and Oden [23] based on the Lennard-Jones 6-12 potential. We have indicated that terms of the order of ρ^3 have been neglected; however, we have also neglected non-additivity effects of the order of ρ^2. The immediately preceding equation has thus been put into a form where it can be used in conjunction with experimental data to significant density—roughly up to a density for which PVT data could be adequately represented in terms up the fourth virial coefficient, but neglecting fifth and higher virial coefficients.

Taking all these factors into consideration, we have shown in fig. 4 the domain of likely applicability of eqn. (22) for determining the intermolecular potential function and the non-additivity effect.

Eqn. (23) can be put into a more practical form for comparison with experimental data. Let

$$A(r;\rho,T) = 1 + I_3(r) + \tfrac{1}{2}[I_3(r)]^2 + \tfrac{1}{2}\rho^2 \bowtie . \quad (24)$$

Then we have the following expression:

$$\frac{A(r;\rho,T)}{I_1(r;\rho,T)+1} = \exp\{\beta\phi(r)\} - \frac{\rho}{I_1(r;\rho,T)+1} g_1^{(NA)}(r). \quad (25)$$

Thus we have a simple functional relationship between the experimental quantities

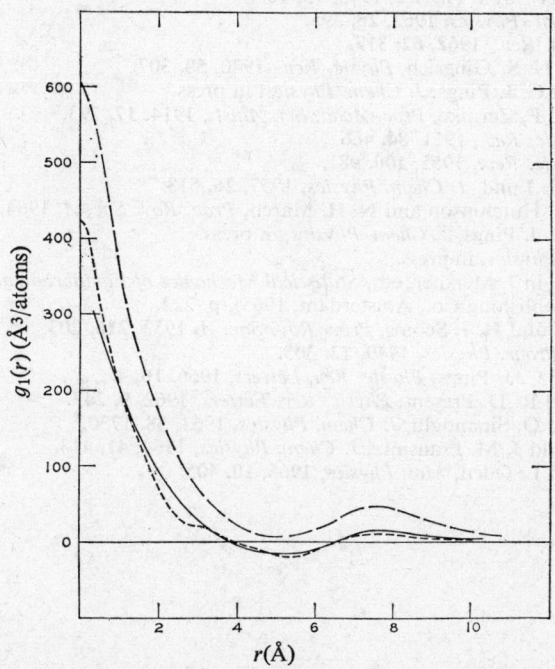

FIG. 5.—Comparison [15] of the three-body double-rooted cluster integral. The theoretical curves are taken from the reduced $g_1^*(r)$ of Henderson and Oden. The experimental curve is the result of applying eqn. (18) to X-ray data at the state labelled 36 in fig. 4.

— — $(3\cdot409)^3 \, g_1^*(r)$ at $T^* = 1$
——— $(3\cdot409)^3 \, g_1^*(r)$ at $T^* = 1\cdot4$
- - - - $g_1(r)$, expt. at $T = 163\cdot1°K$
     $= (1\cdot37) \times (119\cdot5°K)$

$A(I_1+1)^{-1}$ and $\rho(I_1+1)^{-1}$, with the slope determining the non-additivity effect and the intercept the intermolecular potential function. Although the non-additivity term may have dependence on temperature, the intermolecular potential function is temperature-independent; therefore, the application of above expression to the same substance at two different temperatures must yield the same value of the intermolecular potential function if the data are correct.

A study of X-ray diffraction study of fluid argon by Mikolaj and Pings [8] included several states in a region where the above expression should be applicable. However, the points were widely spaced in density, and too few in number to provide any strong test of the applicability of the method suggested here. Nevertheless, these data were sufficient to lend some credibility to an important facet of the development, viz., computation of plausible values of the cluster integrals from eqn. (18). Fig. 5 reproduces a comparison of theoretical values of $g_1(r)$ with values calculated from eqn. (18), using data from a low-density state. Our laboratory is now conducting an experiment to accumulate detailed data for fluid argon with the best possible accuracy in a range of densities for a maximum utility of eqn. (23).

[1] R. W. James, *The Optical Principles of the Diffraction of X-Rays*, (Bell, London, 1954), p. 477.
[2] J. Waser and V. Schomaker, *Rev. Mod. Physics*, 1953, **25**, 671.
[3] H. H. Paalman and C. J. Pings, *Rev. Mod. Physics*, 1963, **35**, no. 2, 389.
[4] N. S. Gingrich, *Rev. Mod. Physics*, 1943, **15**, 90.
[5] K. Furukawa, *Progr. Physics*, 1962, **25**, 395.
[6] R. F. Kruh, *Chem. Rev.*, 1962, **62**, 319.
[7] A. Eisenstein and N. S. Gingrich, *Physic. Rev.*, 1940, **58**, 307.
[8] P. G. Mikolaj and C. J. Pings, *J. Chem. Physics*, in press.
[9] L. S. Ornstein and F. Zernike, *Proc. Acad. Sci. Amst.*, 1914, **17**, 793.
[10] L. Goldstein, *Physic. Rev.*, 1951, **84**, 466.
[11] L. Goldstein, *Physic. Rev.*, 1955, **100**, 981.
[12] A. Reetz and L. H. Lund, *J. Chem. Physics*, 1957, **26**, 518.
[13] M. D. Johnson, P. Hutchinson and N. H. March, *Proc. Roy. Soc. A*, 1964, **282**, 283.
[14] G. Mikolaj and C. J. Pings, *J. Chem. Physics*, in press.
[15] C. J. Pings, *Mol. Physics*, in press.
[16] G. S. Rushbrooke, in J. Meixner, ed., *Statistical Mechanics of Equilibrium and Non-Equilibrium* (North Holland Publishing Co., Amsterdam, 1965), p. 222.
[17] G. S. Rushbrooke and H. I. Scoins, *Proc. Roy. Soc. A*, 1953, **216**, 203.
[18] J. de Boer, *Rept. Progr. Physics*, 1949, **12**, 305.
[19] P. G. Mikolaj and C. J. Pings, *Physic. Rev. Letters*, 1966, **16**, 4.
[20] H. W. Graben and R. D. Present, *Physic. Rev. Letters*, 1962, **9**, 247.
[21] N. R. Kestner and O. Sinanoglu, *J. Chem. Physics*, 1963, **38**, 1730.
[22] A. F. Sherwood and J. M. Prausnitz, *J. Chem. Physics*, 1964, **41**, 413.
[23] D. Henderson and L. Oden, *Mol. Physics*, 1966, **10**, 405.

X-Ray Diffraction Study of Liquid Water in the Temperature Range 4-200°C*

By A. H. Narten, M. D. Danford and H. A. Levy

Chemistry Division, Oak Ridge National Laboratory, Oak Ridge, Tennessee

Received 9th December, 1966

The scattering of X-rays from the free surface of liquid water in equilibrium with water vapour has been analyzed at 4, 25, 50, 75, 100, 150 and 200°C. Deuterium oxide at 4°C was also studied. The diffractometer used was specially designed for the study of liquid structure. The radial distribution functions derived from the experiments are in agreement with most of the previously published work on water showing, however, much higher resolution.

Intensity and radial distribution functions have been computed for a model structure and compared to those derived from experiment. The model assumes an anisotropically expanded ice-I structure, surrounded by a continuous distribution of distances, as an adequate description of the short-range order in water. Occupancy of the large dodecahedral cavities typical for this structure was permitted. The model intensity and radial distribution functions are in quantitative agreement with those derived from experiment at all temperatures. Some thermodynamic properties estimated for the model structure are in essential agreement with those of liquid water.

The first X-ray diffraction patterns from liquid water were obtained by Meyer,[1] Stewart[2] and Amaldi.[3] This work, together with the known properties of the isolated water molecule and the ice lattice, led Bernal and Fowler[11] to propose their model of water structure. Katzoff[4] was the first to apply to water the method of Fourier analysis. Morgan and Warren (1938)[5] analyzed the X-ray scattering from liquid water at five temperatures between the melting and boiling points. Their work led to the abandonment of the Bernal and Fowler model of water structure.

Since 1938, various X-ray diffraction studies of water have been published [6-10]; these investigations have not added to Morgan and Warren's results. It has been the purpose of our work to obtain a set of diffraction data on liquid water which extends and improves upon Morgan and Warren's work both in resolution and temperature range.

EXPERIMENTAL

The diffraction measurements were made with a diffractometer specially designed for the study of liquids. The diffraction pattern from the horizontal surface of liquid water was obtained with a divergent beam technique similar to the Bragg-Brentano system used for powder samples. The instrument provides for simultaneous angular motion of the X-ray tube and the detector about a horizontal axis lying in the liquid surface. This method eliminates sample holder absorption and scattering. Monochromatic MoKα radiation is obtained through the use of a bent and ground crystal monochromator mounted in the diffracted beam. The diffractometer, the procedure for data collection, the various corrections applied to the raw data, and their final evaluation have been discussed elsewhere.[12]

Scattered intensities were measured with various beam divergences, ranging from 0.5 deg. at the lowest scattering angles to 4.0 deg. at the highest angles. The times for a fixed

---

* Research sponsored by the U.S. Atomic Energy Commission under contract with the Union Carbide Corporation.

number of counts, ranging from 100,000 to 600,000, were measured at 0·25 to 1·0 deg. intervals in scattering angle. As the diffraction pattern showed interference throughout the observable range of the instrument [12] (to $s_{max} = (4\pi/\lambda) \sin \theta_{max} = 16$, θ being half the scattering angle), the data are appreciably more extensive than the earlier ones.[1-10]

We have studied the X-ray diffraction pattern of liquid water at 4, 25, 50, 75, 100, 150 and 200°C; deuterium oxide at 4°C was also studied. The experiments at and below 100°C were done at atmospheric pressure, and those above 100°C at the vapour pressure of the sample. Both our raw data and the reduced intensity and radial distribution functions derived from them are available in tabulated form.[13]

RESULTS

The reduced intensity $i(s)$ represents the structurally sensitive part of the total coherent intensity $I(s)$[12, 13] in electron units. It is computed from the equation

$$i(s) = I(s) - \sum_i f_i^2(s), \qquad (1)$$

where $\sum_i f_i^2(s)$ is the part of the scattering ascribable to independent atoms, and the sum is over the stoichiometric unit (one water molecule). A radial distribution function $D(r)$ is obtained by Fourier inversion of (1) according to

$$D(r) = 4\pi r^2 \rho_0 + (2r/\pi) \int_0^{s_{max}} s\, i(s) M(s) \sin (sr) ds, \qquad (2)$$

where ρ_0 is the average number density of molecules, and $M(s)$ is a modification function included to sharpen the features of the radial distribution function (RDF). The modification function used was

$$M(s) = [\sum_i f_i(s)]^{-2}, \qquad (3)$$

where f refers to the coherent scattering amplitudes of oxygen and hydrogen, and summation is again over the stoichiometric unit. This modification function removes the average breadth of the distribution of electron density in the atoms. It also changes the scale so that if $i(s)$ is in electron units, $D(r)$ is in units characteristic of one molecule. The physical meaning of the function $D(r)$ has been discussed elsewhere.[12, 14]

The reduced intensity and radial distribution functions for liquid water are shown in fig. 2 and 3 (circles). There are deviations from a uniform distribution of distances out to 8 Å at room temperature. The first prominent maximum in the RDF, corresponding to nearest neighbour interactions, shifts gradually from 2·82 Å at 4°C to 2·94 Å at 200°C. From the area under this peak, a coordination number of 4·4-4·5 can be computed,* which remains constant over the whole temperature range covered by our experiments. Maxima around 4·5 and 7 Å, corresponding to second and third neighbour interactions, are distinct at room temperature, but disappear gradually with increasing temperature. There is no evidence for a sudden breakdown in the structure of water; if changes in the average configuration around any water molecule take place, they must occur gradually with increasing temperature. The curves for light and heavy water at 4°C are almost identical within experimental error. There is no significant difference in the arrangement of oxygen atoms at this temperature.

* The calculation of average coordination numbers from the area under a RDF peak is not unambiguous. In this case, the lower bound of the first maximum is fairly well defined, but the upper bound is not. The coordination number given here was computed from the parameters of our water model (for details see below and table 1). Its accuracy should be judged by the agreement of the model radial distribution function (solid line, fig. 3) with those derived from experiment (circles, fig. 3) in the region below 3·5 Å.

All of the earlier diffraction studies of liquid water, with the exception of those of the Amsterdam group,[9, 10] have confirmed the results of Morgan and Warren.[5] It is therefore sufficient to discuss only these two studies. Our results are in essential agreement with those of Morgan and Warren, whose data extended to a value of $s_{max} = 12$ at room temperature. Slight differences arise from the higher resolution of our work. The disagreement between Morgan and Warren's work and that of the Amsterdam group (which yields a nearest neighbour distance of 3 Å, and a coordination number of 5) is thus confirmed. We have shown [13] that a value of $s_{max} = 8$, as used in the Amsterdam work, yields radial distribution functions which, for water, show erroneous features in the region of short radial distances.

STRUCTURAL MODEL OF LIQUID WATER

It is not possible to compute radial distribution functions from a known or assumed pair potential for a system interacting with long-range, many-body, non-central forces. However, the experimental radial distribution function for a liquid, together with the known atomic arrangement in the solid and gaseous states, may suggest a model for the liquid structure, which may then be tested against the diffraction data.

For a model of liquid structure to be useful in the present context, it should have a sufficiently detailed geometric basis to permit computation of intensity and radial distribution functions. It must give a detailed description of the arrangement of all atoms around each atom in the stoichiometric unit taken as the origin, and should be consistent with the fact that the distance spectra about each such stoichiometric unit are alike. A distribution of suitably chosen stoichiometric units over a lattice extending to the limits of the sample, would have the required properties. With a description of this kind, it is possible to specify a set of mean radial distances r_{ij} which is needed for the computation of reduced intensity functions according to the equation [12]:

$$i_D(s) = \sum_i \sum_j \exp(-b_{ij}s^2) f_i(s) f_j(s) \sin(sr_{ij})/sr_{ij}. \quad (4a)$$

Here, i is summed over the stoichiometric unit and j over all atoms in the structure. A " temperature factor " $\exp(-b_{ij}s^2)$ is included in (4a); it takes into account the distribution of instantaneous interatomic distances about their respective means r_{ij} both in time and space. The coefficient b_{ij} is one-half the mean square variation in the distance r_{ij} between atom pairs.[12]

If such a model is to be realistic, it must account for the fact that a liquid is not a crystal. We have, in a liquid, only a distribution of distances with maxima in positions for which a lattice is a convenient frame of reference. These positions, which are sharp in a crystal, become increasingly diffuse with radial distance from any origin atom. Thus, the coefficients b_{ij} in (4a) must increase with the distance r_{ij}.

For a model of liquid structure to be tractable, we can terminate the series of terms (4a), which become smaller with increasing distance r_{ij}, at some arbitrary distance, and assume a uniform distribution of distances (continuum) beyond. This corresponds to making a " hole " in a uniform, structureless medium in which to place the discrete interactions of the model structure (4a). The reduced intensity from the continuum of distances with a pair of atoms ik in the stoichiometric unit beginning at r_{ik0}, and extending to the limits of the sample, is given by the equation [12]:

$$i_c(s) = \sum_i \sum_k \exp(-b_{ik0}s^2) f_i(s) f_k(s) 4\pi\rho_0 [sr_{ik0} \cos(sr_{ik0}) - \sin(sr_{ik0})]/s^3. \quad (4b)$$

Here, both i and k are summed over the stoichiometric unit. A " temperature factor " is included in (4b) since the emergence of the continuum will not be sharp. The reduced intensity curve of the model structure can now be computed as the sum of (4a) and (4b):

$$i(s) = i_D(s) + i_C(s). \qquad (4)$$

The model intensity function (4) can be systematically refined to seek a satisfactory fit of the experimental data over the whole angular range.

DESCRIPTION OF THE WATER MODEL

Several crystal structures were examined as a point of departure towards a structural model for liquid water: the α-quartz structure, the cubic ice structure, the chlorine hydrate (clathrate) structure, and the ice-I structure. The clathrate type of model for liquid water proposed by Pauling [16] was investigated in detail. The RDF for the clathrate model was calculated for a nearest neighbour distance of 2·76 Å. Expansion of this distance to that corresponding to the first peak in the observed RDF (2·88 Å at 25°C) leads to an increase of the fraction of molecules inside the clathrate cages in order that the proper density be maintained. As a result, the area under the first peak becomes too small. In view of these difficulties, the Pauling model does not seem adequate to explain our X-ray data.[17]

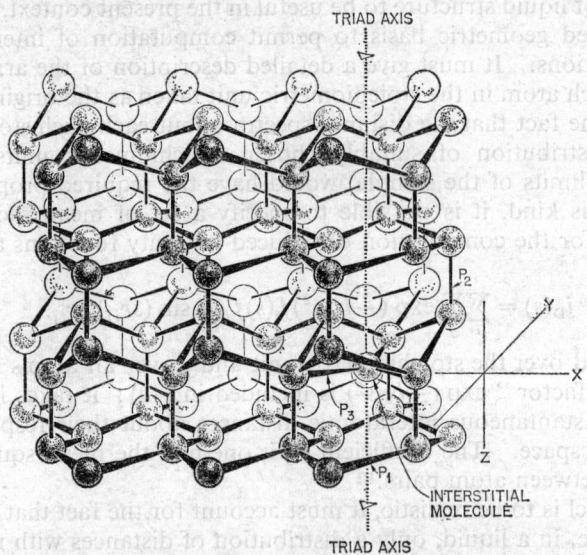

FIG 1.—The water model (ball/stick ratio not to scale).

Among the crystal structures examined, the ice-I lattice was the most promising one; it is shown in fig. 1. Each oxygen atom is tetrahedrally surrounded by other oxygen atoms, forming layers of six-membered puckered rings. Two adjacent layers, related by mirror symmetry, form dodecahedral cavities. In our water model, the ice-I lattice is anisotropically expanded ($P_1 \neq P_2$ in fig. 1), and both vacant lattice sites and occupancy of the cavities by water molecules are permitted, but constrained to conform to the experimental density. For simplicity, the model retains the hexagonal symmetry of the ice-like network.

Intensity curves for this model structure were computed by eqn. (4). Discrete interactions were included for all distances out to approximately 10 Å, with a continuum beyond. The initial agreement being promising, the model was subjected to systematic refinement by iterative non-linear least squares,[15] in which the model intensity function (4) was fitted to values derived from experiment. At this stage, a number of constraints were introduced in order to keep the model as simple as possible and to reduce the number of variable parameters to a minimum. The position of the cavity molecule was restricted to the triad axis (fig. 1). Since exploratory calculations had shown that the inclusion of discrete O—H and H—H interactions did not change the model intensity functions significantly (because of the low scattering power of the one electron in the hydrogen atom), continuous distributions were assumed for these distances. All " temperature factors " corresponding to longer range distances were related to those of the third coordination shell about any origin atom, under the assumption that $b_{ij} \propto r_{ij}$.[18] Also, a number of " temperature factors " corresponding

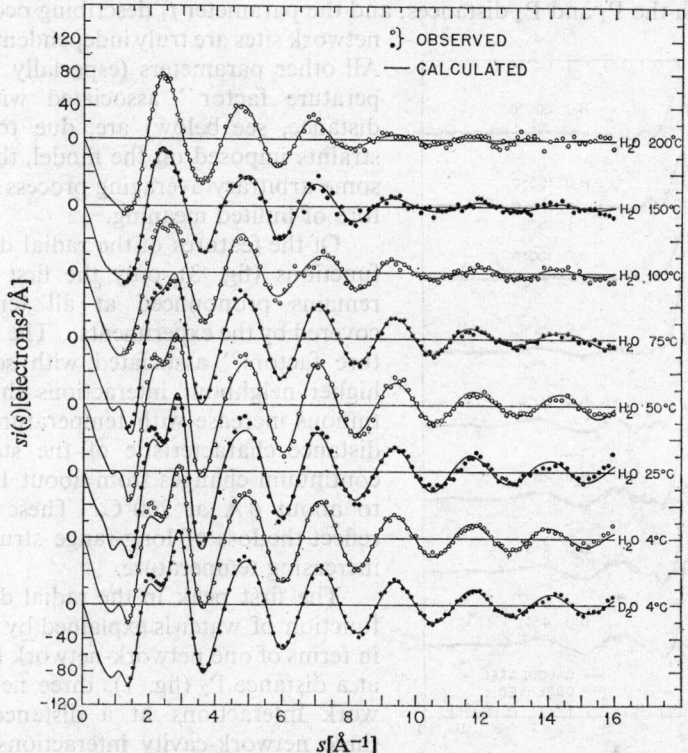

FIG. 2.—Observed and model reduced intensities for liquid water.

to first, second and third neighbour distances were arbitrarily set equal. Finally, only physically reasonable values of the model parameters were allowed in order to minimize the time required for convergence of the fit. Only three distances were treated as independent variables: the two near neighbour O—O network distances parallel and roughly perpendicular to the triad axis (P_1 and P_2 in fig. 1), and the shortest distance from the cavity oxygen atom to the network (P_3 in fig. 1). All other distances (out to 10 Å) were properly related to these near neighbour distances. These three adjustable parameters, together with their associated " temperature factors ", were sufficient to yield a good fit to all but the low angle region of the intensity function. In order to fit this region also, additional " temperature factors " associated with second and third neighbour interactions, were varied and also the distance characteristic of the start of the continuum, and a parameter specifying the occupancy of lattice sites.

Reduced intensity functions obtained from the least-squares refined model are shown in fig. 2 (solid lines), along with the observed data (circles). The corresponding radial distribution functions are shown in fig. 3. For the Fourier inversion of the observed intensity functions, extrapolation from the lowest scattering angle accessible by our technique to zero angle was made using the model intensity curves.

PARAMETERS OF THE MODEL AND THEIR TEMPERATURE DEPENDENCE

The refined parameters used for the calculation of the model intensity and radial distribution functions are shown in fig. 4 and 5. It should emphasized again, that only the three near neighbour distances P_1, P_2, and P_3, the " temperature factor " associated with the P_1 and P_2 distances, and the parameter f_1 describing occupancy of network sites are truly independent variables. All other parameters (especially the " temperature factor " associated with the P_3 distance, see below) are, due to the constraints imposed on the model, the result of some arbitrary averaging process and therefore of limited meaning.

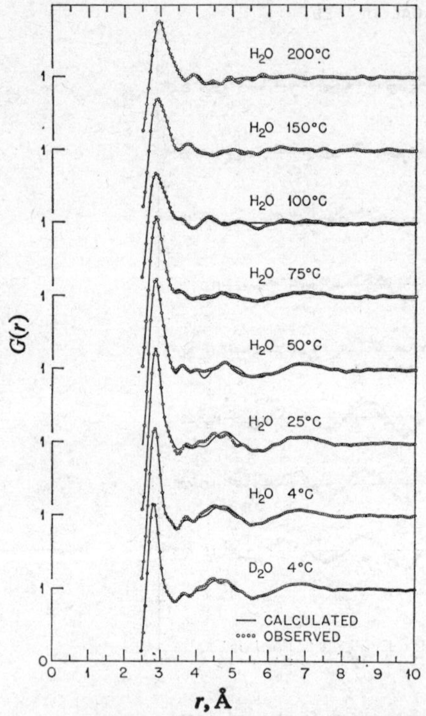

Of the features of the radial distribution functions (fig. 3), only the first maximum remains pronounced at all temperatures covered by the experiments. The " temperature factors " associated with second and higher neighbour interactions show a continuous increase with temperature, and the distance characteristic of the start of the continuum changes from about 10 Å at 4°C to about 6 Å at 200°C. These variations reflect the loss of long-range structure with increasing temperature.

The first peak in the radial distribution function of water is explained by the model in terms of one network-network interaction at a distance P_2 (fig. 1), three network-network interactions at a distance P_1, and three network-cavity interactions at a distance P_3, each of them properly weighted according to the network and cavity occupancy factors.

FIG. 3.—Observed and model radial distribution functions of water.

At 4°C, the distance P_2, between network molecules related by mirror symmetry, is only slightly larger than the corresponding ice distance; with increasing temperature, this distance (fig. 4) contracts below the nearest neighbour distance in ice. The distance P_1 between network molecules related by a centre of symmetry is, at 4°C, about 6 % larger than the corresponding ice distance, and with increasing temperature, this distance goes through a maximum of 3·02 Å at 100°C. The root-mean-square (rms) displacements associated with these network distances (fig. 4) show roughly the same temperature dependence. At temperatures above 100°C, the short network distance P_2 expands, and the long P_1 distance contracts; at 200°C the two network distances differ by an amount much smaller than their respective rms-displacements.

The position of the cavity molecule was constrained to the triad axis (fig. 1). A molecule situated in the centre of the cavity formed by adjacent layers of network molecules would have six nearest network neighbours; the results of our study

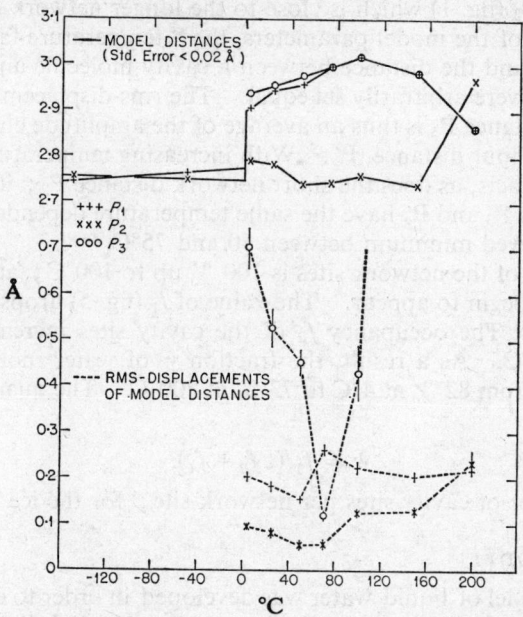

FIG. 4.—Near neighbour model distances and their RMS-displacements.

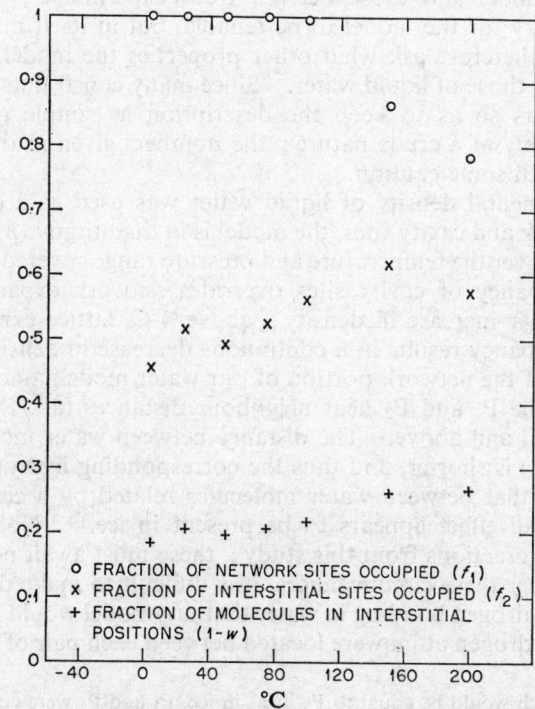

FIG. 5.—Temperature dependence of model parameters.

indicate that the position of the molecule is not at the cavity centre. At the position found, the angle subtended by two nearest network oxygen atoms has approximately the tetrahedral value. Thus each cavity molecules has three nearest network neighbours at a distance P_3 (fig. 1) which is close to the longer network distance P_1.

In the refinement of the model parameters, the "temperature factors" associated with the distance P_3 and the distance between a cavity molecule and its three second nearest neighbours * were arbitrarily set equal. The rms-displacement shown in fig. 4 as associated with distance P_3 is thus an average of the amplitude characteristic of this and the second neighbour distance, P'_3. With increasing temperature, P_3 expands, as does P_1, and P'_3 contracts, as does the short network distance P_2; if the rms-displacements associated with P_3 and P'_3 have the same temperature dependence, their average could show the observed minimum between 50 and 75°C.

The occupancy f_1 of the network sites is 100 % up to 100°C; at this temperature, empty network sites begin to appear. The value of f_1 (fig. 5) drops to 87 % at 150°C and 79 % at 200°C. The occupancy f_2 of the cavity sites increases from 45 % at 4°C to 57 % at 200°C. As a result, the fraction w of water molecules in network positions, decreases from 82 % at 4°C to 73 % at 200°C. The quantities f_1, f_2, and w are related by

$$w = f_1/(zf_2 + f_1), \tag{5}$$

where z is the number of cavity sites per network site; for the ice lattice $z = \frac{1}{2}$.

PROPERTIES OF MODEL

The structural model of liquid water was developed in order to explain the diffraction data, and the agreement between the intensity and radial distribution functions computed for the model and those derived from experiment is gratifying. This agreement is necessary for the model to be tenable, but in itself not sufficient proof for its reality. We therefore ask what other properties the model might have, and how they compare to those of liquid water. Since many constraints were imposed on the model parameters so as to keep the description as simple as possible, these predictions can be only of a crude nature; the numbers given in this section should therefore be used with some caution.

Since the experimental density of liquid water was used as a constraint on the occupancy of network and cavity sites, the model is in quantitative agreement with the P—V—T behaviour over the temperature and pressure range covered by the diffraction experiments. Occupancy of cavity sites overrides network expansion up to 4°C, leading to the familiar increase in density; above 4°C, lattice expansion at almost constant cavity occupancy results in a continuous decrease in density.

The anisotropy of the network portion of our water model, amounting to a 10 % difference between the P_1 and P_2 near neighbour distances (at 75°C), remains pronounced up to 100°C and above. The distance between water molecules related by mirror symmetry (P_2) is shorter, and thus the corresponding hydrogen bond appears to be stronger than that between water molecules related by a centre of symmetry (P_1). A similar small effect appears to be present in ice.[19] Nothing can be said concerning O—H interactions from this study; these must await neutron diffraction investigations. Under these circumstances, it is difficult to make definite statements as to the degree of hydrogen bonding in water that our model would predict. If in the ice-like network a hydrogen atom were located between each pair of adjacent oxygens,

* This distance, which would be equal to P_3 if, as in ice, P_1 and P_2 were equal, is, for the water model, about 10 % larger than P_3.

forming a hydrogen bond, there would be, per mole of water, a fraction wf_1 such interactions; of these, 0.25 wf_1 would be of the mirror symmetric and 0.75 wf_1 of the centrosymmetric type. Since the distance P_2 is comparable to the near neighbour distance in ice-I, the mirror symmetric bonds would presumably be of similar strength as the hydrogen bonds in ice. Around an empty network site there would be a fraction $w(1-f_1)$ " broken " hydrogen bonds. Since, with our assumptions, neither a hydrogen atom nor an unshared electron pair belonging to a network water molecule would point in the direction of a cavity molecule, the network-cavity molecule interactions, fraction $(1-w)$, would be of a different and probably weaker kind than the network-network bonds.

If we apply the term hydrogen bond to any O—H ... O interaction for which the O—O distance is smaller than that computed from the van der Waals radii of oxygen and hydrogen, then the model would predict a distribution of hydrogen bonds; it would change with temperature as does the near neighbour distance distribution, i.e., as the first peak in the radial distribution function of water. This would be in agreement with spectroscopic investigations of the O—H stretching frequency in water.[20]

A crude estimate of the frequencies associated with the translational motion of the network molecules can also be made. If the rms-displacements of the network distances were due to translational vibrations only, and if a network molecule moved independently in the field of its nearest neighbours with a frequency $\nu = (f/M)^{\frac{1}{2}}/2\pi$, where f is the force constant and M the reduced mass, f could be eliminated by the corresponding expression for the energy: $E = \frac{1}{2}kT = \frac{1}{2}f\overline{x^2}$; here $\overline{x^2}$ is the mean square amplitude associated with the translational motion. Using the proper constants, the frequency (in cm^{-1}) is related to the amplitude (in Å) by the approximate expression $\nu \cong (T)^{\frac{1}{2}}/\bar{x}$. At 4°C, $\bar{x} = 0.093$ Å for the mirror symmetric P_2 bond, and the frequency would be 200 cm^{-1}. Similarly, with $\bar{x} = 0.203$ for the motion along the centrosymmetric P_1 bond the frequency computes as 90 cm^{-1}. Bands around 160 and 60 cm^{-1} have been observed in the Raman and inelastic neutron spectrum of water, and assignment of the 160 and 60 cm^{-1} frequency to the motion of water network molecules along the mirror and centrosymmetric hydrogen bonds has been proposed previously on a more intuitive basis.[21] Our model is not in disagreement with this view.

Our model system in a state of statistical equilibrium can be described as a saturated solution of N' vacant network sites (holes) and N'' cavity molecules in an ideal lattice, constituted by $N-N''$ regularly arranged molecules and containing $N-N''+N'$ sites, among which these molecules and the N' holes can be distributed at random. This description corresponds to the assumption that the holes and cavity molecules are not interacting with each other; this assumption is justified so long as N' and N'' are small compared with N, which is not the case with our water model. The number of network holes and cavity molecules can be determined as a function of temperature from the condition of the minimum of that part of the free energy which is due to their presence. The corresponding part of the entropy is proportional to the logarithm of the number of different ways they can be distributed over the respective sites. Employing the customary approximations, the counterpart of the entropy of mixing of a ternary solution is

$$S^M/R = -(w/f_1)[f_1 \ln f_1 + (1-f_1) \ln (1-f_1)] - (1-w)/f_2[f_2 \ln f_2 + (1-f_2) \ln (1-f_2)]. \quad (6)$$

The first term describes the entropy change associated with the formation of vacant network sites (holes), and the second that corresponding to the formation of cavity molecules. For the molal Gibbs free energy of the model we write

$$G = w[f_1 G_N^\circ + (1-f_1) G_H^\circ] + (1-w) G_I^\circ - TS^M. \tag{7}$$

Here G_N°, G_H° and G_I° are hypothetical standard molal free energies of network molecules, network holes, and cavity molecules, respectively, and S^M is defined by eqn. (6). Introducing $\Delta G_H^\circ = G_N^\circ - G_H^\circ$, and $\Delta G_I^\circ = G_N^\circ - G_I^\circ$, eqn. (7) rearranges to

$$G = G_I^\circ + w[\Delta G_I^\circ - (1-f_1)\Delta G_H^\circ] - TS^M. \tag{8}$$

From the condition $dG(f_1, f_2) = 0$ we obtain for the standard free energy change associated with the formation of vacant network sites:

$$\Delta G_H^\circ = (RT/f_1^2)[\ln(1-f_1) + z\ln(1-f_2)], \tag{9}$$

and for the free energy change associated with the transformation of cavity molecules into the network:

$$\Delta G_I^\circ = RT[\ln f_2/(1-f_2) - (z/f_1)\ln(1-f_2)] - (RT/f_1)[f_1 \ln f_1 + (1-f_1)\ln(1-f_1)] + (1-f_1)\Delta G_H^\circ. \tag{10}$$

Eqn. (6-10) reduce to those derived by Frank and Quist [22] in their study of the thermodynamic properties of the Pauling model, for the binary case with $f_1 = 1$.

The quantities ΔG_H° and ΔG_I° can be calculated from eqn. (9) and (10) and the model parameters f_1, f_2 and w; they are shown in table 1. From the temperature dependence of ΔG_H° and ΔG_I° the average enthalpy changes associated with the formation of network holes and cavity molecules, ΔH_H° and ΔH_I°, can be obtained (table 1). The enthalpy change associated with the formation of a network hole must be, at least

TABLE 1.—THERMODYNAMIC PROPERTIES OF THE WATER MODEL. ENERGY UNITS IN kcal/mole; ENTROPIES IN kcal/mole deg.; w IS THE FRACTION OF MOLECULES IN LATTICE POSITIONS; f_1 THE LATTICE OCCUPANCY, AND N THE AVERAGE NUMBER OF NEAREST NEIGHBOURS

T(°K)	w	f_1	N	ΔG_H°	ΔG_I°	ΔH_V model	ΔH_V water	ΔS_V model	ΔS_V water
277·2	0·81$_5$	1	4·3$_7$	—	0·06$_2$	9·7	10·72	0·035	0·0387
298·2	0·79$_6$	1	4·4$_1$	—	0·24$_4$	9·7	10·51	0·033	0·0352
323·2	0·80$_3$	1	4·3$_9$	—	0·19$_3$	9·7	10·25	0·030	0·0317
348·2	0·79$_2$	1	4·4$_2$	—	0·32$_5$	9·7	9·99	0·028	0·0287
373·2	0·7$_8$	0·9$_9$	4·4	−4	0·4$_5$	9·7	9·71	0·026	0·0260
423·2	0·7$_4$	0·8$_7$	4·5	−2·$_8$	0·8$_8$	9·6	9·09	0·023	0·0215
473·2	0·7$_3$	0·7$_9$	4·5	−3·$_0$	0·7$_7$	9·6	8·35	0·020	0·0177

$$\Delta H_H^\circ = -9.9 \pm 4.3 \qquad \Delta H_I^\circ = -1.06 \pm 0.23$$

within the accuracy of this discussion, approximately equal to the evaporation energy of a network molecule, in our water model. For the total evaporation enthalpy of the model, we may thus write

$$\Delta H_V = w\Delta H_H^\circ + (1-w)(\Delta H_H^\circ - \Delta H_I^\circ). \tag{11}$$

The model evaporation enthalpies and the corresponding entropies $\Delta S_V = \Delta H_V/T$ are compared with the experimental values in table 1. From the temperature dependence of the model evaporation enthalpies, the specific heat of the model can be obtained as approximately 9 cal/mole at room temperature. The experimental value for water is 18 cal/mole, but we do not consider this disagreement as significant in view of the approximate nature of this thermodynamic treatment. The assumption of temperature dependent values for ΔH_H° and ΔH_I° would raise the model c_p value into the neighbourhood of the experimental value for liquid water.

CONCLUSIONS

The X-ray diffraction data on liquid water presented here yield information on the average atomic arrangement around any oxygen atom taken as the origin. The proposed structural model for water was developed to explain the diffraction data. Reduced intensity functions computed for the model are in quantitative agreement with the X-ray data on liquid water over the whole angular range covered by our experiments. Radial distribution functions obtained by Fourier inversion of the model intensity functions are in agreement with those derived from experiment to distances of 10 Å and beyond. The same model, with proper adjustment of its parameters, explains the X-ray data over the whole temperature range covered by our experiments. Agreement of this model with the diffraction data is necessary but in itself not sufficient proof of its reality. On the other hand, the model has properties which are not in disagreement with the thermodynamic properties of water, and it may be helpful in the interpretation of the many strange properties of water. In similar manner, other proposed models of water [23] which have a sufficiently detailed geometrical basis to permit computation of intensity and radial distribution functions can be tested against the diffraction data, with agreement a necessary condition for the model to be tenable.

[1] H. H. Meyer, *Ann. Physik*, 1930, **5**, 701.
[2] G. W. Stewart, *Physic Rev.*, 1931, **37**, 9.
[3] E. Amaldi, *Physik. Z.*, 1931, **32**, 914.
[4] S. Katzoff, *J. Chem. Physics*, 1934, **2**, 841.
[5] J. Morgan and B. E. Warren, *J. Chem. Physics*, 1938, **6**, 666.
[6] L. Simons, *Soc. Sci. Fennica, Commentationes Phys. Math.*, 1939, **10**, no. 9.
[7] C. Finbak and H. Viervoll, *Tidsskr. Kjemi, Bergvesen Met.*, 1943, **3**, 36.
[8] G. W. Brady and W. J. Romanow, *J. Chem. Physics*, 1960, **32**, 306.
[9] C. L. van Panthaleon van Eck, H. Mendel and W. Boog, *Disc. Faraday Soc.*, 1957, **24**, 200; *Proc. Roy. Soc. A*, 1958, **247**, 472.
[10] J. Heemskerk, *Rec. Trav. Chim.*, 1962, **81**, 904.
[11] J. D. Bernal and R. H. Fowler, *J. Chem. Physics*, 1933, **1**, 515.
[12] H. A. Levy, M. D. Danford and A. H. Narten, *Data Collection and Evaluation With an X-Ray Diffractometer Designed for the Study of Liquid Structure* (ORNL-3960, May 5, 1966).
[13] A. H. Narten, M. D. Danford and H. A. Levy, *X-Ray Diffraction Data on Liquid Water in the Temperature Range 4 to 200°C* (ORNL-3997, September, 1966).
[14] J. Waser and V. Schomaker, *Rev. Mod. Physics*, 1953, **25**, 671.
[15] W. R. Busing and H. A. Levy, OR GLS, *A General Fortran Least Squares Program* (ORNL-TM-271, August 1962).
[16] L. Pauling, in *Hydrogen Bonding* (D. Hadzi and H. W. Thompson, ed.), (Pergamon Press, London, 1959).
[17] M. D. Danford and H. A. Levy, *J. Amer. Chem. Soc.*, 1962, **84**, 3965.
[18] J. Frenkel, *Kinetic Theory of Liquids* (Dover Publications, New York, 1955).
[19] S. La Placa and B. Post, *Acta Cryst.*, 1960, **13**, 503.
[20] T. T. Wall and D. F. Hornig, *J. Chem. Physics*, 1965, **43**, 2079. M. Falk and T. A. Ford, *Can. J. Chem.*, 1966, **44**, 1699.
[21] Y. V. Gurikov, *Zhur. Struct. Khim.*, 1963, **4**, 824.
[22] H. S. Frank and A. S. Quist, *J. Chem. Physics*, 1961, **34**, 604.
[23] J. L. Kavanau, *Water and Solute-Water Interactions* (Holden-Day, San Francisco, 1964).

Infra-Red Absorption of HDO in Water at High Pressures and Temperatures

By E. U. Franck and K. Roth

Institut für Physikalische Chemie, Technische Hochschule,
Karlsruhe, Englerstr. 11/Germany

Received 16th January, 1967

By use of a specially designed cell with a sapphire window the absorption of the OD-stretching vibration of HDO in H_2O has been measured at frequencies from 2200 to 2900 cm^{-1} and at temperatures and pressures from 30 to 400°C and from 50 to 4000 bars respectively. At the supercritical temperature of 400°C and pressures below 200 bars (corresponding to a density of water of 0·1 g/cm³) the rotational structure of the vibration band of free water molecules is observed. At higher density only one intensive absorption maximum with simple shape is observed at all temperatures. This is considered as support for the continuum model for water in the liquid and in the dense supercritical state.

New information on the structure of liquid water has recently been derived from near infrared and Raman spectra [1-12]. The frequency and intensity of the absorption of the oxygen-hydrogen vibrations indicate the existence and the extent of hydrogen bonding. The OD-vibration of dilute HDO in H_2O is particularly suited for such investigations because of the absence of interference from other frequencies and for other reasons.[1, 2, 8, 13] The temperature dependence of this vibration is of special interest. Wall and Hornig [1] and Falk and Ford [2] have obtained important results which support the assumption of a continuum model for liquid water.

The infra-red spectrum of liquid water in the overtone region above 5000 cm^{-1} at saturation pressure up to the critical point at 374°C and 221 bars has been measured by Luck.[9] Other authors have also recently published spectra in this frequency region for liquid water at saturation pressure and elevated temperatures.[10-12] The OD-vibration of HDO, however, has only been determined up to 130°C.[2] No information about the pressure or density dependence of this vibration was available. Therefore, it was the purpose of this work, to investigate separately the influence of temperature and density on the OD-stretching frequency of HDO. These investigations had to be extended to supercritical temperatures in order to observe the variation of the absorption from very low to very high density of water at constant temperature.

It should be possible to determine the conditions under which OD-vibration not affected by hydrogen bonding is detectable. To obtain this information measurements were made to temperatures and pressures up to 400°C and 4000 bars respectively.

EXPERIMENTAL

An optical cell of the reflection type similar in some ways to that used by Welsh [19] was designed. The cell has a single window, made of a colourless synthetic sapphire of 10 mm thickness. Attached to the surface of the sapphire is a platinum-iridium mirror. Spacers of gold foil determine the distance between the mirror and sapphire. This space, filled with the fluid, provides a path length of twice the distance between the mirror and sapphire surfaces. Thus the path length is independent of the applied pressure. The aperture of the sapphire window is 8 mm. The body of the cell is made from a non-corrosive nickel alloy. It is covered by the coils of the heating wire and enclosed in a double-walled brass case cooled with water. The cell body contains two thermocouple wells. A detailed description of the cell will be given elsewhere.

The housing of the Perkin-Elmer model 521 grating spectrometer was flushed with dry air. It was furnished with a Micro Specular Reflectance Accessory which had been slightly changed in order to mount the high-pressure cell outside the normal sample area. A 1 : 1 slit image could be produced inside the cell on the Pt-Ir mirror from which the beam was reflected. The beam is refocused on the entrance aperture of the instrument by a toroidal mirror. A narrow stainless-steel capillary connects the cell to the pressure generating unit. This unit consists of a hand pump, a pressure intensifier* and a separator vessel in which the pressure is transmitted from oil to water. The pressure is measured by calibrated Bourdon gauges. The D_2O† was 99·7 % pure; the mixtures of D_2O and H_2O were prepared by weighing.

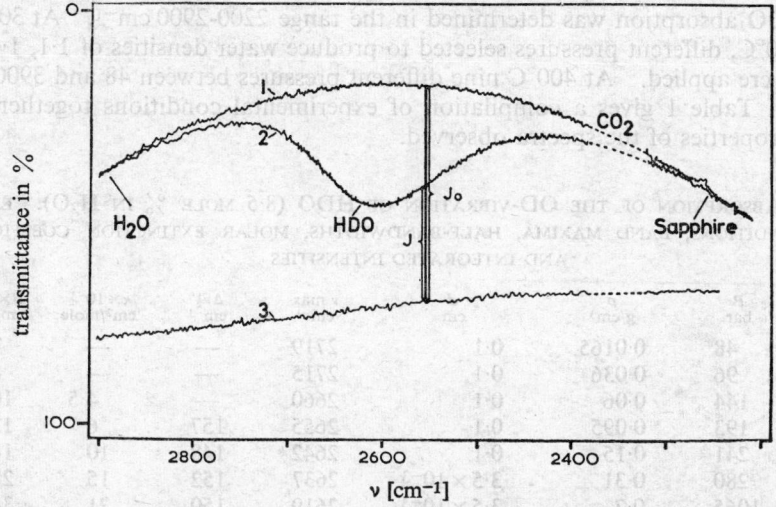

FIG. 1.—One set of original curves of the % transmittance as a function of frequency ν in cm⁻¹ at 400°C and 3900 bars (0·9 g/cm³); path length, 35 μ. 1, background absorption of H_2O and sapphire; 2, absorption of a 8·5 mole % solution of HDO in H_2O; 3, zero line, representing light reflected by the water-sapphire surface and light emitted by the hot cell body; --- region of CO_2 absorption with reduced reliability.

The accuracy of the temperature measurements, at the highest temperatures is ±5°C. The pressure is correct within ±5 bars below 250 bars and within ±50 bars beyond 1000 bars. The water density has been calculated using the VDI-steam-tables [21] up to 1000 bars and the experimental PVT-data of Maier and Franck [14] at higher pressures. The spectrometer was calibrated using the water vapour bands, the CO_2 doublet and polystyrene foil with the micro-reflectance unit and the empty cell in position. The frequencies are correct to within ±2 cm⁻¹. The path length was determined using the interference fringes of the empty cell. For every transmittance curve of HDO in H_2O the spectrum of pure H_2O at equal temperatures and pressures had to be determined. Fig. 1 gives an example for 400°C and 3900 bars. Curve 1 is the transmittance of pure H_2O and sapphire; curve 2 represents the solution of HDO in H_2O with a path length as before. Curve 3 was determined without the Pt-Ir mirror; it represents the black-body radiation of the heated cell filled with the

*Harwood Engineering
†Farbwerke Hoechst

HDO+H$_2$O mixture together with the light reflected by the inner surface of the sapphire. From such curves the extinction coefficient κ of HDO and the integrated band intensity B have been evaluated using the relations

$$\kappa = \frac{\overline{M} \log_{10}(J_0/J)}{x_{\text{HDO}}\rho_{\text{H}_2\text{O}}d},$$

$$B = \int_{\nu_1}^{\nu_2} \kappa d\nu.$$

$\overline{M}$ is the average molecular weight of the mixtures, x_{HDO} the mole fraction of HDO using an equilibrium constant of 3·96,[3, 15] $\rho_{\text{H}_2\text{O}}$ denotes the density of water in g/cm^3 at temperature T and pressure P. d is the path length in cm and J_0 and J in % are the transmittance values according to fig. 1.

RESULTS

The HDO absorption was determined in the range 2200-2900 cm^{-1}. At 30, 100, 200 and 300°C, different pressures selected to produce water densities of 1·1, 1·0 and 0·9 g/cm^3 were applied. At 400°C nine different pressures between 48 and 3900 bars were used. Table 1 gives a compilation of experimental conditions together with the main properties of the spectra observed.

TABLE 1.—ABSORPTION OF THE OD-VIBRATION OF HDO (8·5 MOLE % IN H$_2$O). EXPERIMENTAL CONDITIONS, BAND MAXIMA, HALF-BANDWIDTHS, MOLAR EXTINCTION COEFFICIENTS AND INTEGRATED INTENSITIES

T °C	P bar	ρ g/cm^3	d cm	ν max cm^{-1}	$\Delta\nu_{\frac{1}{2}}$ cm^{-1}	$\kappa \times 10^{-3}$ cm^2/mole	$B \times 10^{-5}$ cm/mole
400	48	0·0165	0·1	2719	—	—	7
400	96	0·036	0·1	2715	—	—	8·5
400	144	0·06	0·1	2660	—	4·5	10
400	193	0·095	0·1	2655	157	6	12
400	241	0·15	0·1	2642	148	10	18
400	280	0·31	3·5×10^{-3}	2637	152	15	28
400	1065	0·7	3·5×10^{-3}	2619	150	21	38
400	2055	0·8	3·5×10^{-3}	2613	157	22	41
400	3900	0·9	3·5×10^{-3}	2605	167	23	45
300	2180	0·9	3·5×10^{-3}	2595	—	28	—
200	600	0·9	3·5×10^{-3}	2578	—	35	—
300	5000	1·0	3·5×10^{-3}	2587	153	29	58
200	2800	1·0	3·5×10^{-3}	2568	195	33	70
100	1000	1·0	3·5×10^{-3}	2540	195	42	85
30	100	1·0	3·5×10^{-3}	2507	168	55	99
100	4400	1·1	3·5×10^{-3}	2535	—	45	—
30	3080	1·1	3·5×10^{-3}	2505	—	56	—

Fig. 2 demonstrates the variation of the OD-absorption with temperature at constant density. The decrease of frequency and maximum extinction was already expected from the isobaric infra-red [2, 5] and Raman [1, 6] observations. At densities of 0·9 g/cm^3 and higher, no trace of a second absorption is detectable. At lower temperatures the shape of the bands is almost Gaussian, a fact which has been emphasized by Falk and Ford.[2] Above 200°C, however, the shape becomes increasingly asymmetric. The wings of the bands seem to disappear always in the same frequency region; only the maxima are shifted to higher frequency with increasing temperature.

The isothermal behaviour of the OD-absorption at one supercritical temperature is shown by fig. 3. At the lowest density, which is 28 times the density of water

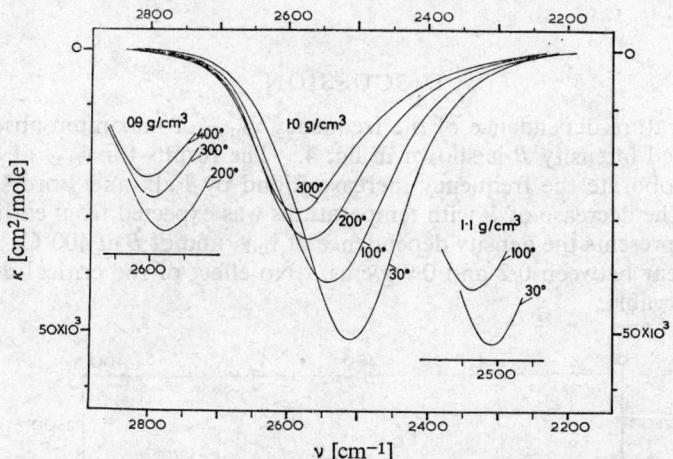

FIG. 2.—Molar extinction coefficient κ in cm²/mole of the OD-stretching vibration as a function of frequency ν in cm⁻¹. Absorption curves at constant densities of water of 0·9, 1·0 and 1·1 g/cm³ and at temperatures of 30, 100, 200, 300 and 400°C.

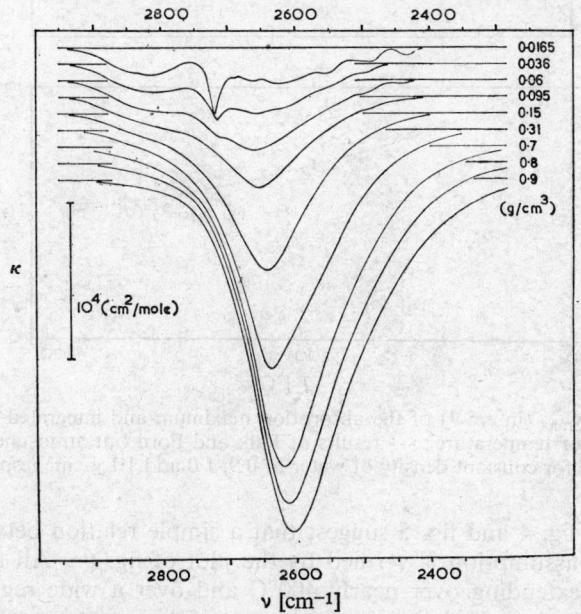

FIG. 3.—Molar extinction coefficient κ in cm²/mole of the OD-stretching vibration as a function of frequency ν in cm⁻¹ at a constant temperature of 400°C and at different densities of water (g/cm³). Note the different base lines of the individual curves.

vapour at normal boiling conditions, the R-, Q- and P- branches of the OD-vibration band are clearly observable. The peak of the Q-branch is at 2719 cm⁻¹. Benedict, Gailar and Plyler give 2720±5 cm⁻¹ for dilute HDO gas at room temperature. This Q-branch was no longer observable in the present work at densities higher than 0.1 g/cm³, e.g., at pressures beyond 200 bars. The structures in the P- and R-branches at 400°C and 0.0165 g/cm³ (48 bars) are in accord with the contours of the vibration-rotation band of the free HDO molecule observed in the gas at atmospheric pressure.[16, 17]

DISCUSSION

The temperature dependence of the frequency ν_{max}, of maximum absorption and of the integrated intensity B is shown in fig. 4. The results for ν_{max} at a density of 1.0 g/cm³ corroborate the frequency increase found by Falk and Ford[2] at isobaric conditions. The decrease of B with temperatures was expected from earlier observations. Fig. 5 presents the density dependence of ν_{max} and of B at 400°C. The curves are almost linear between 0.2 and 0.9 g/cm³. No effect of the critical density (0.32 g/cm³) is observable.

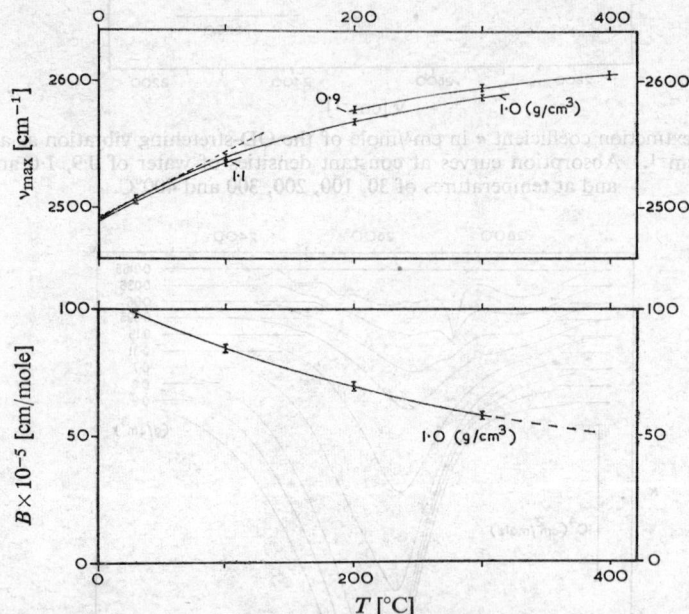

FIG. 4.—Frequency ν_{max} (in cm⁻¹) of the absorption maximum and integrated intensity B (in cm/mole) as a function of temperature; --- results of Falk and Ford[2] at atmospheric pressure. The curves are for constant density of water of 0.9, 1.0 and 1.1 g/cm³ respectively.

The curves in fig. 4 and fig. 5 suggest that a simple relation between $\bar{\nu}_{max}$ and B may exist. This assumption is verified by the plot of fig. 6. All the experimental points, although extending over nearly 400°C and over a wide region of densities, are lying within the range of experimental uncertainty on one curve, which is only slightly curved. The extrapolated value of $\nu_{max} = 2670$ cm⁻¹ for $B = 0$ is lower than the frequency of maximum absorbance of the observed Q-branch of free water molecules at the lowest density investigated (see fig. 3). One might presume that the extrapolated value of ν_{max} reflects the combined influence of the surrounding polar molecules on the OD-groups without hydrogen bonding. Other authors have obtained curves of the type of fig. 6 by compiling frequency shifts and intensity changes for several different hydrogen-bonded compounds in one diagram.[20]

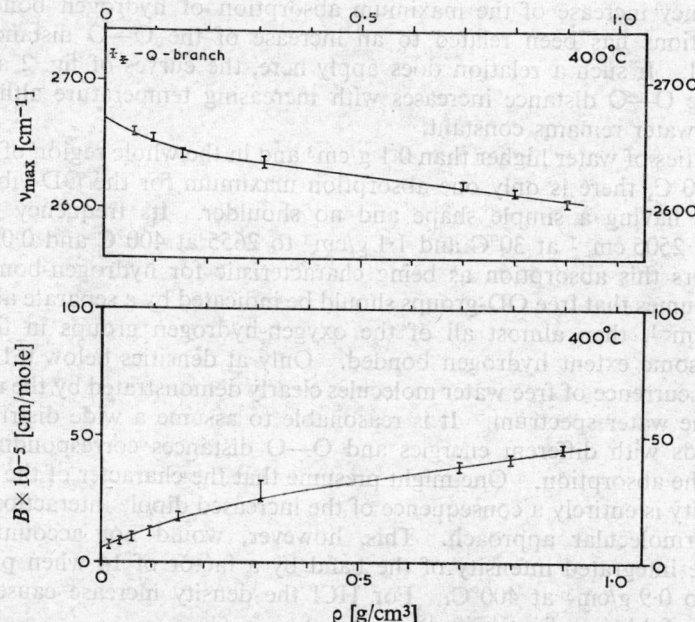

Fig. 5.—Frequency ν_{max} (in cm^{-1}) of the absorption maximum and integrated intensity B (in cm/mole) as a function of density of water (in g/cm^3) at 400°C. In the upper left corner the maxima of the Q-branch at densities of 0·0165 and 0·036 g/cm^3 are indicated (see fig. 3).

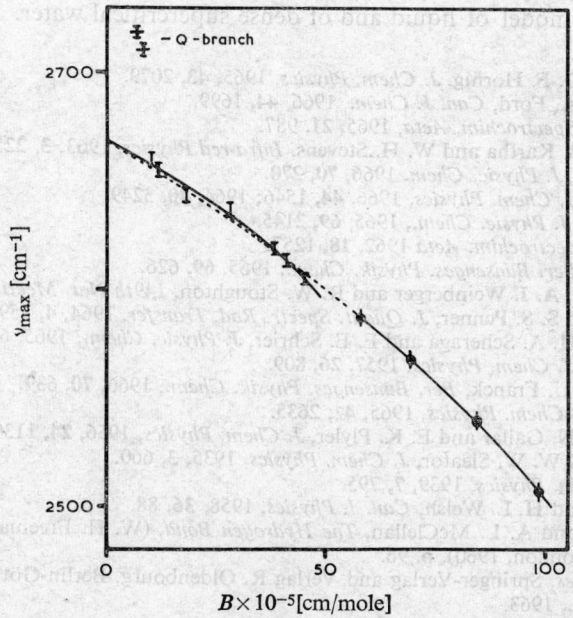

Fig. 6.—Frequency ν_{max} (in cm^{-1}) of the absorption maximum plotted against the integrated intensity B (in cm/mole). I, points at 400°C and different densities of water: ●, points at different temperatures and density 1·0 g/cm^3; +, maxima of the Q-branch at densities of 0·0165 and 0·036 g/cm^3 (see fig. 3); ---, extrapolation.

The frequency increase of the maximum absorption of hydrogen bonded OH- and OD-vibrations has been related to an increase of the O—O distance of the hydrogen bond. If such a relation does apply here, the curves of fig. 2 and fig. 5 imply, that the O—O distance increases with increasing temperature although the density of the water remains constant.

At all densities of water higher than 0·1 g/cm^3 and in the whole region of temperatures up to 400°C, there is only one absorption maximum for the OD-vibration of HDO in H$_2$O having a simple shape and no shoulder. Its frequency gradually increases from 2505 cm^{-1} at 30°C and 1·1 g/cm^3 to 2655 at 400°C and 0·095 g/cm^3. If one considers this absorption as being characteristic for hydrogen-bonded OD-groups and assumes that free OD-groups should be indicated by a separate absorption around 2700 cm^{-1}, then almost all of the oxygen-hydrogen groups in this range should be to some extent hydrogen bonded. Only at densities below 0·1 g/cm^3 at 400°C is the occurrence of free water molecules clearly demonstrated by the rotational structure of the water spectrum. It is reasonable to assume a wide distribution of hydrogen bonds with different energies and O—O distances corresponding to the broadness of the absorption. One might presume that the character of the spectrum at higher density is entirely a consequence of the increased dipole interaction because of closer intermolecular approach. This, however, would not account for the increase of the integrated intensity of the band by a factor of 14 when proceeding from 0·0165 to 0·9 g/cm^3 at 400°C. For HCl the density increase caused only a twofold or threefold rise of intensity.[18]

Thus, the infra-red spectrum of the OD-vibration of HDO in H$_2$O gives no indication of non-hydrogen-bonded OD groups or of defined small clusters of water molecules at a density higher than 0·1 g/cm^3. In accordance with the conclusion of Wall and Hornig[1] and of Falk and Ford[2] these spectra are considered as support for the continuum model of liquid and of dense supercritical water.

[1] T. T. Wall and D. F. Hornig. *J. Chem. Physics*, 1965, **43**, 2079.
[2] M. Falk and T. A. Ford, *Can. J. Chem.*, 1966, **44**, 1699.
[3] C. A. Swenson, *Spectrochim. Acta*, 1965, **21**, 987.
[4] J. G. Bayly, V. B. Kartha and W. H. Stevens, *Infra-red Physics*, 1963, **3**, 221.
[5] K. A. Hartmann, *J. Physic. Chem.* 1966, **70**, 270.
[6] G. E. Walrafen, *J. Chem. Physics*, 1966, **44**, 1546; 1964, **40**, 3249.
[7] D. P. Stevenson, *J. Physic. Chem.*, 1965, **69**, 2145.
[8] R. E. Weston, *Spectrochim. Acta* 1962, **18**, 1257.
[9] W. A. P. Luck, *Ber. Bunsenges. Physik. Chem.*, 1965, **69**, 626.
[10] W. C. Waggener, A. J. Weinberger and R. W. Stoughton, 149*th Nat. Meeting A.C.S.*, 1965.
[11] R. Goldstein and S. S. Penner, *J. Quant. Spectr. Rad. Transfer*, 1964, **4**, 359, 441.
[12] M. R. Thomas, H. A. Scheraga and E. E. Schrier, *J. Physic. Chem.*, 1965, **69**, 3722.
[13] R. D. Waldron, *J. Chem. Physics*, 1957, **26**, 809.
[14] S. Maier and E. U. Franck, *Ber. Bunsenges. Physik. Chem.*, 1966, **70**, 639.
[15] R. E. Weston, *J. Chem. Physics*, 1965, **42**, 2635.
[16] W. S. Benedict, N. Gailar and E. K. Plyler, *J. Chem. Physics*, 1956, **24**, 1139.
[17] E. F. Barker and W. W. Sleator, *J. Chem. Physics*, 1935, **3**, 660.
[18] W. West, *J. Chem. Physics*, 1939, **7**, 795.
[19] W. F. J. Hare, and H. L. Welsh, *Can. J. Physics*, 1958, **36**, 88.
[20] G. C. Pimentel and A. L. McClellan, *The Hydrogen Bond*, (W. H. Freeman and Comp. San Francisco and London, 1960), p. 96.
[21] *VDI-Steam Tables*, Springer-Verlag and Verlag R. Oldenbourg, Berlin-Göttingen-Heidelberg-München 6th ed., 1963.

Spectroscopic Studies Concerning the Structure and the Thermodynamic Behaviour of H_2O, CH_3OH and C_2H_5OH

By Werner A. P. Luck

Hauptlaboratorium der Badischen Anilin- & Soda-Fabrik AG
67 Ludwigshafen/Rh., Germany

Received 16th January 1967

The i.-r. spectroscopic determination of non-H-bonded OH-groups in water and alcohols are in agreement with the thermodynamic behaviour of these liquids. It is possible to calculate the specific heats, the heats of vaporization, the surface energies and the density with these spectroscopic results together with a simple model of the liquids. This method also gives the density maximum and the minimum of the specific heat of H_2O. The conformity with the thermodynamic properties shows that these measurements can be employed to develop better theories of liquids and that the approximation methods used for the interpretation of the i.r. spectra are satisfactory.

Infra-red spectra [1-7] of H_2O, CH_3OH and C_2H_5OH in the temperature region from $-50°C$ to $+400°C$ and comparison with solution spectra [8] have shown that in liquids these compounds have less non-H-bonded OH-groups than the most theories of liquids claim. An exact interpretation of the i.-r. spectra is not possible.[9-14]

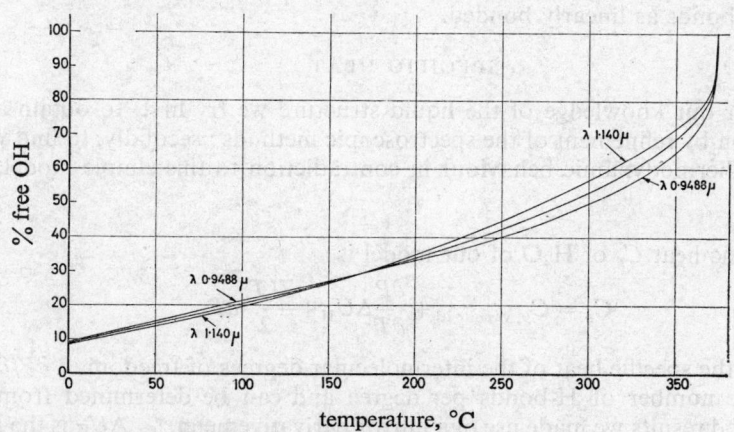

Fig. 1.—Percentage P of non-H-bonded H_2O-molecules determined by $0.9488\,\mu$- and $1.140\,\mu$-i.r. bands.[5,6]; middle line: mean values.

The spectra of liquids and solutions are similar, but in liquids there are many more bands [14] of energetic unfavourable H-bonds from Pople's point of view.[15] Therefore, only approximation methods can be used to interpret the spectra. We think the best approximation method is to determine the percentage of non-H-bonded OH-groups (fig. 1). To take into account the cooperative effects [3, 16] we need a model of the water structure (fig. 2) with fissure planes of free OH-groups (compare the Bjerrum defects in the theory of the dielectric constant[17]) and closed H-bonds. Assuming a flickering cluster model we have intermediate states of H-bonds with unfavourable angles or distances.[9, 11, 18] To prove the applicability of this method we attempt in

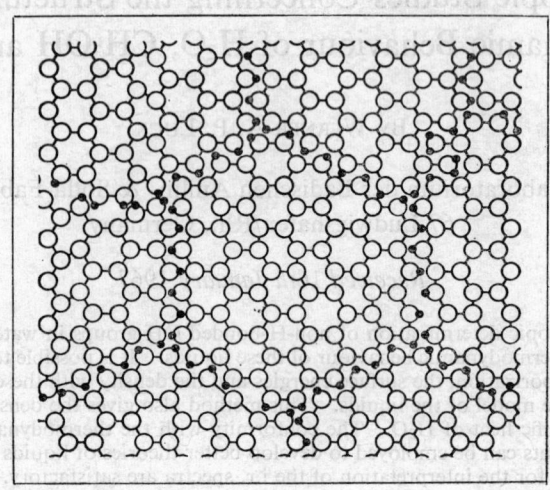

water model

FIG. 2.—Simplified cluster model of the water structure at about 0°C. O—O, O-atoms bound with H-bonds; Q, non-H-bonded O—H groups at the cluster surfaces.

this paper to calculate the thermodynamic behaviour from the spectroscopic results assuming a two-species model of free OH-groups and ice-like H-bonded groups. Energetically unfavourable H-bonds are partially counted as free OH and less perturbed H-bonds as linearly bonded.

SPECIFIC HEAT

To further our knowledge of the liquid structure we try first, to obtain a better approximation by refinement of the spectroscopic methods; secondly, to find whether there is any thermodynamic behaviour in contradiction to this simple model.

WATER

The specific heat C_v of H_2O of our model is

$$C_v = C_{v,\text{ vapour id}} + \frac{\partial P}{\partial T}\Delta U_H + \frac{Z(T)}{2}aR. \qquad (1)$$

$C_{v,\text{ vapour id}}$ is the specific heat of the intermolecular degrees of freedom. $\partial P/\partial T$ is the change of the number of H-bonds per degree and can be determined from fig. 1. To obtain good results we made use of a mirror derivativemeter.* ΔU_H is the H-bond energy per mole; we take $\Delta U_H = \Delta U_S - W_H = 8$ kcal/mole. Z is the coordination number in the liquid state; a is a constant, $R = 1.986$ cal/mole; $ZaR/2$ is the contribution of the intermolecular forces of non-H-bond type to the specific heat, and is not exactly known. In addition, we assume that

$$Z(T)aR/2 = (4/2)(1-P)R, \qquad (2)$$

and use the experimental temperature function $(1-P)$ of fig. 1. Fig. 3 shows that

*Ott, Kempten, Germany.

eqn. (1) gives good agreement between the experimental values of C and the values derived from our simple model. The disagreement in the temperature region 525-625°K is of the similar magnitude to the approximations in eqn. (2). This is expected of our model because the cluster size in this temperature region is smaller than 6 molecules. We should correct the value $Z = 4$, and take account of the

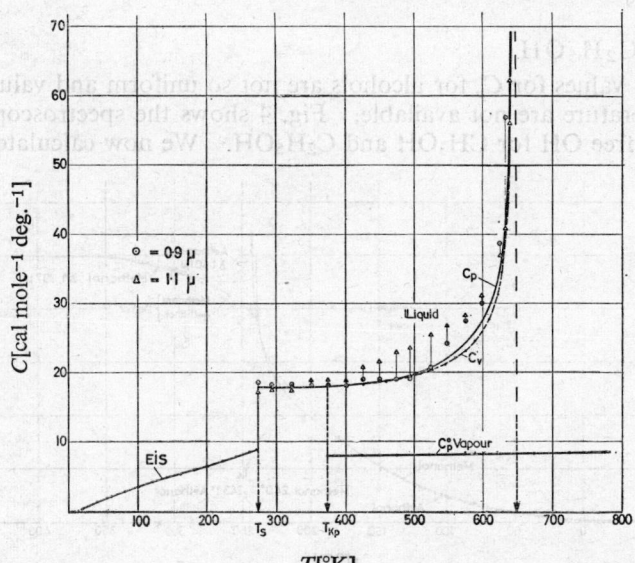

FIG. 3.—Specific heats of water ——— obs.[19]; ⊙, calc. with 0·95 μ band and eqn. (1); △, calc. with 1·14 μ band and eqn. (1).

number of free molecules, which are neglected in our model. The spectroscopic analysis has shown that the number of free molecules can be neglected (smaller than 1 %) for $t < 200°C$; its increase is more than 1 % for $t > 200°C$. Other disagreements in fig. 3 are of the same magnitude as the errors in the spectroscopic method. Table 1

TABLE 1.—SPECIFIC HEAT OF H_2O

$T°K$	C_v vapour	$\frac{\delta P}{\delta T}\Delta U$		$2(1-P)R$		C_v theor.	
		0·94μ	1·1μ	0·94μ	1·1μ	0·94μ	1·1μ
273	6	8·8	7·75	3·56	3·6	18·46	18·1
323	6	9·2	8·5	3·4	3·4	18·6	18·2
373	6·1	9·3	9·9	3·15	3·16	18·55	19·1
423	6·1	10·3	12·1	2·9	2·9	19·3	21·1
473	6·15	10·55	14·5	2·6	2·6	19·3	23·2
523	6·2	12·2	17·3	2·4	2·2	20·8	25·7
573	6·3	19·5	20·3	1·98	1·7	27·8	28·3
623	6·4	31·2	29·6	1·4	1·1	39·0	37·1
638	6·4	76·7	51·2	1·1	0·9	84·2	59·5

shows the magnitude of the different factors in eqn. (1). $\partial P/\partial T$ of the 1·1μ band, which gives our best values, is nearly constant up to 35°C and then increases slowly for increasing temperatures. Thus, eqn. (1) and (2) together with fig. 1 give a minimum of the specific heat at about 35°C in agreement with experiments. This is caused by the factor $2R(1-P)$ cal/mole deg. which decreases from 0°C to 35°C from 3·622

118   I.R.-SPECTRA AND BEHAVIOUR OF H_2O, CH_3OH AND C_2H_5OH

to 3·481 cal/mole deg. The difference is 0·14 The experimental difference is
$$C_p(0°C) - C_p(35°C) = 18·11 - 17·95 = 0·16 \text{ cal/mole deg.}$$
We have shown that additions of salt change P in the sequence of the lyotropic ion series.[4] Small change of P and especially of $\partial P/\partial T$ should change the temperature of the specific heat minimum. The specific heats of salt solutions are in keeping with this conclusion.[29]

CH_3OH AND C_2H_5OH

Experimental values for C_p for alcohols are not so uniform and values of C_v and for higher temperature are not available. Fig. 4 shows the spectroscopically determined values of free OH for CH_3OH and C_2H_5OH. We now calculate in a similar

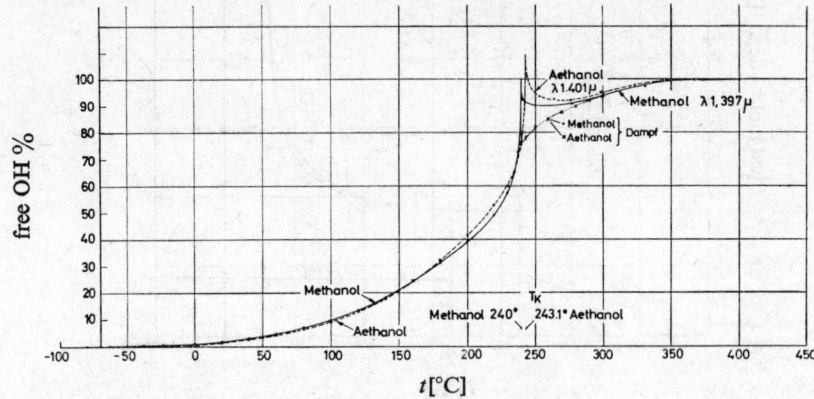

Fig. 4.—Percentage P of non-H-bonded CH_3OH and C_2H_5OH molecules in the liquid state, determined by the 1·4 μ band.[14] *

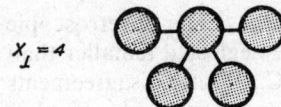

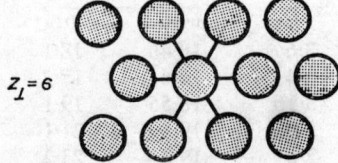

Fig. 5.—Simplified model for the liquid state of alcohols: chains of H-bonded molecules perpendicular to the paper plane, coordination number of these chains in bulk, $Z = 6$; at the surface, $X = 4$.

way the C_v-values. We take as a model CH_3OH chains of H-bonded molecules. Every chain has six neighbour-chains (fig. 5). It is possible to obtain good values of C_v with the formula,

$$C_v = C_{v,\text{ vap. id.}} + \frac{\partial P}{\partial T}\Delta U_H + (1-P)\frac{8}{2}R, \qquad (3)$$

and a value $\Delta U_H = 4$ kcal/mole.

* The peaks near T_c are caused by the density gradient in the gravity field.[6] For $T > T_c$ the optical density of the CH-band is nearly constant in the upper side of our cell. The OH-band is constant only for $T > T_c$ (H_2O). That means that for alcohols at T_c not all H-bonds are open.

The agreement between C_v, expt. and C_v determined by eqn. (3) is of similar magnitude as the errors in our spectroscopic values P, of the differences of the experimental values and the uncertainty between C_p and C_v in the liquid state (fig. 6).

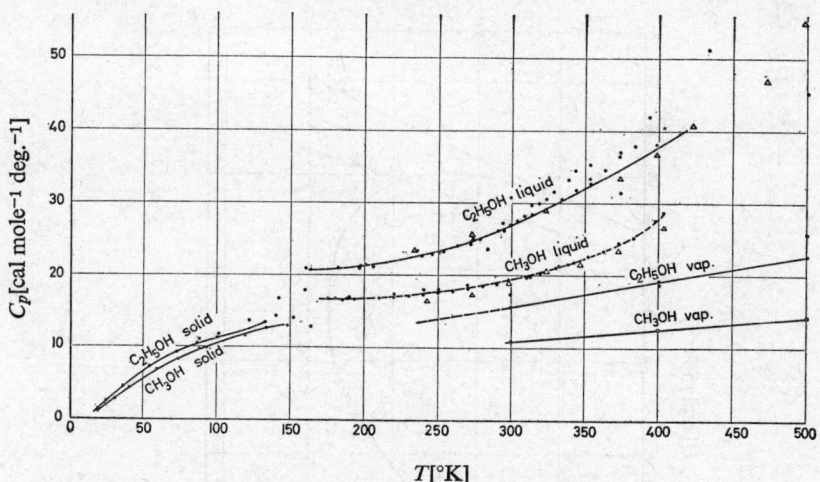

FIG. 6.—Specific heats of CH_3OH and C_2H_5OH. ○, obs. value of different authors;[20] △, calc. with fig. 4 and eqn. (3).

Most doubtful is the factor $ZaR/2$. Fortunately it is the smallest one, and its influence is not very large. (Our assumption has some similarity to that of Kincaid and Eyring,[21] who have assumed that some rotational degrees of freedom become librations in the liquids and increase the specific heat by about 1 cal/mole deg.).

HEAT OF VAPORIZATION

WATER

The inner vaporization energy L_v can be determined from

$$L_v = (1-P)\Delta U_S + PW_H - (1-P)2RT - (U_{\text{vap. id.}} - U_{\text{vap. real}}). \qquad (4)$$

$(1-P)\Delta U_S$ is the energy of the closed H-bonds. We take $\Delta U_S = \Delta U_H + W_H = 11.64$ kcal/mole, and $\Delta U_S = L_v(°C) + L_M$ is the sum of H-bond ΔU_H and van der

TABLE 2.—HEAT OF VAPORIZATION H_2O (KCAL/MOLE)

$T°K$ 0.95μ	1.1μ	$(1-P)$	$(1-P)\Delta U_S$	PW_H	$(1-P)\Delta U_S + PW_H$	$(1-P)2RT$	W_{real}	L_v calc.	L_v expt.
300	309	0.875	10.18	0.45	10.63	1.07	0	9.6	9.8
353	363	0.815	9.49	0.67	10.16	1.16	0.03	9.0	9.07
410	416	0.745	8.67	0.93	9.60	1.22	0.07	8.3	8.4
507	487	0.625	7.27	1.36	8.63	1.22	0.32	7.1	7.2
573	535	0.5	5.82	1.8	7.62	1.11	0.8	5.7	5.72
610	585	0.4	4.66	2.18	6.84	0.95	1.3	4.59	4.3
617	594	0.375	4.36	2.27	6.63	0.91	1.47	4.2	4
628	608	0.333	3.88	2.4	6.28	0.82	1.76	3.7	3.5
640	631	0.25	2.91	2.7	5.61	0.64	2.4	2.47	2.4
643	640	0.2	2.33	2.91	5.24	0.51	3.54	1.2	1.6

Waals interaction W_H. We obtain this value as the sum of the heat of vaporization at 0°C and the energy of melting L_M. ($L_M = 1.43$ kcal/mole is the sum H-bonds of the energy 0·8 kcal/mole to open 10 % of the H-bonds, the energy 0·35 kcal/mole to change 20 % of the H-bonds in energetically unfavourable bonds and the change in the energy of the van der Waals interaction of about 0·25 kcal/mole). PW_H is the van der Waals interaction of the free H-bonds. We take $W_H = 3·64$ kcal/mole.

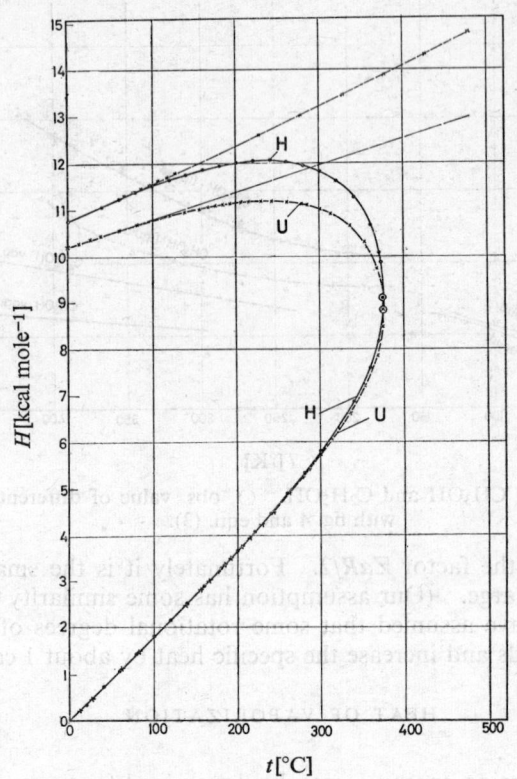

FIG. 7.—Heat function H and internal energy U above, saturated vapour state;[19] below, liquid state;[19] straight lines, extrapolated ideal gas state.

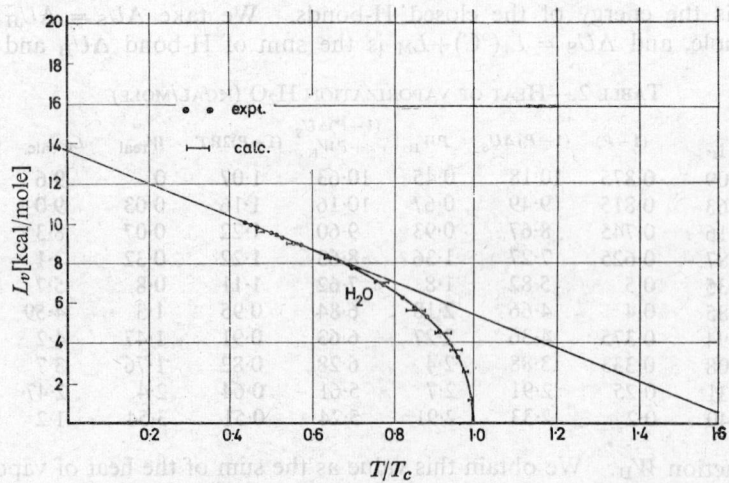

FIG. 8.—Internal heat of vaporization L_v of H_2O [19] ●, expt.; —. calc. with 0·9 μ and 1·1 μ band.

The factor $(1-P)2RT$ has the same meaning as in the calculation of C_v. It gives the heat content of the intermolecular degrees of freedom. The experimental values $L_{v,\text{expt.}}$ give the energy to transfer 1 mole from the liquid to the real vapour state. Our calculation gives the energy of transfer of liquid to the ideal vapour state. Therefore we require the value of W_{real} in eqn. (4). We obtain it from the difference between the real heat content of the vapour from thermodynamic tables [19] and the linear extrapolated ideal vapour state (fig. 7). Table 2 shows the different factors of eqn. (4). Table 2 and fig. 8 show that we obtain a good agreement between eqn. (4) combined with the experimental P-values, and the experimental L_v values within the limits of error of our spectroscopic method.

CH_3OH AND C_2H_5OH

In a similar way, we calculate L_v of CH_3OH and C_2H_5OH from the equation,
$$L_v = (1-P)U_S + PW - 8/2RT \tag{5}$$
For alcohols we have only found $L_{v,\text{expt.}}$ for temperatures less than 130°C. Therefore we do not need a correction for the real gas state, which is only important for higher temperatures with higher vapour pressures. We get $L_{v,\text{expt.}}$ from $L_p - p\Delta V = L_{v,\text{expt.}}$. We take $\Delta U_S(CH_3OH) = 10.7$ kcal/mole; $\Delta U_S(C_2H_5OH) = 12$ kcal/mole.

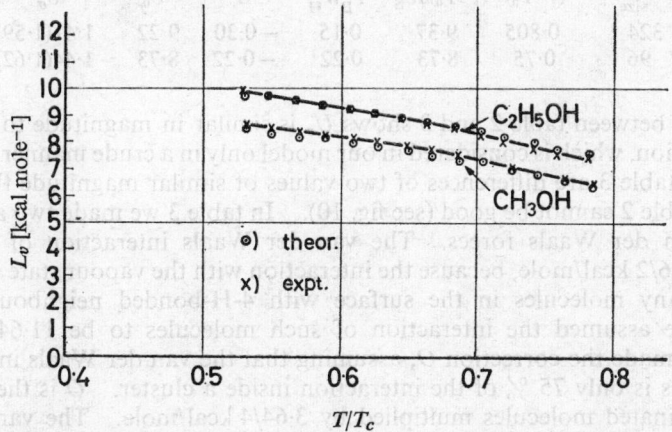

FIG. 9.—Internal heat of vaporization of CH_3OH and C_2H_5OH ×, expt.[22]; ○, calc. by eqn. (6) and fig. 4.

These values are obtained by extrapolation of $L_{v,\text{expt.}}$ to the melting point and adding the heat of melting. W is the van der Waals interaction of the free OH-groups. We take $W = 3.6$ kcal/mole, the same value taken for H_2O.

Fig. 9 shows that eqn. (5) together with our experimental P-values are in good agreement with the experiments. Especially the greater change of L_v with temperatures above 50°C ($T/T_c > 0.63$) agrees with the greater increase of P with T in this temperature range.

In the same way we can write eqn. (5) for lower P-values:
$$L_v = (1-P)\Delta U_H + (6/2)W_D + PW - (8/2)RT \tag{6}$$
with $\Delta U_H = (4+3.6)$ kcal/mole $= 7.6$ kcal/mole; $W_D(CH_3OH) = 1.03$ kcal/mole; $W_D(C_2H_5OH) = 1.47$ kcal/mole. In eqn. (6) we separate the van der Waals interaction W_D of the rest of the molecules in the H-bonded chains. This interaction 3.6 kcal/mole of the H-bonded OH groups is included in U_H.

SURFACE ENERGY

The surface energy $U\sigma$ is defined by [23, 24, 14]

$$U_\sigma = \sigma_M - T\partial\sigma_M/\partial T, \qquad (7)$$

where σ_M is the molar surface tension. To calculate $U\sigma$ we need a specific model.

WATER

We take for water a model of tridymite-like clusters and calculate the energy content of the (0001) basic plane for clusters of 324 and 96 molecules. The surface energy is given by

$$U_\sigma = [(1-P)\Delta U_S + PW_H]_{\text{cluster}} - [(1-P_0)\Delta U_S + P_B W_H - 0]_{\text{surface}}, \qquad (8)$$
$$U_\sigma = U_{\text{cluster}} - U_0.$$

P_0 is the amount of non-H-bonded OH-groups at a surface. P_B is the amount of non-H-bonded OH-groups at the border-line, which have van der Waals interaction with neighbouring clusters. We obtain the values given in table 3.

TABLE 3.—SURFACE ENERGY OF WATER: $U\sigma$ (KCAL/MOLE)

$t°C$	cluster size	$(1-P_0)$	$(1-P_0)\Delta U_S$	$P_B W_H$	O	U_0	U_σ	U_σ expt.
32	324	0.805	9.37	0.15	−0.30	9.22	1.41(1.59)	1.61
83	96	0.75	8.73	0.22	−0.22	8.73	1.44(1.62)	1.66

A comparison between table 2 and 3 shows U_σ is similar in magnitude to the van der Waals interaction, which is considered in our model only in a crude manner. Secondly the results of table 3 are differences of two values of similar magnitude therefore the accuracy of table 2 cannot be good (see fig. 10). In table 3 we made two assumptions about the van der Waals forces. The van der Waals interaction of the surface molecules is 3·6/2 kcal/mole, because the interaction with the vapour state is neglected. There are many molecules in the surface with 4-H-bonded neighbours. In our calculation we assumed the interaction of such molecules to be 11·64 kcal/mole. Therefore we made the correction O, assuming that the van der Waals interaction of such molecules is only 75 % of the interaction inside a cluster. O is the percentage of four-coordinated molecules multiplied by 3·64/4 kcal/mole. The van der Waals interaction of three-coordinated molecules at the surface is only included in our calculation as the interaction in the three H-bonds, i.e. corresponding to 75 %. The interaction of these 3-coordinated molecules should be smaller by the smaller interaction with the second next neighbours. Assuming this effect to be 10 % of 3·6 kcal/mole we get the results in parenthesis in table 3. In addition, the surface energy of the other planes of the tridymite-like clusters would be larger. The (0001) planes in table 3 are the planes with the highest energy content and would be preferred in a crystal-like state. X-ray investigations have shown that the ice structure grown at the surface of undisturbed water is orientated with (0001) parallel to the water surface.[30] This may point to the preference of this plane at the surface of liquid water. But in the flickering cluster model we would expect a fraction of energetic unfavourable faces too. It would be unwarranted to give exact values of all these effects in our rough model.

However, we can state that our model is not in disagreement with the observed surface energy. The increase of U_σ with temperature is only known for liquids with H-bonds. Our model gives the possibility to understand this anomalous effect by the cluster structure. It is only possible to make this rough approximation in the low temperature region where there are large clusters. For higher temperatures we have to take into account that the partition function of the cluster size would be different at the surface and in bulk. The percentage of unfavourable H-bonds would be

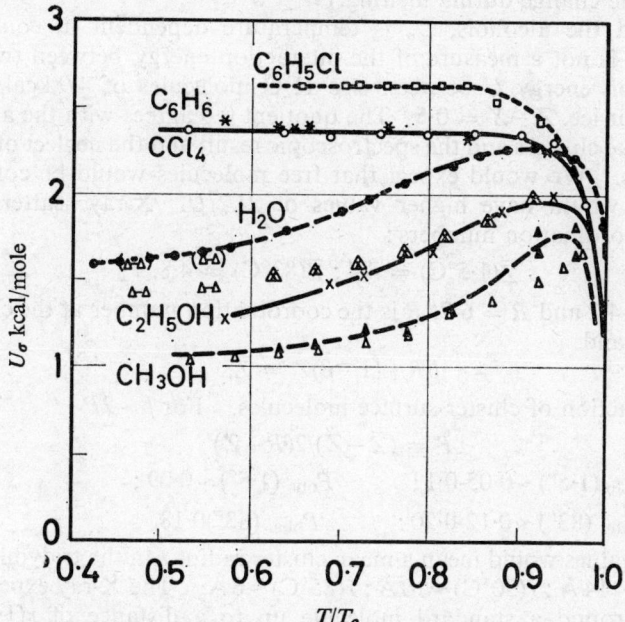

FIG. 10.—Surface energy U_σ expt. values: □, C_6H_5Cl; ●, H_2O; —, C_6H_6; ×, C_2H_5OH; ○, CCl_4; △, CH_3OH; calc. with eqn. (8) △, H_2O; calc. with eqn. (10), ▲, C_2H_5OH; △, CH_3OH.

different between the surface and in bulk too. Only for large cluster sizes may we expect that both these effects are not large. The increase of U_σ in the temperature region $T/T_c > 0.7$ can only be understood by these effects. The decrease of U_σ in the region $T/T_c > 0.9$ for all liquids is due to the increase of the vapour pressure in this region, i.e., the difference of the coordination numbers at the surface and in bulk decreases.

ALCOHOLS

We calculate the surface energy of alcohols from eqn. (9),

$$U_\sigma = [(1-P)\Delta U_H + (6/2)W_D + PW] - [(1-P)_0 \Delta U_H + (4/2)W_D + 2P_0 W/3] \quad (9)$$

(see our model, fig. 5). For low temperatures, for low P-values, we put $P = P_0$ and

$$U_\sigma = W_D + \tfrac{1}{3} PW \quad (10)$$

Fig. 10 shows that eqn. (10) together with the spectroscopic P-values (fig. 4) agrees well with the experimental values in a way not expected from our rough model with $P = P_0$.

4-COORDINATION NUMBER

For normal liquids, eqn. (11) is valid :[14]

$$U_\sigma = [(Z-X)/2](3/2)RT_c \quad (11)$$

where Z is coordination number in bulk, and X is coordination number at the surface.

For a face-centred cubic configuration one would expect $Z - X = 3$. For CCl_4, C_6H_6, C_6H_5Cl and C_2H_5—O—C_2H_5, $Z - X$ is 2·88-2·76.[14] This may mean that for these ideal liquids the coordination number 12 is valid with defects of 5-10 %. (The percentage disagreement of the value $Z - X = 3$ is of similar magnitude as the percentage volume change during melting.)

For H_2O and the alcohols, U_σ is temperature dependent in contradiction to eqn. (9) and RT_c is not a measure of the interaction energy between two molecules. For an interaction energy U between two H_2O molecules of 4·9 kcal/mole we get $2U_\sigma/U \sim 0·6$. For ice, $Z - X = 0·5$ The quotient 0·6 agrees with the assumption of large tridymite-like clusters and the spectroscopic result and the neglect of the presence of free molecules. We would expect that free molecules would be concentrated at the surface and would have higher values of $2U_\sigma/U$. X-ray scattering results [25] give the mean coordination numbers:

$$\bar{Z}(1·5°C) = 4·4; \quad \bar{Z}(83°C) = 4·8.$$

Assuming $Z = 4-4·2$ and $R = 6-7$, R is the coordination number at the cluster-surface inside the liquid and

$$\beta R + (1-\beta)Z = \bar{Z}, \tag{12}$$

where β is the fraction of cluster surface molecules. For $\beta \sim 2P$

$$P = (\bar{Z}-Z)/2(R-Z) \tag{13}$$

Then $P_{calc.}(1·5°) \sim 0·05$-$0·1$; $\quad P_{obs.}(1·5°) \sim 0·09$;

$P_{calc.}(83°) \sim 0·12$-$0·20$; $\quad P_{obs.}(83°) 0·18$.

The observed P values would mean a mean cluster radius r in the tridymite-like cluster model of $\bar{r}(0°C) \sim 14 \text{Å}$; $\bar{r}(30°C) \sim 10 \text{Å}$; $\bar{r}(85°C) \sim 6 \text{Å}$. The X-ray experiments show ordered zones around a standard molecule up to a distance of $r(1·5°C) > 8·5 \text{Å}$; $r(30°C) > 8·5 \text{Å}$; $r(83°C) \sim 7 \text{Å}$.

The radial partition curves of masses around a standard molecule given by the X-ray method agree with the assumption that the disorder mainly causes a decrease of the distance between the second-next neighbours. This could mean an effect of the H-bonds of unfavourable angles, which would not greatly change the distance between the first-next neighbours. In a similar way, an opening of H-bonds by molecular rotation could decrease the distance to the second-next molecules.

DENSITY

The density-temperature function of H_2O was interpreted by a two-species model;[26] more disordered groups were found than estimated from our experiments. This arises because the assumption that the density of the ordered volumes is the same as in ice. This neglects the energetically unfavourable H-bonds, which the spectra show are present. Therefore we believe that in a two-species model we should assume a higher mean density of the ordered zones than in ice. Our spectroscopic results cannot give direct information on the density of the different H-bonded and non-H-bonded zones. For a model similar to that used to deduce the other eqn. of this paper, we can evaluate the density curve (fig. 11) by the formula:

$$1/\rho = (1-P)V_i + PV_B; \tag{14}$$

volume of ice-like regions:

$$V_i(\text{cm}^3\text{g}^{-1}) = 1·0350(1+1·741\ 10^{-4}t(°C)),$$

volume of disordered regions:

$$V_B(\text{cm}^3\text{g}^{-1}) = 0·64006(1+5·7249\ 10^{-3}t(°C)).$$

The volume expansion of the H-bonded groups is taken to be similar to the expansion of ice. The expansion of the unbonded groups is adjusted from the experimental density at 100°C. Eqn. (14) gives a rough approximation of the density (fig. 11). The deviation for higher temperatures means that we cannot neglect free molecules with a higher volume in this region and one cannot assume a linear volume expansion till T_c (this has to be so for normal liquids, too).[26] The known density maximum at

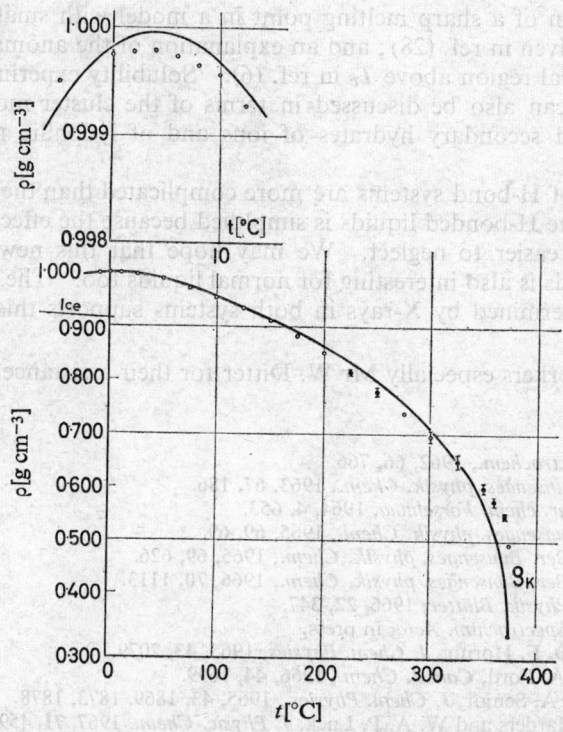

FIG. 11.—Density of H_2O. ○, calc. with eqn. (14).

4°C may be understood by eqn. (14), which, however, is very sensitive to small changes of P. With $P(0°C) = 0.088$ and $P(10°C) = 0.101$, in agreement with our measurements, the density maximum is given by eqn. (14) too (see fig. 11). This sensitivity of the density maximum on P agrees with the observation that the maximum is changed by salt additions.[27] We have found salt additions change P too.[4] We did not search for the best constants in eqn. (14); it is possible that there are better ones.

DISCUSSION

Every equation of this paper by itself is somewhat hypothetical; but the combination of them with the same assumptions has more significance and are also consistent with each other. In this way, fig. 1 and 4 would be interesting if they were theoretical figures; but we recall that they are experimental ones. We do not believe that our equations and our model are correct for the liquid structure. New experiments and discussions of the relaxation times τ should give new information to improve this rough model.

The i.-r. ice band-maximum changes little with decreased temperatures; i.e., the energy of the H-bonds of ice increases slightly at lower temperatures. But τ increases with lower temperatures. This could mean that τ is coupled with a proton-rotation.

The smaller proton mobility in liquid water in comparison with that in ice has to conform with the presence of large clusters. The mobility at the cluster surfaces may determine the mobility in the liquid state.

An interpretation of a sharp melting point in a model with small change of the degree of order is given in ref. (28); and an explanation of the anomalous behaviour of H_2O in the critical region above T_c in ref. (6). Solubility experiments of ions or organic molecules can also be discussed in terms of the cluster model. We must expect primary and secondary hydrates of ions and of lyophilic molecules [3, 4] in such solutions.

The behaviour of H-bond systems are more complicated than the normal liquids. But the theory of the H-bonded liquids is simplified because the effect of the second-next neighbours is easier to neglect. We may hope that this new knowledges of the H-bonded liquids is also interesting for normal liquids too. The similarity of the ordering effects determined by X-rays in both systems supports this statement.

I thank my coworkers especially Mr W. Ditter for their assistance and for helpful discussions.

[1] W. Luck, *Z. Elektrochem.*, 1962, **66**, 766.
[2] W. Luck, *Ber. Bunsenges. physik. Chem.*, 1963, **67**, 186.
[3] W. Luck, *Fortschr. chem. Forschung*, 1964, **4**, 653.
[4] W. Luck, *Ber. Bunsenges. physik. Chem.*, 1965, **69**, 69.
[5] W. A. P. Luck, *Ber. Bunsenges. physik. Chem.*, 1965, **69**, 626.
[6] W. A. P. Luck, *Ber. Bunsenges. physik. Chem.*, 1966, **70**, 1113.
[7] W. A. P. Luck, *Physik. Blätter*, 1966, **22**, 347.
[8] W. A. P. Luck, *Spectrochim. Acta*, in press.
[9] T. T. Wall and D. F. Hornig, *J. Chem. Physics*, 1965, **43**, 2079.
[10] M. Falk and T. A. Ford, *Can. J. Chem.*, 1966, **44**, 1699.
[11] V. Vand and W. A. Senior, *J. Chem. Physics.*, 1965, **43**, 1869, 1873, 1878.
[12] G. Böttger, H. Harders and W. A. P. Luck, *J. Physic. Chem.*, 1967, **71**, 459.
[13] W. A. P. Luck, *Can. J. Chem.*, in press.
[14] W. A. P. Luck, *Ber. Bunsenges. physik. Chem.*, 1967, in preparation.
[15] J. A. Pople, *Proc. Roy. Soc. A*, 1951, **205**, 163.
[16] H. S. Frank, *Proc. Roy. Soc. A*, 1958, **247**, 481. H. S. Frank and W. Y. Wen, *Disc. Faraday Soc.*, 1957, **24**, 133.
[17] C. Jacard, *Ann. N.Y. Acad. Sci.*, 1965, **125**, 390. A. Steineman and H. Gränicher, *Helv. physic. Acta*, 1957, **30**, 554.
[18] W. Luck, *Naturwiss.*, 1965, **52**, 25, 49. W. A. P. Luck, *Naturwiss.*, 1967, **54**, in press.
[19] J. H. Keenan and F. G. Keyes, *Thermodynamic Properties of Steam* (John Wiley & Sons, New York, 1936).
[20] O. Maass and L. T. Waldbauer, *J. Amer. Chem. Soc.*, 1925, **47**, 1. G. S. Parks, *J. Amer. Chem. Soc.*, 1925, **47**, 338. C. Drucker and H. Weissbach, *Z. physik. Chem.*, 1925, **117**, 223. K. K. Kelley, *J. Amer. Chem. Soc.*, 1929, **51**, 180. E. F. Fiock, D. C. Ginnings and W. B. Holton, *Bur. Stand. J. Res.*, 1931, **6**, 886. W. Timofejew, *Iswiestja d. Kiew. polyt. Inst.*, 1905, *I. Diss.* (Kiew 1905), 340 S. J. C. M. Li, K. S. Pitzer and E. V. Ivash, *J. Chem. Physics*, 1955, **23**, 1814. G. S. Parks, *J. Amer. Chem. Soc.*, 1925, **47**, 338. K. K. Kelley, *J. Amer. Chem. Soc.*, 1929, **51**, 779. G. S. Parks and H. M. Huffmann, *J. Physic. Chem.* 1927, **31**, 1842. E. F. Fiock, D. C. Ginnings and W. B. Holton, *Bur. Stand. J. Res.*, 1931, **6**, 886. G. E. Gibson, G. S. Parks and W. M. Latimer, *J. Amer. Chem. Soc.*, 1920, **42**, 1537. Blacet, Leighton and Bartlett, *J. Physic. Chem.*, 1931, **35**, 1935. A. Battelli, *Rend. Lincei*, 1907, **16**, [1], 243, *Cim.*, 1907, **13**, 418. Regnault, *Mem. l'Acad.*, 1862, **26**, 262. W. Sutherland, *Phil. Mag.*, 1888, **26**, 298. Hirn, *Ann. Chim. Physique*, 1867, **10**, 32. H. A. G. Cherrin, *Petr. Ref.*, 1961, **40**, 127. K. A. Kobe and R. E. Pennington, *Petr. Ref.*, 1950, **29**, nr. 9, 135.

[21] J. F. Kincaid and H. Eyring, *J. Chem. Physics*, 1938, **6**, 625.
[22] E. F. Fiock, D. C. Ginnings and W. B. Holton, *Bur. Stand. J. Res.*, 1931, **6**, 886.
[23] G. Kortüm, *Einführung in die chem. Thermodynamik* (Verlag Chemie, Weinheim, 1960), 3. Aufl., S. 420.
[24] K. L. Wolf, *Physik und Chemie der Grenzflächen* (Springer-Verlag Berlin-Göttingen-Heidelberg, 1957).
[25] J. Morgan and B. E. Warren, *J. Chem. Physics*, 1938, **6**, 666. M. D. Danford and H. A. Levi, *J. Amer. Chem. Soc.*, 1962, **84**, 3965. O. J. Samoilow, *Die Struktur von wässrigen Elektrolytlösungen* (Teubner, Leipzig, 1961), S. 38.
[26] K. Grjotheim and J. Krogh-Moe, *Acta Chim. Scand.*, 1954, **8**, 1193.
[27] R. Wright, *J. Chem. Soc.*, 1919, **65**, 119.
[28] S. E. Bresler, *Acta Physicochim*, 1939, **10**, 491. J. Frenkel, *Kinetische Theorie der Flüssigkeiten* (VEB Verlag Wissenschaften, Berlin; Clarendon Press Oxford, 1957).
[29] M. Eigen and E. Wicke, *Z. Elektrochem.*, 1951, **55**, 354. E. Wicke, M. Eigen and Th. Ackermann, *Z. physik. Chem.*, 1954, **1**, 340. Th. Ackermann, *Z. Elektrochem.*, 1958, **62**, 411.
[30] U. Yoshida and T. Tsuboi, *Mem. Sci. Kyoto Univ. A*, 1929, **12**, 203.

GENERAL DISCUSSION

Dr. Mansel Davies (*Aberystwyth*) said: The spherical-molecule liquids naturally occupy a special position in theoretical treatments and have great areas of interest in the monatomic liquids, metals and fused salts, but in the field of molecular liquids those of nearly spherical form (HCl, CCl_4, CH_3CCl_3, camphor, etc.) are far from typical liquids. They are a major sub-set of the class II liquids of Hill.[1] Respects in which they are " abnormal " liquids include: (i) the marked differences between the activation energies for the viscosity and for the molecular reorientation (i.e., rigid dipole relaxation) processes:

$$\Delta H^*(\tau \text{ rotational}) < \Delta H^*(\eta);$$

(ii) the differences between the effective specific volume parameters $b > b'$ in $(1/\eta) = A(v-b)$; $(1/\phi) = A'(v-b')$, where v is the specific volume, A and A' are (Batschinski) constants, and $\phi = 2kT\tau$; (iii) the abnormally small enthalpy (or entropy) of crystallization of the spherical-molecule liquids; (iv) other " abnormalities " are listed in Timmermans' volume.[2] As Nora Hill has suggested, features (i) and (ii) can be used as criteria to predict that such spherical-molecule liquids will crystallize to solids having considerable rotational mobility in the solid (" rotator phase ") state, which is the immediate cause of (iii).

Although local anisotropy plays an important role in most molecular liquids the detailed structural study of the spherical-molecule examples is greatly to be desired and could be markedly advanced by first studying the corresponding rotator-phase crystal features.[3] The correlation of the changes in properties on melting, with the addition in these cases of only translational molecular mobility, should help to unravel the patterns in molecularly anisotropic liquids.

Dr. J. N. Sherwood (*Strathclyde University*) said: Following their remarks upon the similarity between the molecular properties of the rotator phase solids and those of the corresponding melt, Davies, and Powles, have commented that these solids could well serve as model systems for the study of the structure and properties of the liquid state. With this possibility in mind we have been examining the structural properties of rotator phase solids. Previously, comments upon the structure of these materials were confined to observations upon the lack of long-range order, as instanced by X-ray diffraction studies,[4] and speculations upon the extreme plasticity of these solids.[4] Our initial studies of self-diffusion and plastic flow in several of these solids permit some further speculations on the nature of this unique phase.

Self-diffusion measurements show that translational molecular mobility is high. The self-diffusion coefficient at the melting point $D_m \approx 10^{-7}$ cm^2 sec^{-1} compared to a much lower value for non-rotator phase solids, $D_m \approx 10^{-11}$ cm^2 sec^{-1}. If we consider this phase as a solid, then the rate of self-diffusion will be proportional to the defect concentration and hence these figures imply a considerably higher defect content in the rotator phase solid. The energies ΔH_d, involved in the self-diffusion

[1] N. E. Hill, *Proc. Roy. Soc. A*, 1957, **240**, 101; *Trans. Faraday Soc.*, 1959, **55**, 2000.
[2] J. Timmermans, *Les Constantes Physiques des Composés Organiques Cristallisés* (Masson et Cie., Paris, 1953).
[3] C. Clemett and M. Davies, *Trans. Faraday Soc.*, 1962, **58**, 1705, 1718. G. Corfield and M. Davies, *ibid.*, 1964, **60**, 10.
[4] W. J. Dunning, *J. Physics Chem. Solids*, 1961, **18**, 21.

process can be rationalized on the basis of a vacancy diffusion process for both types of solid.[1] The pre-exponential factors in the equation

$$D = D_0 \exp(-\Delta H_d/RT)$$

are much higher, however, than would be expected for a normal vacancy process ($D_0 = 10^6$ cm² sec⁻¹, cyclohexane[2]). On the basis of this, we have suggested that the principal point defect in the rotator phase solids may be a highly relaxed vacancy. This would correspond to a small liquid-like region in the lattice and could result in 0·1 % of the lattice being in a disordered state. Studies of diffusion in impurity-doped crystals confirm this interpretation.[3]

In such a highly disordered system, the considerable plasticity of the solid might result from a vacancy creep process in the single crystal.[4] (For metals such a mechanism only holds for micro-crystalline solids). Creep studies[3] have confirmed that the rotator phase solids are highly plastic (100 times more so than metals at similar reduced temperatures) and that the activation energy ΔH_c for the creep process is equal to that for self-diffusion (Pivalic acid, $\Delta H_d = 21·8\pm 0·1$ kcal mole⁻¹, $\Delta H_c = 22·4\pm 0·7$ kcal mole⁻¹). The creep strain, however, is proportional to the 5th power of the stress whereas an exponent of unity would be expected for vacancy creep. Exponents of this order are characteristic of creep taking place by a dislocation climb mechanism. Analysis of the experimental data indicates that the dislocation content of the crystals studied is $\sim 10^5$ per cm². This figure is in reasonable agreement with etch pit counts which we have made; these yield apparent dislocation contents of $>10^4$ per cm². Thus, there is sufficient crystallinity in the solid for dislocations to be present and to have an effect upon the properties of the crystals.

We conclude from this evidence that the rotator phase solids are fundamentally crystalline but that there is a high proportion of disorder in the solids. At the melting point the solid loses its remaining degree of crystallinity with the characteristically low entropy of fusion, $\Delta S_f < 5$ cal/mole deg. How close in structure these materials are to liquids can only be decided after further structural studies, but as an intermediate phase such studies may well shed further light upon the nature of the liquid state; the above comments refer to polyatomic rotator phase solids and not to rare gas solids. The latter appear to behave normally.[1]

Dr. G. Caglioti, Dr. M. Corchia and **Dr. G. Rizzi** (*CNEN, Ispra, Italy*) said: In a programme on the structure of liquid metals,[5,6] and resuming a previous investigation on the crystal physics of zinc,[7] Corchia, Rizzi and myself have recently measured at the CNEN laboratory of Ispra the structure factor $S(Q)$ of liquid zinc at 470°C, by conventional diffraction of 1 Å neutrons in a well collimated (~ 25 min arc) geometry. Our $S(Q)$ does not exhibit any evidence for the existence of the unusual bump obtained in 1941 by X-ray diffraction in the region of wave vector transfer $Q \simeq 1·5$ Å⁻¹,[8] while in the rest of the diffraction pattern the agreement between X-ray and neutron data is only qualitative. The radial distribution function $4\pi r^2 g(r)$ obtained by Fourier inversion of our neutron data is consistent with the short-range

---

[1] J. N. Sherwood, *Conference on Point Defects in Non-metallic Solids* (Proc. British Ceram. Soc., 1967), to be published.
[2] G. M. Hood and J. N. Sherwood, *Molecular Crystals*, 1966, **1**, 97.
[3] H. M. Hawthorne and J. N. Sherwood, to be published.
[4] W. J. Dunning, *J. Physics Chem. Solids*, 1961, **18**, 21.
[5] P. Ascarelli, *Physic. Rev.*, 1966, **143**, 36.
[6] P. Ascarelli and G. Caglioti, *Nuovo Cimento, B*, 1966, **43**, 375.
[7] G. Borgonovi, G. Caglioti and J. J. Antal, *Physic. Rev.*, 1963, **132**, 683.
[8] C. Gamertsfelder, *J. Chem. Physics*, 1941, **9**, 450.

structure of the liquid to be expected on the basis of the structure and dynamical properties of the corresponding crystal. It shows a sharp peak representing a well-separated shell of ten first nearest neighbours, at a distance (2·60 Å) slightly smaller than the distance (2·67 Å) between the first six nearest neighbours in the corresponding crystal. Further studies are under way to obtain the ion-ion potential from the diffraction data, as well as to ascertain the nature of a small anomaly seemingly appearing at 2·72 Å^{-1}, just before the first diffraction peak (at $Q = 2·9$ Å^{-1}) in the experimental $S(Q)$. The results reported here will appear soon in *Nuovo Cimento B*, 1967, **49**, 222.

Dr. D. I. Page (*A.E.R.E., Harwell*) said: Results of some work at Harwell on the diffraction scattering of neutrons by heavy water, to compare with the X-ray data

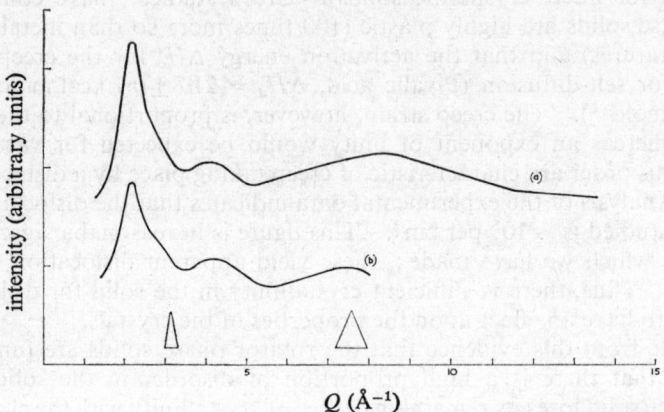

Fig. 1.—Neutron diffraction scattering from D$_2$O at 295°K. (a) $\lambda_0 = 0·835$ Å; (b) $\lambda_0 = 1·365$ Å.

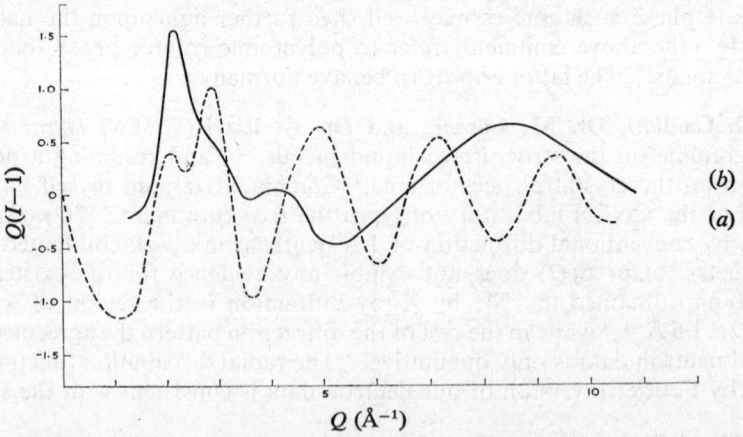

Fig. 2.—Comparison of X-ray and neutron scattering data from water at room temperature.
(a) X-ray. Narten, Danford & Levy. O.R.N.L. 3997. (b) Neutron.

of Dr. Narten, are shown. The measurements were made on a conventional diffractometer using a neutron beam from the "hot source" in DIDO. This is a block of moderator at high temperature which enhances the flux of short wavelength neutrons allowing large momentum transfers to be measured.

Fig. 1 shows the best fit to the raw data and the resolution function of the instrument at two incident wavelengths. The statistical error on a single point is about twice the line thickness. With the incident wavelength of 0·835 Å, a value of $Q = 14$ was reached. There is little structure apart from the main peaks.

Fig. 2 shows the corrected data plotted as a function of $Q(I-1)$ to compare with the X-ray data. There is a correlation between the first two maxima but little similarity after that. This can be qualitatively accounted for by realizing the X-rays are scattered predominantly by the oxygen atoms while the neutrons are mainly " seeing " the hydrogen atoms. Thus the oxygen atoms which are much more localized than the hydrogen atoms give rise to a sharp first peak in the X-ray radial distribution function; on transforming this, the almost sinusoidal variation of the X-ray data is obtained. The less localized hydrogen atoms give a more blurred R.D.F. and hence a much smoother diffraction pattern. The first peak in the diffraction patterns (corresponding to intermolecular scattering) appears as a doublet in both cases; again, the difference in shape could be due to the radiations " seeing " different atoms and consequently the location of the molecular scattering centres would not be the same for neutrons and X-rays. We are trying to find a suitable model to predict the neutron scattering data—as Dr. Narten has done for the X-ray case. We conclude that X-ray and neutron scattering are complementary techniques rather than competing ones.

Mr. J. W. Perram and **Dr. S. Levine** (*Manchester University*) said: We have been examining lattice models with the view to explaining some of the properties of liquid water in terms of co-operative hydrogen bonding, as envisaged by Frank and Wen [1] and elaborated on by Nemethy and Scheraga [2] (N.S.). There has been much criticism of N.S.'s " significant structure " theory of water, on spectroscopic grounds and on their use of adjustable parameters. There are also objections to their statistical mechanical treatment, which should be discussed. We start with their partition function for N molecules

$$Q_{NS} = \sum_{\mathbf{n}} (N!/\prod_{i=0}^{4} n_i!) \exp(-E(\mathbf{n})/kT) \cdot \prod_{i=0}^{4} f_i^{n_i}, \qquad (1)$$

where n_i is the number of water molecules with $i(=0,1,...,4)$ hydrogen bonds, $E(\mathbf{n})$ the energy of a particular distribution $\mathbf{n}(=n_0,...,n_4)$ of hydrogen bonds and f_i is the single molecule partition function which accounts for vibrational, rotational and translational states. The combinatorial factor $N!/\prod_{i=0}^{4} n_i!$, which is supposed to be the degeneracy of the energy level $E(\mathbf{n})$, is, however, in error. For example, many of the configurations included in this factor are geometrically impossible. Apparently N.S. partly avoid this difficulty by restricting the terms in the partition sum to those corresponding to the hydrogen-bonded clusters of Frank and Wen. However, they do not show that clusters follow from a proper statistical mechanical theory.

To illustrate the inadequacy of (1), we have considered the following simple model: (i) no *a priori* restrictions, due to clusters, are assumed; (ii) the energy $E(\mathbf{n})$ of a configuration is proportional to the total number of bonds, i.e., $E(\mathbf{n}) = -rE_H$, where E_H is the so-called energy of the hydrogen bond and $r = \frac{1}{2}\sum_{i=0}^{4} in_i$ is the number of such bonds. This is equivalent to N.S.'s assumption of equal energy spacings between the 5 hydrogen-bonded molecular species. (iii) All the $f_i(=f)$ are equal.

[1] H. S. Frank and W.-Y. Wen, *Disc. Faraday Soc.*, 1957, **24**, 133.
[2] G. Nemethy and H. A. Scheraga, *J. Chem. Physics*, 1962, **36**, 3382.

This may be a reasonable approximation for all species except $i = 0$, but experiments suggest that the number n_0 is small.[1] If we imagine the O atoms as forming a tetrahedral lattice, then the $2N$ mid-points of the lines joining adjacent O atoms also form a tetrahedral lattice and we can assign energy states 0 and $-E_H$ (one hydrogen bond) to each of these $2N$ points. The degeneracy corresponding to r hydrogen bonds is $\binom{2N}{r}$, the number of ways of distributing r objects among $2N$ sites. The partition function is therefore

$$Q = f^N \sum_{r=0}^{2N} \binom{2N}{r} \exp \frac{rE_H}{kT} = f^N \left(1 + \exp \frac{E_H}{kT}\right)^{2N}. \quad (2)$$

In contrast, (1) is a multinomial expansion, viz.,

$$Q_{NS} = f^N \left[1 + \exp \frac{E_H}{2kT} + \exp \frac{E_H}{kT} + \exp \frac{3E_H}{2kT} + \exp \frac{2E_H}{kT}\right]^N$$

$$= \left[f\left(\exp \frac{5E_H}{2kT} - 1\right) \bigg/ \left(\exp \frac{E_H}{2kT} - 1\right)\right]^N. \quad (3)$$

We have compared the entropy S_H due to the hydrogen bond distributions in (2) and (3), taking the value $E_H = 1.4$ kcal/mole. In the temperature range 280-370°K, (2) gives an increase in S_H from 1·1 to 1·6 (cal/deg. mole) whereas, according to (3), this increase is from 1·7 to 2·1. In our simplified model, $r \to N$, i.e., half the bonds remain unbroken, as $T \to \infty$. All thermodynamic functions are well behaved, our water neither boils nor freezes and it possesses no short-range order compatible with the existence of clusters. Furthermore, both this model and that of N.S. have neglected the residual entropy (considered by Nagle [2]) due to the two directions available to the hydrogen bond.

The basis of Frank and Wen's concept of clusters is that one hydrogen bond promotes the formation of other hydrogen bonds. Thus, the energy spacing E_H should depend on the number i of hydrogen bonds per molecule. N.S. discuss this briefly and suggest that allowance is made for unequal spacing by restricting the summation in (1), but that nevertheless equal spacing is an acceptable approximation. Our calculations show, however, that equal spacing is incompatible with the assumption of cluster formation, a point which has also been stressed by Gurikov.[3] It seems necessary, therefore, to postulate unequal spacing from the start and work on this problem is in progress. One technique which can be used is familiar in the Ising problem, the absence or presence of hydrogen bonds corresponding to the two directions of electron spin. In addition, the implications of the Samoilov model [4] as treated by Gurikov,[3] who introduces interstitial molecules and vacant sites (similarly as Narten, Danford and Levy) as well as hydrogen bonding, are being studied. Our investigations indicate that the quantitative predictions of N.S.'s theory and of the similar theory by Vand and Senior [5] should be viewed with some reserve.

Dr. W. A. P. Luck (*Ludwigshafen/Rh.*) said: In answer to Perram and Levine I would mention that the N.-S. paper was a pioneering one but only a first approximation. The "unsharp" isosbestic points and the differences between the spectra of

[1] D. P. Stevenson, *J. Physic. Chem.*, 1965, **69**, 2145.
[2] J. F. Nagle, *J. Math. Physics*, 1966, **7**, 1484.
[3] Yu. V. Gurikov, *Zhur. Strukt. Khim.* 1965, **6**, 817.
[4] O. Ya. Samoilov, *Structure of Aqueous Solution of Electrolytes and Hydration of Ions* (English trans., Consultants Bureau, New York, 1965).
[5] V. Vand and W. A. Senior, *J. Chem. Physics*, 1965, **43**, 1869, 1874, 1878.

pure alcohol and the solution show that the assumption of an equal energy spacing is approximate. In addition, the energy difference of the so-called free molecules in the N.–S. paper compared with ice-like bonded molecules is only 2·64 kcal/mole. The sublimation energy of 11·6 kcal/mole gives the real difference (ice-vapour like) molecules. Therefore we do not agree with some spectroscopic tests of the N.–S. theory and the bands allied to the different N.–S. species. In our nomenclature, the free species of the N.–S. paper are energetically unfavourable to H-bonding. The free OH-groups of our nomenclature are neglected in the N.–S. theory. This is the reason that our percentage of free OH is much smaller that in the N.–S. theory. Scheraga has now devised a new theory which is much better as a first approximation.

Dr. W. A. P. Luck (*Ludwigshafen/Rh.*) said: It is easy to show that Franck and Roth's and our experiments agree. If we have an equilibrium of two species with two different bands, then it depends on the frequency distance $\Delta\nu$ of these bands, the half width $\Delta\nu_{\frac{1}{2}}$ and the quotient of the optical density whether we observe two bands,

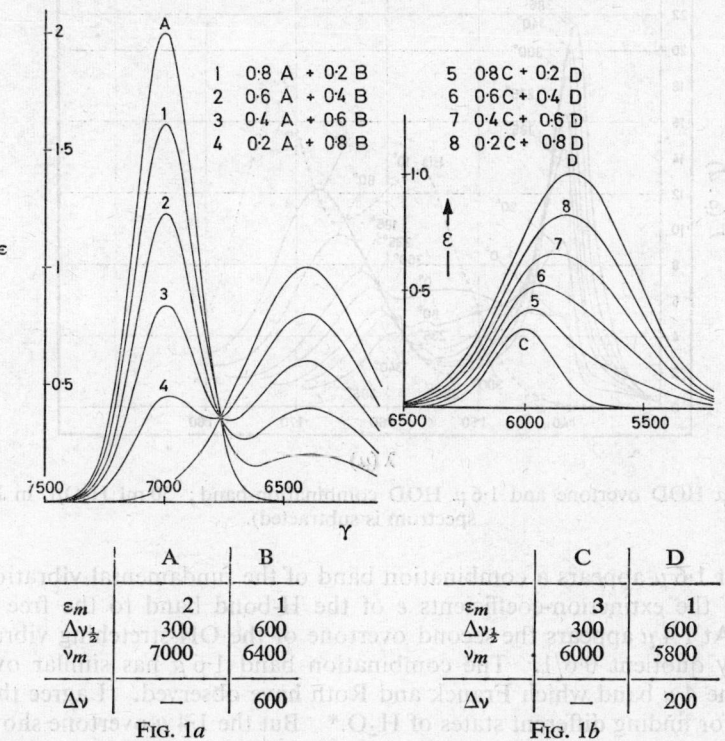

	A	B		C	D
ε_m	2	1	ε_m	3	1
$\Delta\nu_{\frac{1}{2}}$	300	600	$\Delta\nu_{\frac{1}{2}}$	300	600
ν_m	7000	6400	ν_m	6000	5800
$\Delta\nu$		600	$\Delta\nu$		200

FIG. 1a   FIG. 1b

one main band with peaks, one unsymmetrical band or only one band. For example, the overlapping of two bands with the same extinction-coefficients always gives only one band if $\Delta\nu < 0.85\Delta\nu_{\frac{1}{2}}$. There are many experimental observations of one-band systems of an equilibrium of two species with two overlapping bands.[1] Fig. 1 shows two theoretical examples of an equilibrium corresponding to two overlapping bands:

$$\varepsilon = \varepsilon_m \exp\left[-4\ln 2\left(\frac{\nu_m - \nu}{\Delta\nu_{\frac{1}{2}}}\right)^2\right].$$

[1] W. Luck, *J. Soc. Dyers Col.*, 1958, **74**, 221; *Angew. Chem.*, 1960, **72**, 57.

Fig. 1a corresponds to the experimental conditions of the HOD overtone band. Fig. 1b corresponds to the experimental conditions of the HOD combination band and should be similar in the fundamental region. Fig. 1 shows that it is not unusual to observe one band without peaks in the combination or fundamental region, and to observe separate bands in the overtone region. The experimental H_2O spectra are more complicated because the H-bond bands are composed of a system of bands. In OH H-bonding the $\Delta\nu$ between the free OH-band and the H-bonded band is smaller in the fundamental and combination bands than in the overtone region.[1] In addition, the intensity of the H-bond-band is higher in the fundamental region than the free OH-band. In the overtone region it is reversed: the intensity of the H-bond band is smaller than the free OH-band. Therefore it is easier to observe free OH or NH-bands in the overtone region (cp. fig. 1 and 3 in ref. (2)). This outstanding advantage of the overtone bands can be observed especially with the HOD spectra 1·3-1·8 μ

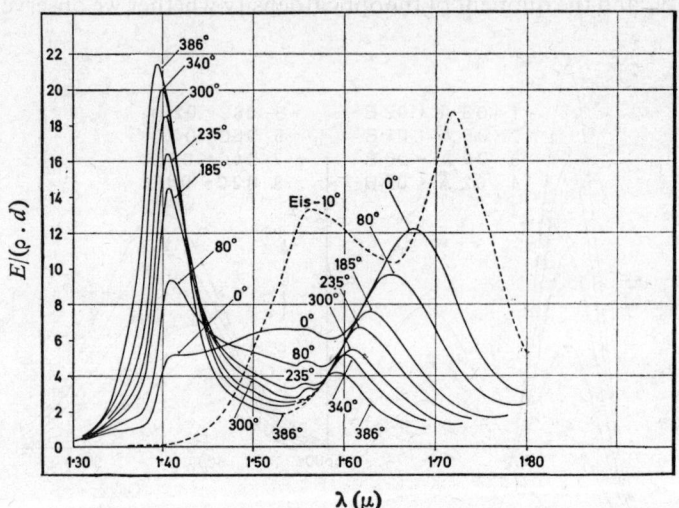

FIG. 2.—1·4 μ HOD overtone and 1·6 μ HOD combination-band; 50 ml H_2O/l. in D_2O (D_2O-spectrum is subtracted).

(fig. 2). At 1·6 μ appears a combination band of the fundamental vibrations with a quotient of the extinction-coefficients ε of the H-bond band to the free OH-band of 4·5/1. At 1·4 μ appears the second overtone of the OH-stretching vibration with an intensity quotient 0·6/1. The combination band 1·6 μ has similar overlapping effects as the 4 μ band which Franck and Roth have observed. I agree this band is not useful for finding different states of H_2O.* But the 1·4 μ overtone shows a band maximum belonging to more or less free OH. Taking the supercritical spectra— which are temperature independent for constant density—as the standard state for a fluid-like interaction of non-H-bonding we obtain from this isolated 1·4 μ HOD overtone-band the same results for free OH that we obtain with four different H_2O bands (fig. 3). This good agreement shows clearly that in the overtone-region the overlapping of different bands does not affect our method. Even so, this experimental

[1] W. A. P. Luck, *Ber. Bunsenges*, 1965, **69**, 626.
[2] W. Luck, *Z. Elektrochem.*, 1961, **65**, 355.
* For an attempt to analyze different species with the 3 μ fundamental band, see W. K. Thompson, W. A. Senior and B. A. Pethica, *Nature*, 1966, **211**, 1086.

agreement (fig. 3) of different bands shows that a variation of ε with temperature may be unimportant too. The statement that the HOD fundamental stretching band would be the best one to study the water structure is not valid, if we include the overtone-spectra.

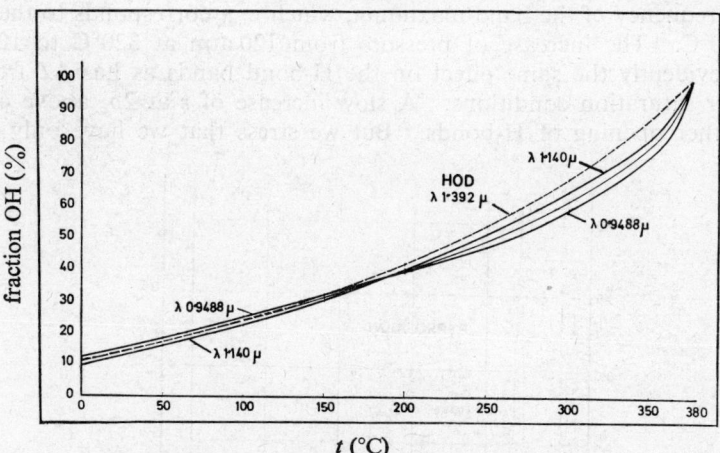

FIG. 3.—The % free OH P determined by the two H_2O bands 1·14 and 0·95 μ agrees well with the determination of the 1·39 μ HOD band.

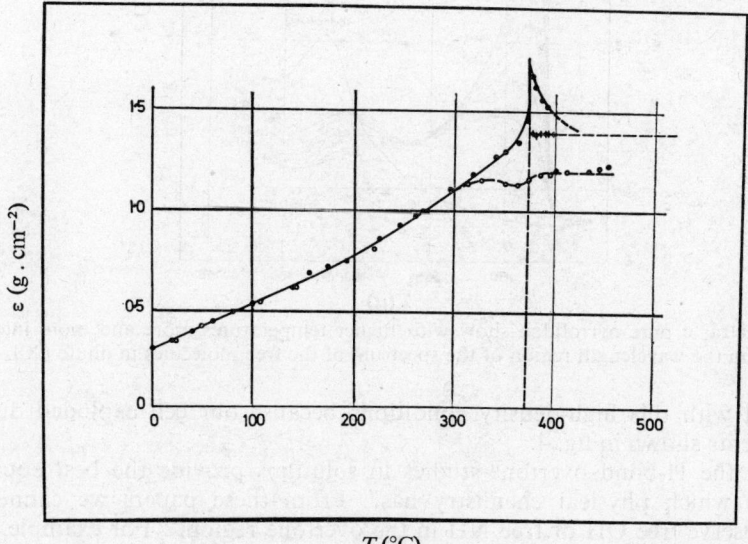

FIG. 4.—H_2O extinction coefficient ε at the wavelength 1·143 μ (free OH-region) : ●, liquid state $ρ_c$; +, vapour state $ρ_c$; ○, liquid state $2ρ_c$.

Franck and Roth observe with decreasing T an increase of the high intensity H-bond band with the corresponding $Δν$. The same change was observed in the supercritical T-region with increasing $ρ$ from $ρ_c$ to $3ρ_c$. That means an increasing p from 240 to 2000 atm. This could be an indication of induced H-bonding by p or $ρ$.

Since the H-bonding is an equilibrium this is expected. We have made measurements of the 1·1 μ H$_2$O band at $2\rho_c$ (fig. 4). For $T > 320°C$, and this density $2\rho_c$, the optical density in the free OH-region is more or less constant and lower than for the density ρ_c, as expected from Franck and Roth's results. Our band-system has a decreasing intensity with increasing H-bonds. Even so, we have observed at $2\rho_c$ and $T > 320°C$ a constant frequency of the band maximum, which ν_{max} corresponds to the saturated state of 320°C. The increase of pressure from 120 atm at 320°C to 1200 atm at 450°C has evidently the same effect on the H-bond bands as has ΔT from 320 to 374°C under saturation conditions. A slow increase of ε at $2\rho_c$ above 430°C may show a further opening of H-bonds. But we stress that we have only made one

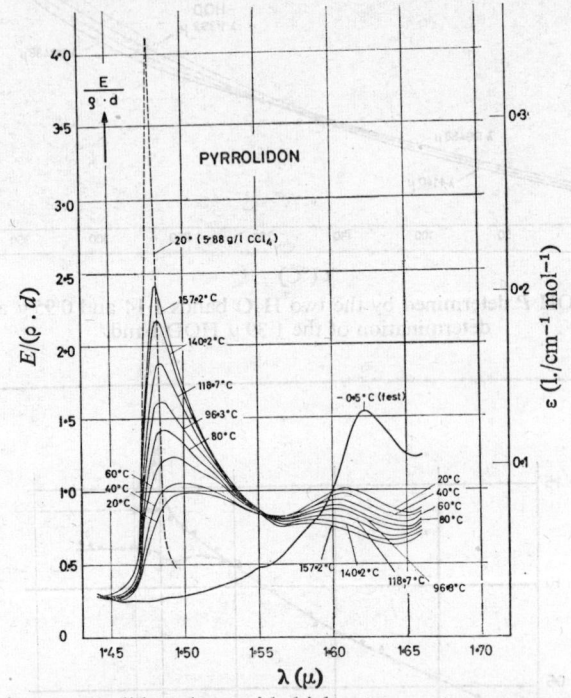

FIG. 5.—Spectra of pure pyrrolidon show with higher temperatures more and more intensity and a maximum in the wavelength region of the spectrum of the free molecules in dilute CCl$_4$-solutions.

experiment with this high-density conditions because our cell exploded during the measurements shown in fig. 4.

I think the H-bond overtone-studies in solutions provide the best equilibrium-knowledge which physical chemistry has. From these papers we cannot doubt that we observe free OH or free NH in the overtone region. For example, for pyrrolidon the equilibrium constant for dimerization is constant with change of weight concentration of a factor of 10^3.[1] We know in this case especially well the free NH-band. Fig. 5 shows that heating pure pyrrolidon gives a change of spectra in the direction of this free NH-band. We obtained the same results with CH$_3$OH, C$_2$H$_5$OH, 1-3 propandiol, 1-4 butandiol, 1-5 pentandiol, 1-4 butindiol and N-ethyl-acetamide too.[2] Comparing the CH$_3$OH solution-spectra with the CH$_3$OH

[1] W. A. P. Luck, *Naturwiss.*, 1965, **52**, 25.
[2] W. A. P. Luck, *Spectrochim. Acta*, 1967, in press.

T-dependent-spectra in bulk we see that we not only have two species, free OH and linear H-bonded, but also different types of energetically unfavourable H-bond bands.[1] I agree with Franck and Roth that in this region of different H-bonds there may be, more or less, a continuous distribution of different H-bonds with energy contents $U < \Delta U_H$. But all OH-groups with $U > \Delta U_H$ are in similar states from the point of view of H-bond bands. This is one reason why we prefer only to discuss quantitatively the percentage P of free OH. The second reason is that in this frequency region all overlapping effects are minimal.

The intensity of the free OH-bands may change with a change of molecular environment. But this change cannot be so large that it is impossible to make approximative statements. An exact interpretation of the H_2O spectra is impossible, so we have to make approximative statements because a knowledge of water structure is so important.

Many of own measurements at lower densities agree nevertheless with Franck and Roth in showing smaller intensities. In the small p-region there is an increase of intensity of a rotation-structured spectra with increasing pressure.[2] But we have little information what happens if the disturbed rotation changes to a libration.

At a maximum a limit of 5-20 % free OH at 0°C is expected; this only means that we do not know how many hundreds of molecules are in the flickering clusters. But the exact number of molecules in a cluster is not so important for our understanding the water structure; it was important to show that most theories have assumed as yet too many free OH-groups.

Prof. H. S. Frank (*University of Pittsburgh and Mellon Institute*) said: I express my admiration of the work reported by Narten *et al.*, by Franck *et al.* and by Luck. Each, by difficult and painstaking experiment, has established new conditions which any acceptable model for water will have to satisfy, and each has, therefore, made an important contribution to the ultimate solution of the water problem. None of the authors has purported to say the last word about that problem, and each one has wisely emphasized that the interpretation of his data which he favours is not necessarily unique. That their interpretations could not all be right is clear, for none of the three is in agreement with either of the other two. Franck considers that only one " kind " of O—H bonding in liquid water need be assumed at any temperature or density. Narten specifies two types of water molecules, which should therefore show two kinds of bonding, but makes the relative proportions of the two very insensitive to temperature changes, whereas Luck not only distinguishes between " bonded " and " unbonded " O—H entities, but gives numbers which make their proportions much more temperature-sensitive.

One of the principal problems in discussion of the water structure is the difficulty in finding experimental evidence which *requires* either the acceptance or the rejection of any given model. To find a model with which one set of new data are consistent, or which they suggest, is relatively easy, but uniqueness of interpretation is another matter. Thus, for all the attractiveness of the inferences Luck draws from the effect of temperature changes on his spectra, I worry about not really understanding the laws which govern the addition of intensities in the overtone and combination bands which he has studied; and therefore consider his work likely to be more useful as illustrating and refining a model which will have been established on other grounds, than as providing the initial proof for such establishment. Similarly, while the data of Narten, Danford and Levy seem to add in an important way to our experimental

[1] W. Luck, *Ber. Bunsenges*, 1963, **67**, 186.
[2] G. Kortüm and W. Luck, *Z. Naturforsch.*, 1951, **6a**, 191, 305, 313.

knowledge of liquid H_2O and D_2O, the model that they propose could be proved to be unique only if it could be shown that no alternative starting structure, with an equal number of adjustable parameters, could be refined to give calculated radial distribution curves which would fit the data as well as their present ones do. And in the meantime, the fact that, on their present model, the fraction of water in the framework form changes so slowly with temperature has the thermodynamic consequence that there can be little difference in molal enthalpy between framework and interstitial molecules, which, if true, would have remarkable implications for the nature of the bonding in the two states.

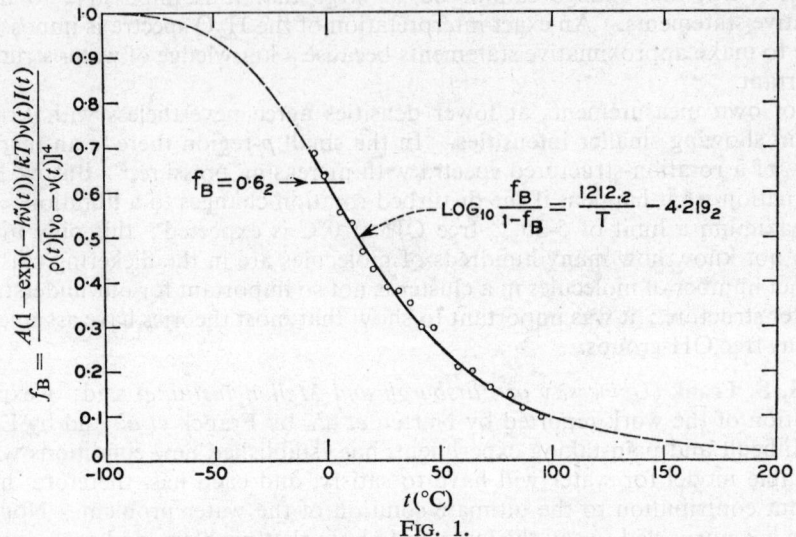

FIG. 1.

In this connection, it is worth looking at another set of data which suggests strongly that some form of water is indeed disappearing fairly rapidly as room temperature water is heated. These data, taken by G. E. Walrafen in the Bell Laboratories,[1] are intensities of Raman scattering at frequencies near 175 cm^{-1}. This band, which presumably is the counterpart of the ice scattering near 220 cm^{-1}, is thought to arise from the vibration against each other of oxygen atoms linked by hydrogen bonds. As shown in fig. 1, reproduced from Walrafen's paper, the corrected intensity of this band drops by almost half between 0 and 25°C and does so in the way that would be observed if the fraction f of the scattering material and that $(1-f)$, of the non-scattering material, were related by an equilibrium constant $K = f/(1-f)$ which obeyed conventional thermodynamic laws.

The question then arises how this result is compatible with the fact that Franck and Roth (along with others who have studied the O-D stretch of HOD in H_2O) get an infra-red band which superficially is simple. The answer is that bands which "superficially" are simple may, in fact, be resultants of 2 or more component bands. This is illustrated in fig. 2, which was constructed by Dr. W. A. Senior using the National Heart Institute's curve analyzer [2] located in Mellon Institute, which was kindly placed at our disposal by the Petroleum Fellowship. Here two Gaussians are seen to add up to something which, on superficial inspection, looks like another Gaussian. If there are two component bands which are farther separated in central

[1] G. E. Walrafen, *J. Chem. Physics*, 1966, **44**, 1546.
[2] W. A. Senior, *Ann. N.Y. Acad. Sci.*, 1964, **115**, 644.

frequency a shoulder will appear, and if the component bands correspond to chemical species which are in equilibrium, so that a change in conditions (temperature, for example) causes more of one to be formed at the expense of the other, then, either with or without overt shoulders in the individual plots, the curves corresponding to different conditions will often display the so-called isosbestic phenomenon (fig. 3).

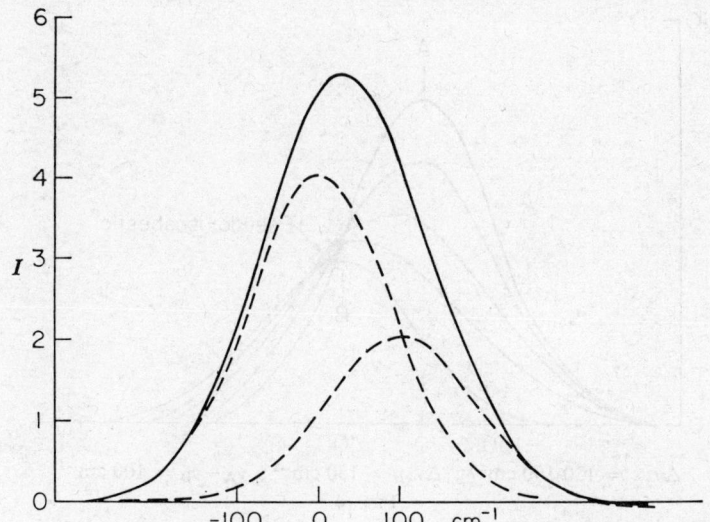

$\Delta\nu_{\frac{1}{2}A} = \Delta\nu_{\frac{1}{2}B} = 130 \text{ cm}^{-1}$; $\nu_A - \nu_B = 100 \text{ cm}^{-1}$; $\varepsilon_A C_A = 4$; $\varepsilon_B C_B = 2$. (See Curve 3).

FIG. 2.

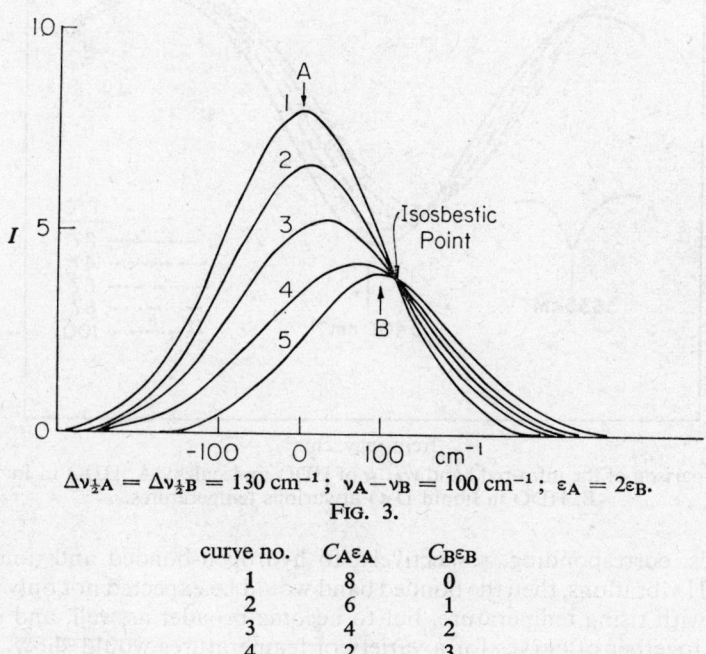

$\Delta\nu_{\frac{1}{2}A} = \Delta\nu_{\frac{1}{2}B} = 130 \text{ cm}^{-1}$; $\nu_A - \nu_B = 100 \text{ cm}^{-1}$; $\varepsilon_A = 2\varepsilon_B$.

FIG. 3.

curve no.	$C_A\varepsilon_A$	$C_B\varepsilon_B$
1	8	0
2	6	1
3	4	2
4	2	3
5	0	4

$C_A + C_B = \text{const.}$

140   GENERAL DISCUSSION

The appearance of such a pattern is often taken by chemical spectroscopists to betoken the existence of an equilibrium, e.g., the mixture of acid and basic forms of a coloured indicator changes in the course of a titration and successive spectral curves show isosbestic behaviour. The existence of an equilibrium need not, however, produce a " perfect " isosbestic. If, e.g., the O—H stretch, say, of HOD in D_2O consisted

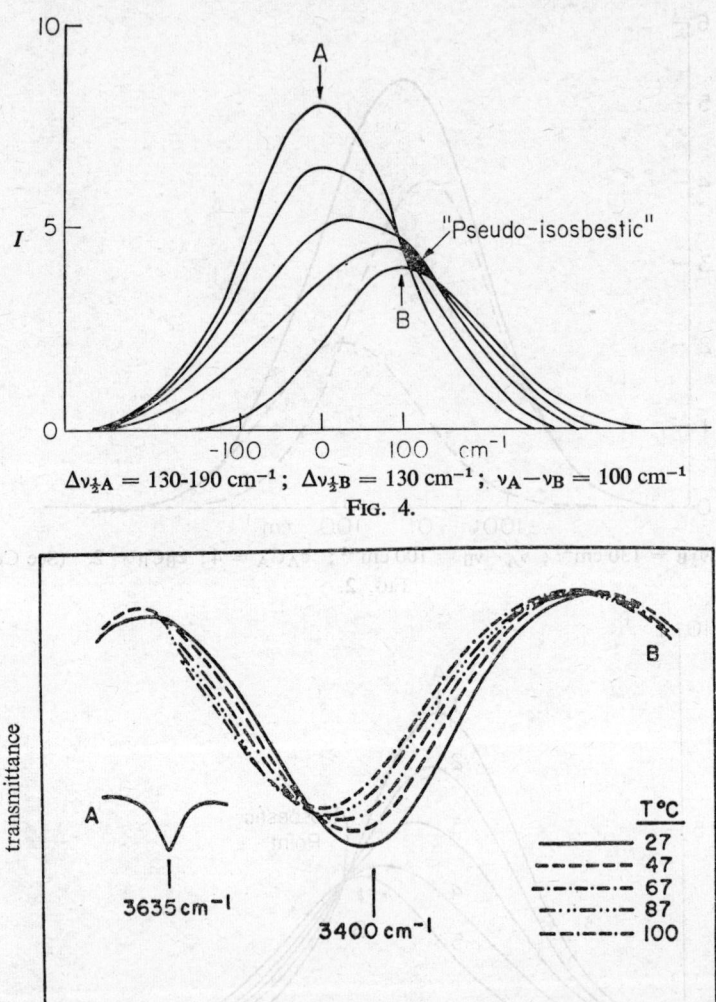

$\Delta\nu_{\frac{1}{2}A} = 130\text{-}190 \text{ cm}^{-1}$; $\Delta\nu_{\frac{1}{2}B} = 130 \text{ cm}^{-1}$; $\nu_A - \nu_B = 100 \text{ cm}^{-1}$
Fig. 4.

Fig. 5.—Comparison of the infra-red band ν_{O-H} of HDO molecules: A, HDO in in $DCCl_3$, 27°; B, HDO in liquid D_2O at various temperatures.

of two bands, corresponding, respectively, to hydrogen-bonded and non-hydrogen-bonded O—H vibrations, then the bonded band would be expected not only to decrease in intensity with rising temperature, but to become broader as well, and in this case the plotting together of curves for a variety of temperatures would show a modified, or pseudo-isosbestic, behaviour. Fig. 4 shows how this would come about, and fig. 5, a set of absorption curves taken by K. A. Hartman, Jr. of the du Pont Central

Experimental Station [1] shows that some such thing really is observed. This is consistent with, but does not prove, the idea that two distinguishable kinds of O—H stretching motions are in liquid water.

The objection has been made that " unbonded " O—H groups ought to absorb at much higher frequencies, where no absorption is observed. Here the new findings of Franck and Roth assume great importance, for they seem to me to confirm that an unbonded OH or OD in liquid water at a density of 1·0 g/cm^3 need not be expected to absorb at the frequency found in the dilute vapour. If the v_{max} against T curve of their fig. 4, for $\rho = 1\cdot 0$ g/cm^3 is extrapolated to higher temperatures, there seems little doubt that it will level off to an asymptotic v_{max} well below 2700 cm^{-1}, i.e., well below the Q branch O—D absorption in HOD vapour. But if the temperature varied from 400 to 500, 600 - - - 1000 - - - °C, there is also little doubt that it would become increasingly inappropriate to describe the HOD molecules as hydrogen bonded. That is, at high densities, Franck and Roth have shown—to me at least—that there is a non-hydrogen-bonded interaction between HOD molecules which lowers the frequency of the OD absorption in a way qualitatively similar to that produced by hydrogen bonding. This is consistent with the inference that there are two kinds of strong cohesive forces between water molecules that can be drawn from the fact that the vapour pressure curves of H$_2$O and D$_2$O against temperature cross each other.[2] If this be granted, then the smoothness and apparent simplicity of the O—H and O—D stretch curves found at any one temperature by Wall and Hornig,[3] by Hartman, by Falk and Ford [4] and by Franck and Roth, no longer has any cogency as an argument for a one-species model, and the two-species inference from the pseudo-isosbestic curves of Hartman and from Walrafen's Raman data becomes credible.

Dr. W. A. P. Luck (*Ludwigshafen/Rh.*) said: In answer to Frank's contribution, the different overtone bands of H$_2$O, D$_2$O and HOD that we have observed all have isosbestic points that are not sharp. Therefore, as a first approximation we may assume a two-species model. But all these " isosbestics " are not good ones.[5] We obtained the same result from the argument that the sum of free OH and linear-bonded OH do not add up to 100 %,[1] i.e. the reason that the isosbestic points are not good is because of the existence of more than two species.

With free molecules, they have similar vibration frequencies as in the vapour state; but they are disturbed in the fluid state. Therefore we have not obtained any indication of rotation structure in the fluid state, but have observed disturbed rotation structure of H$_2$O in CCl$_4$ solutions and in the vapour state at smaller pressures as in the saturated state.

I agree that all the new experimental data from X-ray scattering, Raman- and i.-r.- spectra are not contradictory. Different authors have made different interpretations with different approximations; we would need a special meeting of all these people to make progress in our knowledge of the water structure.

Dr. J. Padova (*S.N.R.C., Yavne, Israel*) said: With reference to the paper by Luck, I would like to state that measurements of the absorptivity of water at 960 mμ in NaNO$_3$ solutions were carried out at 25°C in our laboratory by I. Abrahamer. The molar absorptivity ε showed a linear increase with concentration of NaNO$_3$

---

[1] K. A. Hartman, Jr., *J. Physic. Chem.*, 1966, **70**, 270.
[2] I. Kirschenbaum, *Physical Properties and Analysis of Heavy Water* (McGraw-Hill, New York, 1951), p. 25.
[3] F. T. Wall and D. F. Hornig, *J. Chem. Physics*, 1965, **43**, 2079.
[4] M. Falk and T. A. Ford, *Can. J. Chem.*, 1966, **44**, 1699.
[5] W. Luck, *Ber. Bunsenges.*, 1963, **67**, 186.

up to saturated solutions. From the two-species model of free OH and ice-like H bonded groups used by Luck, it may be shown that the percentage of free OH groups is proportional to the absorptivity of water, pointing thereby to the similar effect of temperature and salt concentration on free OH groups percentage (cf. fig. 1 of Luck's paper) and confirming the structure breaking effect of $NaNO_3$.

Prof. M. L. Josien (*Faculté des Sciences de Paris*) said: In the course of a systematic infra-red study of intermolecular associations, we have obtained data concerning the association of water with proton acceptors and donors. (*a*) In ternary mixtures, when a proton acceptor is added to a carbon tetrachloride solution of water, the water molecule yields two kinds of complexes: HOH...B and B...HOH...B.[1,2] Fig. 1 shows, e.g., the evolution of absorption between 3800 and 3400 cm^{-1} as a function of

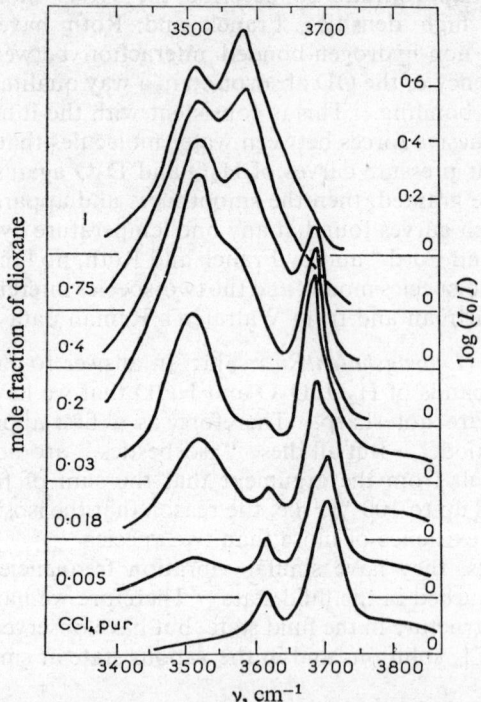

FIG. 1.—Stretching frequencies of water in carbon tetrachloride+dioxane mixtures. f.m.: dioxane molar fraction, water concentration = 0·006-0·05 mole/l.; pathlength = 30·3 mm. The product (water concentration × pathlength) has been kept constant.

the molar fraction of dioxane added to a carbon tetrachloride solution. The free molecules H_2O absorb at 3613 (v_1) and 3708 cm^{-1} (v_3), while the 1-1 complex absorbs at 3510 and 3683 cm^{-1}, and the 1-2 complex at 3512 and 3583 cm^{-1}. For all the proton acceptors studied, if a 1-1 complex is formed, there remains an absorption around 3700 cm^{-1}; on the contrary, in the 1-2 complexes (cf. table 1) the frequencies of the v_1 and v_3 vibrations are lowered by a similar value, although the difference ($v_3 - v_1$) decreases progressively with the strength of the proton acceptor and the intensity ratio $I(v_1)/I(v_3)$ increases to about 1.

[1] P. Saumagne and M. L. Josien, *Bull. Soc. Chim.*, 1958, 813.
[2] P. Saumagne, *Thèse* (Bordeaux, 1961).

Fig. 2 shows, for ethyloxide, a series of curves recorded in 1960 in order to analyse the influence of temperature on the equilibrium between the 1-1 and 1-2 complexes. The spectra were obtained with a single-beam spectrometer P.E. 112; the absorption bands of atmospheric water vapour were not compensated for. At 40°C, water was found mainly in the state of a 1-2 complex, while the amount of 1-1 complex (v_1 3700 cm^{-1}, v_3 3560 cm^{-1}) was predominant around the temperature of 300°C.

TABLE 1

solvent	v_1 (cm^{-1})	v_3 (cm^{-1})	(v_3-v_1), cm^{-1}	$I(v_1)/I(v_3)$
acetonitrile	3543	3636	93	0·88
cyclohexanone	3530	3610	80	0·90
diethylether	3518	3590	72	0·97
dimethylsulphoxide	3440	3505	65	1
pyridine	3411	3485 (sh.)	—	

$(I(v_1)/(I(v_3))$ in the gas is ca. 0·1).

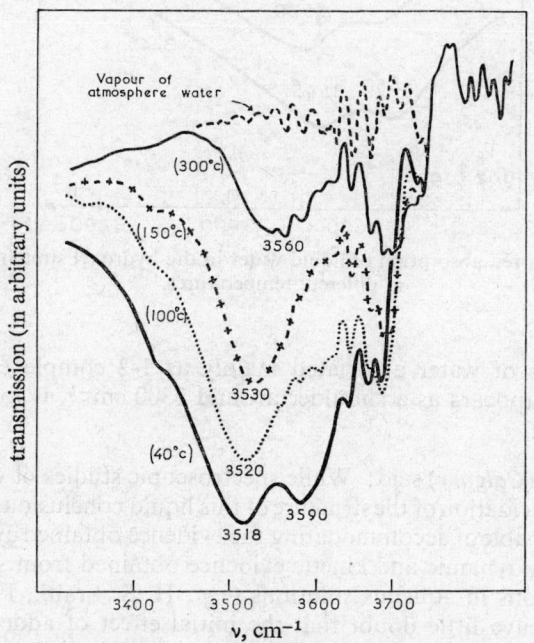

FIG. 2.—Stretching frequencies of water in diethyl oxide; effect of temperature; saturated solution; pathlength = 0·3 mm at high temperatures.

(b) The stretching frequencies of water are not very sensitive to complexing by hydrogen bonding of the oxygen atom.[1] Under the influence of a very strong acid, such as trifluoroacetic acid, a decrease of only 22 cm^{-1} is observed for the frequencies v_1 and v_3.

(c) The above data lead to the interpretation of the spectrum of liquid water in terms of being a complex of the 1-2 type since, in the limits of sensitivity of infra-red spectroscopy, no absorption around 3700 cm^{-1} can be observed.[2]

[1] J. de Villepin, A. Lautie and M. L. Josien, *Ann. Chim.*, 1966, **1**, 365.
[2] *Congr. Slow Neutron Scattering* (Vienna, 1960).

(d) Fig. 3 shows the evolution of the water spectrum as a function of temperature. In view of the preceding remarks, we propose the following interpretation: the two maxima which progressively occur around 3545 and 3650 cm^{-1} are related to the

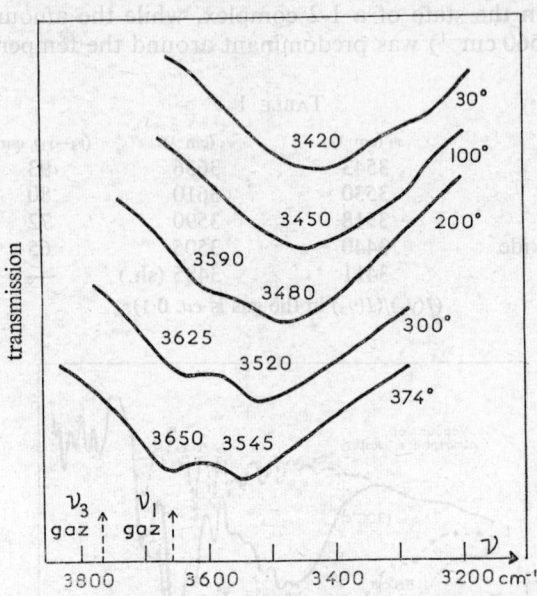

FIG. 3.—Infra-red absorption of liquid water in the hydroxyl stretching region at different temperatures.

v_1 and v_3 vibrations of water associated mainly as 1-2 complexes; the frequency v_2, whose overtone appears as a shoulder around 3300 cm^{-1}, is lowered as the temperature increases.

Prof. J. B. Hyne (*Calgary*) said: While spectroscopic studies of water are of prime importance in the elucidation of the structure of this liquid conclusions drawn from such evidence must be capable of accommodating the evidence obtained by other techniques. In particular, thermodynamic and kinetic evidence obtained from studies of aqueous solutions and reactions in aqueous solutions (e.g., H. S. Frank, F. Frank and Ives, Arnett *et al.* etc.) leave little doubt that the initial effect of added cosolvents is to " buttress " the existing pure water structure and not destroy it. Accordingly, any molecular model of water structure must be capable of rationalizing these observed effects. While the model of Norten, Danforth and Levy and that of Luck provide either interstitial holes or interfaces between cluster surfaces which might be " buttressed " by added non-aqueous species, the lack of " defined small clusters of water " as suggested by Frank and Roth would render rationalization of the structure buttressing effect of additives difficult.

While the conclusion of Luck that H_2O, CH_3OH and C_2H_5OH in the liquid state have less non-H-bonded OH-groups than most theories claim is, in itself, an intuitively acceptable one, the relative percentages of non-H-bonded molecules in water compared with the two alcohols is surprising. In fig. 1 the percentage of " free " H_2O molecules is shown to be approximately 15 % at 50°C while in fig. 4 the corresponding amount of " free " alcohol is less than 5 %. This means that the alcohols, which form linear hydrogen bonded chains, are *more* hydrogen bonded than water which is capable of forming three-dimensional hydrogen bonded structures. It might also be noted that at 50°C the alcohols are much closer to their boiling points than is water. Although Luck does point out that the curves in fig. 1 and 4 are experimental and not theoretical, would he care to comment on this question of the *relative* amounts of " free " species in water compared with the alcohols.

Dr. W. A. P. Luck (*Ludwigshafen/Rh.*) (*communicated*). In answer to Padova I refer to an earlier paper,[1] in which is given a detailed discussion about the salt effects on free OH in aqueous solutions.

In answer to Prof. Josien. The absorption at 3700 cm^{-1} in the " 1-1 complexes " shows a residue of free OH, as is verified by the spectra given by Josien in fig. 1 and by the temperature-effect given in fig. 2. We can recognize in fig. 1 with medium concentrations of acceptors a shoulder of free OH-band. With higher concentrations this shoulder increases to a single new peak. This means that this peak belongs to a free OH-group of a molecule whose second OH-group is H-bonded.[2-4]

The second peak of the " 2-1 complexes " is also observed by Mohr, Wilk and Barrow.[5] But these authors refer to the two peaks belong to H-bond-bands of the v_1 and the v_3 vibrations which change the intensities with the change of symmetry during the change from a 1-1 to a 1-2 complex. With different acceptors the difference between these two H-bond-bands is at about 90 cm^{-1}.[4] The difference between v_1 and v_3 is also 90 cm^{-1}.

The two peaks with $\Delta v \sim 100$ cm^{-1} observed in fig. 3 at higher temperatures belong to these two vibrations v_1 and v_3 of more or less unbonded OH-groups. Perhaps these peaks may be disturbed by the density gradient near the critical point [6] or by higher pressure in Saumagne's cell. Josien's remark shows the difficulty in the analysis of the OH fundamental vibration. This is one more reason for preferring the overtones or the HOD spectra.

In answer to Hyne. I think the reason that the free OH of the alcohols is smaller than the water values is the structure-difference between chain-like aggregation of alcohols and network-building of water. Comparing the number of molecules per aggregate (or cluster) at corresponding temperatures we find there are not such large differences between alcohols and water [7] (fig. 2.30).

Prof. M. Magat (*Faculté des Sciences de Paris*) said: I have a few remarks to make about the problem of liquid water. The first remark concerns theoretical calculations. Rushbrooke has pointed out that no precise theoretical calculations were possible on any liquids except the monoatomic. I would appeal to the theoreticians to recognize that water is of paramount importance—be it only for biology—and attempts should be made to attempt a theoretical treatment of its structure and properties, even using oversimplified models for the charge distribution in the water molecule, as in the old Bernal and Fowler model. Computers should allow one to go much further than in the old calculation by these authors and by myself.

I was gratified to hear Franck's report on recent progress concerning the variation of the intensity of Raman bands attributed to intermolecular vibrations and librations

[1] W. A. P. Luck, *Ber. Bunsenges*, 1965, **69**, 69.
[2] W. A. P. Luck, *Spectr. Chim. Acta* in press.
[3] W. A. P. Luck, *Ber. Bunsenges*, 1965, **69**, 626.
[4] W. A. P. Luck, *Fortschr. chem. Forschung*, 1964, **4**, 653.
[5] S. C. Mohr, W. D. Wilk and G. M. Barrow, *J. Amer. Chem. Soc.*, 1965, **87**, 3048.
[6] W. A. P. Luck and W. Ditter, *Ber. Bunsenges*, 1966, **70**, 1113.
[7] W. A. P. Luck in *Physico-chemical Processes in Mixed Aqueous Solvents*, ed. F. Franks, (Heinemann Educ. Books Ltd., London, 1967), p. 35.

as a function of temperature. Indeed this careful and precise work confirms exactly my findings of some 30 years ago based on much fewer and much less precise measurements: a particularly rapid decrease of these intensities is observed between 25 and 50°C. The intensity at 70°C is much lower than at 20°C, which cannot be simply interpreted as a disappearance of hydrogen bonds.

The third point concerns the problem of " free " water molecules. Mrs. Reinisch (in our laboratory) has recently made a careful survey of results of different methods on the question of the existence of " freely rotating " water molecules, which probably can be also called " not hydrogen-bonded water molecules ". The results are unfortunately contradictory. The situation as summarized by Mrs. Reinisch is as follows.

methods used	existence (+) or non-existence (−) of H-bonds
infra-red	−
Raman spectra	? (a)
neutron scattering	+ (b)
n.m.r.	− (c)
X-ray structure	+ (?) (d)
dielectric constant	+ (?) (e)

(a) Raman spectra give no definite evidence except perhaps the appearance above 30°C of a band near 3600 cm^{-1} of a frequency not very different from that of the gas.

(b) Palevsky et al.[1] insists that the existence of some movements may be interpreted as rotations of free molecules. This was not confirmed by Jacrot,[2] Larsson is sceptical,[2] and Palevsky did not mention it in his later papers.

(c) Detailed information on n.m.r. results were given here by Powles.

(d) The X-ray studies, e.g., that presented here by Narten, Danford and Levy indicate for water a co-ordination number of 4·4. Since a water molecule can form only 4 hydrogen bonds, some molecules not involved in hydrogen bonds must be present even if the distances involved are close to H-bond distances.

(e) This is the most difficult point. Ice I has at high frequencies a dielectric constant $\varepsilon_\infty = 3\cdot2$. This was established by Lamb a few years ago and never contested. Liquid water even close to 0°C has a dielectric constant $\varepsilon_\infty = 5\cdot0 \pm 0\cdot5$ at frequencies lying just below the intermolecular vibrational frequencies. The Onsager correlation g factor may be determined *a priori* by statistical mechanical or electrostatical considerations. Thus, Kirkwood and Oster[3] for water; Onsager and Dupuis,[4] Coulson and Eisenberg,[5] Hollins[6] for ice (which g factor must not be very different from that of water) found a g value $2\cdot1 < g < 2\cdot9$, in approximate agreement with the experimental g that one obtains assuming ε_∞ for liquid water $= n^2$ (which is improbable), or $\varepsilon_{\infty \, \text{water}} \equiv \varepsilon_\infty$ for ice $= 3\cdot2$.

However, if one takes $\varepsilon_\infty = 5\cdot0$, the correlation factor becomes $g = 1$,[7] i.e., there is no correlation between water molecules, a highly improbable situation unless there is some kind of compensation of effects. Hence, either the dielectric constant $\varepsilon_\infty = 3\cdot2$ of liquid water is due partly to molecules involved in H-bonds as in ice and partly

[1] *Physic. Rev.*, 1960, **119**, 872.
[2] *Congr. Slow Neutron Scattering* (Vienna, 1960).
[3] *J. Chem. Physics*, 1943, **11**, 175.
[4] *Rendiconti S.I.F.*, X Corso, 1960, p. 294.
[5] *Proc. Roy. Soc. A*, 1966, **291**, 445.
[6] *Proc. Physic. Soc.*, 1964, **84**, 1001.
[7] *Trans. Faraday Soc.*, 1963, **59**, 344.

to free water molecules. Then the correlation factor is reasonable, but there is a complete contradiction between infra-red and dielectric results. Or the difference between ε_∞ in ice and in water is to be explained by some unknown effects (deformations?) and we have to explain why the correlation factor in water is $g = 1$.

The fourth points concerns difficulties in interpreting the intermolecular frequencies. There is just one frequency, about 160-180 cm^{-1}, that was observed in Raman spectra, in infra-red and in neutron scattering. Since it is not affected by isotopic substitution, it seems generally agreed that it is some kind of breathing frequency. Heinloth [1] has observed by neutron scattering the same band in ice. A band not affected by isotopic substitution and located at 60 cm^{-1} was observed by Bolla in Raman spectra and by neutron scattering. It was never observed in the infra-red, even where techniques as sensitive as those developed by Dr. Gebbie [2] at the N.P.L. were used.

The last point deals with the bands at 475 and 685 cm^{-1}. Cartwright and Rubens observed the 475 cm^{-1} band in the i.-r., but this was not confirmed by the later authors,[3] i.e., it exists only in the Raman spectrum. The 685 cm^{-1} is active in both Raman and i.-r. spectra, but it was not observed by Palevsky in his neutron scattering experiments; this is surprising especially as it must be due to movements of the hydrogens. Indeed, these two bands are sensitive to substitution of D to H and must therefore be attributed to the libration of the water molecule; the first band corresponds then to the libration around the binary axis. But this is in contradiction with theory: the calculations show that 500 cm^{-1} corresponds to the frequency of libration around an axis perpendicular to the molecular plane. Perhaps the i.-r. spectra should be re-examined very carefully in this region.

Finally, a suggestion concerning a possible exploitation of i.-r. results on the OD band presented by Franck, who traced the precise form of this band at different temperatures. From the accurate measurements of the radial distribution functions given by Narten, Danford and Levy, we know the average distances at these various temperatures. We can hence correlate the average distance between neighbouring molecules with the average frequency for the same compound. It may then be possible to deduce from the intensity distribution of the i.-r.-band the distribution of distances between first neighbours that could be compared with the radial distribution function. A significant disagreement could be an indication of orientational deviations of water molecules of the ideal positions as the intermolecular distance increases.

Prof. H. S. Frank (*University of Pittsburgh and Mellon Institute*) said: It should be made clear in connection with the discussion of water as a mixture that no one that I know of considers that there are any free H_2O molecules in the liquid, if by this is meant free in the sense in which a molecule is free in the dilute vapour. Otherwise, there is not much definiteness, among the propments of a mixture model, regarding the " species " of which water is a mixture. Of the species that may be present, the only kind which seems relatively easy to characterize would consist of clusters or chunks of 4-co-ordinated molecules connected by bonds which are in some sense space-filling, as in ice or in the clathrate frameworks. That such a structure should support vibrational motions similar to the 220 cm^{-1} " hindered translation " motion, or to the 400-1000 cm^{-1} " hindered rotation ", or librational motions in ice seems reasonable, and that the intensities of the Raman or i.-r. bands which these lead to should decrease with rising temperature, also seems reasonable in a general

[1] *Congr. Slow Neutron Scattering* (Vienna, 1960).
[2] *Nature*, 1966, **210**, 790.
[3] *Optics and Spectr.*, 1961, **10**, 278; *J. Opt. Soc. Amer.*, 1966, **56**, 64.

sense. What it is that disappears, however, and what is produced when this happens, is far from obvious. I have not seen, e.g., any clear description of the normal modes of the ice lattice with which the 220 cm^{-1} frequency or the 400-1000 cm^{-1} frequencies are associated. In what sort of configuration space (e.g., a space of how many dimensions) must a representative point move to trace out these vibrations, and what sort of trace does it describe? Walrafen considers that the vibrating unit has C_{2v} symmetry and suggests that it be visualized as a tetrahedron of $5H_2O$ molecules—a central one and the 4 that are bonded around it. This, according to him, is also the unit in liquid water, and when the intensity of the 175 cm^{-1} Raman band falls off with rising temperature (those in the librational range fall off at just the same rate) he thinks that the bonds break co-operatively, leaving " unbonded ", but densely packed H_2O molecules.

It would appear, however, that another possibility exists, and that what disappears with rising temperature is not in the first instance the bonding, but rather the symmetry of the vibrating groups, and that this causes the disappearance of the scattering power at the frequencies under discussion. Even in that case, however, it would be necessary to recognize two kinds of material—not, now, " bonded " and " unbonded ", but the kind that can scatter at the intermolecular frequencies and the kind that cannot—and this, again, would conflict with the " uniform average " models.

Some people believe in the existence of some " covalent " contribution or " mutual distortion " contribution to the electron configuration in a hydrogen bond, and that the magnitude of this contribution is expected to fall off sharply as the bond bends—i.e., as the O—H line bends out of the O - - - O line of centres. When this bending angle is small, the symmetry of the co-ordination pattern is favoured, as in ice. When the bending gets greater it might well do so co-operatively, and the " electrostatic plus covalent " environment of the O—H stretch might be replaced by an " electrostatic only " environment corresponding, perhaps, to the cosine-law energetic interaction between water dipoles postulated by Pople.[1] In that case, the two species might be " covalent H-bond water ", and " Pople water ", both characterized by large cohesive energy densities, but spectroscopically distinguishable. If they were sharply distinguishable in the overtone and combination absorptions this would also account for Luck's observations.

Dr. Brigitte Eckstein (*Aachen*) said: A poly-paracrystalline structure, analogous to the " flickering cluster model " postulated by Luck for water, was found to be an admissible model for molten metals near their melting point. Thus assuming a strong connection between the structure of the melt and the corresponding crystal, various thermal properties of molten metals were calculated, based on a generalized theory of lattice defects in crystals.[2] These calculated values of thermal expansion, compressibility, atomic heat, entropy of fusion and atomic radii agree within plausible limits with the experimental data. A theoretically derived linear relation between melting temperature and activation energy of the vacancies in the crystal also is in good agreement with the experimental findings. Furthermore, the model gives a good understanding of the mechanisms of melting and of crystallization from the melt.[3]

Notwithstanding their great chemical difference, water and molten metals exhibit corresponding structural features. Probably the model will prove admissible for other simple melts, and it may be taken as a basis for a comprehensive theory of condensed matter.

[1] Pople, *Proc. Roy. Soc. A*, 1951, **205**, 163.
[2] B. Eckstein, *Phys. stat. sol.*, 1967, **20**, 83.
[3] B. Eckstein and H. Peibst, *Rev. hautes temp.*, in press.

Radiation Scattering Studies of the Structure and Transport Properties of Liquids*

By P. A. Egelstaff

Solid State Physics Division, A.E.R.E., Harwell

Received 27th January, 1967

The use of radiation scattering techniques to study problems in liquid state physics has several advantages. These include the detailed nature of the information which can be obtained on structural and dynamical properties, the definiteness of the interpretation which may be given to the data and the exceedingly wide range in types of sample and experimental circumstances which can be covered. To deploy these advantages to the full requires powerful sources and special experimental methods which are still under development. A review is given of the techniques and theory of radiation scattering work emphasizing the relation between neutron and X-ray methods. The possibility of studying electron shell movements by measuring the ratio of X-ray to neutron intensities is discussed.

Broadly, the kinds of experiment fall into two classes: (a) those in which the scattered intensity is measured as a function of the momentum transferred ($\hbar Q$) by the radiation to the specimen, giving the function $S(Q)$, and (b) those in which the intensity is measured as a function of both the momentum transferred and the energy transferred ($\hbar \omega$) by the radiation to the specimen, giving the function $S(Q,\omega)$. The former are used to obtain information on atomic positions while the latter experiments (coupled with the former) are used to derive dynamical information. Both kinds are discussed and some methods of interpreting $S(Q)$ and $S(Q,\omega)$ are described.

Co-operative modes of motion in the system, particularly for wavelengths of the order of the spacing between atoms, may be observed as peaks in $S(Q,\omega)$. The relationship between this kind of data and general transport coefficients is discussed. In addition, the spectral density of the velocity correlation function for atomic motions may be obtained from $S(Q,\omega)$, and this relationship is outlined. This paper covers only the theoretical background to the field.

1. INTRODUCTION

The mathematical discussion of the properties of condensed matter is normally carried out by considering either the system as a continuum or the details of the atomic structure and the atomic motions. It is the aim of radiation scattering work to derive information concerning the latter properties. Then it is possible (in principle) to construct a theory which will predict the macroscopic properties employed in the continuum discussion. Considerable progress has been made for crystalline solids, the primary reason being that the structure and the thermal motion can be separated and that the structure is simplified through the symmetry relations of the crystal lattice. Unfortunately this is not the case for glasses and liquids, where the various pictures tend to get inter-mingled. In these cases it is important that a detailed understanding of the microscopic behaviour is attempted to enhance theoretical progress. With molecular structures the positions and the vibrational

---

* This paper is a condensation of the following papers by the author:

Microscopic Transport Phenomena in Liquids, *Reports Progr. Physics*, 1966, **29**, 333.

Radiation Scattering Data on Liquid Metals (Conference on Properties of Liquid Metals, Brookhaven National Lab., Sept. 1966).

Use of Pulsed Neutron Sources in Solid and Liquid State Physics, (I.A.E.A. Panel on Research Applications of Pulsed Reactors, Dubna, July 1966).

modes of the different atoms can be studied and discussed theoretically with some confidence, but the interaction of large molecules is a difficult problem and the experimental material provided by radiation scattering work is of great value.

It is important to study the structure and thermal motion of the different classes of condensed matter throughout the entire diagram of state, which represents a formidable task. There are many different types of radiation available and each may be used in a number of ways. Owing to the wide variety of samples, temperatures, pressures and techniques which one would like to cover, one must consider the detailed properties of each technique to see where it may be best used. While the general use of radiation scattering methods to study condensed matter cannot be questioned, it is possible to discuss the detailed use of these methods for any given problem. Part 5 of this paper is therefore devoted to comments on the different available techniques, their features and the experimental ranges which may be covered.

Other sections of the paper are concerned with the results which may be obtained with these methods. It will be emphasized that the data obtained by neutron and X-ray methods should be combined into one larger interpretation covering the nuclear and electronic positions (and motions) taken separately. In an ideal case it would be possible to separate out these two kinds of effects from the complete data. Such a development, however, requires significant improvements in the quality of the experimental data, and it is therefore necessary to examine each source of error and attempt to minimize it. For this reason some of the major sources of error are listed in §3 and brief comments made; this list is illustrative rather than exhaustive. Only the theoretical background will be discussed here, for experimental data reference should be made to the papers cited above.

2. NUCLEAR SCATTERING OF NEUTRONS

The cross-section for the scattering of radiation by matter has already been described (e.g., Van Hove,[1] Sjolander.[2]) The method followed is (essentially) the same for each kind of radiation, differing only in detail, and consequently we give the principal steps which are followed in one case only, viz., the scattering of thermal neutrons. The steps in the cross-section calculation are as follows. (a) For low energy (thermal) neutrons only s-wave nuclear scattering is important (because the neutron wavelength $\gg$ nuclear diameter). (b) s-Wave scattering cross-sections (for an isolated stationary nucleus) are spherically symmetric and independent of neutron energy. (c) The nuclear size is much smaller ($\sim 10^{-5}$) than the neutron wavelength and the interatomic distances hence for the ith nuclear potential $V(r)$ (after Fermi),

$$V_i(r) = \text{constant } \delta(\mathbf{r}-\mathbf{r}_i)$$

where r_i is the position of the ith nucleus. (d) The overall perturbation is small (i.e., although the nuclear potential is strong within its range, the intensity scattered by a single nucleus is small) so that the Born approximation is valid. (e) The constant in (c) is determined by fitting the Born cross-section for epi-thermal neutrons to the measured " free atom " cross-section. This constant is written as $2\pi\hbar^2 b/m$, where m is the neutron mass and b is a length (positive for hard-sphere scattering). [The free-atom cross-section is equal to $4\pi(A/A+1)^2 b^2$, where A is the ratio of nuclear to neutron mass.] (f) Therefore, the scattering amplitude for a system of N atoms is

$$a(\theta) \sum_{n=1}^{N} b_n \int d\mathbf{r}' \exp(i\mathbf{Q}\cdot\mathbf{r}')\delta(\mathbf{r}'-\mathbf{r}_n).$$

The essential point is that the scattering amplitude in the Born approximation is expressed as the Fourier transform of the scattering potential. Since the scattering potential consists of a δ-function point for each atom we get a Fourier transform of the atomic positions. (g) If the atoms are moving about on a timescale comparable with the value of $\hbar/\delta E$ in table 1 below, then the time dependence of the atomic positions given in the formula in (f) above must be considered. Essentially the radiation suffers a Doppler shift, which is taken into account by considering the energy spectrum of the scattered radiation. The condition for the conservation of energy may be represented as a Fourier transformation, so that the scattering amplitude involves a second Fourier transformation between time and energy. In this case it depends upon both the momentum and the energy transferred in the scattering process.

One final point is that an observable cross-section is given by the square of the scattering amplitude and hence it involves a product of two terms of the kind given under (f). The two δ-functions give a "pair correlation function", so that the cross-section finally becomes the Fourier transformation of the pair correlation given at eqn. (1) [the form of the correlation function shown here applies to a classical system, eqn. (1) and (2) are taken from Van Hove [1] to whom this formalism is due],

$$G(r,\tau) = \frac{1}{N} \sum_{n,m} <\delta(\mathbf{r}+\mathbf{R}_n(0)-\mathbf{r}_m(\tau))> \qquad (1)$$

where $r_n(\tau)$ is the position of the nth atom at time τ. The cross-section is

$$\frac{d^2\sigma}{d\Omega d\omega} = b^2 \frac{k}{k_0} \int \exp i(\mathbf{Q} \cdot \mathbf{r} - \omega\tau) \{G(r,\tau)-\rho\} d\mathbf{r}d\tau, \qquad (2)$$

where b is the scattering length for a single bound atom and ρ is the mean density.

It is possible to consider two types of correlation function. Referring to the first is the case for which the two atoms n and m are the same in eqn. (1); this self-correlation function describes the average motion of a single atom. The second type is that for which n and m may have any values, so that all atoms in the system are considered. This function is the coherent correlation function. The techniques which are used in neutron scattering work to separate the G function into these two parts depend upon the fact that different isotopes of the same element may have different scattering lengths and also that different spin states of the same isotope may have different scattering lengths. Thus the separation depends upon making measurements with the system in the same chemical state but in different nuclear states.

3. SCATTERING OF X-RADIATION BY ELECTRONS

For electromagnetic radiation the scattering potential is no longer a δ-function as given under (c) above. Instead, it is a distributed potential having a size equal to that of the atom, so that we take a convolution of the atomic positions with the potential for a single atom. Since the Fourier transform of a convolution is a product of transforms, it is necessary to calculate the Fourier transform of the scattering potential for a single atom (i.e., the "form factor") which appears as a factor in the observed scattering amplitude. This point may be understood by considering the general formula for the scattering of X-rays by a liquid written in terms of an electronic space time correlation function.[2] This function is defined by eqn. (3):

$$G_e(\mathbf{r},\tau) = \frac{1}{N} \int d\mathbf{r}' <\rho(\mathbf{r}',0) \cdot \rho(\mathbf{r}'+\mathbf{r},\tau)>, \qquad (3)$$

where $\rho(r,\tau) = \sum_1 \rho_1^o(r-R_1(\tau),\tau)$ is the electron density distribution and $\rho_1^o(t,\tau)$ is the electron density around the lth nucleus. In terms of this correlation function the cross-section may be written down in a form, eqn. (4) analogous to eqn. (2):

$$\left(\frac{d^2\sigma}{d\Omega d\omega}\right)_{X\text{-}rays} = \frac{B}{2\pi} \int \exp\left[i(\mathbf{Q} \cdot \mathbf{r} - \omega\tau)\right] \cdot \{G_e(\mathbf{r},\tau) - \rho_e\} d\mathbf{r} d\tau, \quad (4)$$

where B is a constant and ρ_e is the mean electron density.

Two assumptions are now made in the standard theory: (a) the internal states of the atoms are not excited by the X-ray scattering process, and (b) the electrons follow the nuclei rigidly. These two assumptions allow the cross-section to be rewritten as

$$\left(\frac{d^2\sigma}{d\Omega d\omega}\right)_{X\text{-}rays} = \frac{B}{2\pi} |F(Q)|^2 \int \exp\left[i(\mathbf{Q} \cdot \mathbf{r} - \omega\tau)\right] \cdot \{G(\mathbf{r},t) - \rho\} d\mathbf{r} d\tau, \quad (5)$$

where

$$F(Q) = \int \exp(iQ \cdot r) \cdot <\rho^\circ(r)> dr.$$

This form is similar to eqn. (2) for neutrons and if the form factor $F(Q)$ is known then it is possible to derive from X-ray scattering the nuclear space time correlation function $G(r,\tau)$.

In X-ray scattering work the energy resolution is insufficient to allow the spectrum of the scattered X-rays to be determined. For this reason the X-ray scattering cross-section consists of an integral over all possible values of ω. Provided Q is constant it is then possible to write down the expression obtained by integrating over ω in either eqn. (2) or (5). This result is

$$S(Q) = \int S(Q,\omega) d\omega = \int d\omega \int \exp\left[i(\mathbf{Q} \cdot \mathbf{r} - \omega\tau)\right] \cdot \{G(\mathbf{r},t) - \rho\} d\mathbf{r} dt$$

$$= \int \exp(iQ \cdot \mathbf{r}) \cdot \{G(\mathbf{r},0) - \rho\} d\mathbf{r}, \quad (6)$$

where $S(Q)$ is defined by this equation. The usual pair distribution function $g(r)$ is given by $g(r) = [G(r,0)/\rho] - \delta(r)$.

A physical description of these equations may be given for a classical system. In eqn. (1) the space time correlation function G is the probability of finding an atom at the position $(\mathbf{r},\tau)$ given that there was an atom at the origin at time $\tau = 0$. Thus the co-ordinates $\mathbf{r}$ and τ are the relative positions of two atoms. The function $G(r,\tau)$ may be divided into two parts: (i) a "self" term which describes the motion of the atom which was at the origin at time $t = 0$, and hence the "self" diffusion of this atom, and (ii) a "distinct" term describes the average motion of all other atoms relative to this origin. Eqn. (3) represents the same function for electrons. It describes the probability of finding electron density at the position (r,τ) given that there was (effectively) an electron at the origin at time $\tau = 0$. In eqn. (5) this probability was factored assuming that the electrons are associated with particular nuclei, and consequently the major effects are to be expressed through the positions and motions of the nuclei. Assumptions (a) and (b) given before eqn. (5) ensure that the only time dependence appearing in the G function (eqn. (3)) arises from the motion of the nuclei. In this case the correlation function for $\tau = 0$ is a convolution of the nuclear pair distribution function with a function representing the average electron cloud around a nucleus. The Fourier transformation of this convolution yields the expression (5) for the X-ray cross-section.

Previously, the function $F(Q)$ was known by calculation to much greater accuracy than $S(Q)$, so that it was natural to use the X-ray data to derive $S(Q)$. But $S(Q)$

may be now obtained by neutron scattering to an accuracy of $\sim 2\%$, which is significantly smaller than the error of the calculated $|F(Q)|^2$. As a result it is desirable to reverse the normal procedure and to divide $S(Q)$ out of the X-ray data leaving $|F(Q)|^2$ as the experimentally determined quantity. The theoretical uncertainty in $F(Q)$ arises from three causes: (i) the free atom values of $F(Q)$ are uncertain to $\sim 5\%$; (ii) the free atom value is modified in the liquid environment by several %; (iii) the thermal motion modifies $F(Q)$, and in particular introduces a small temperature dependence.

Item (iii) arises when the electron cloud moves relative to the nucleus. Some evidence for this occurrence may be obtained by considering crystalline solids, particularly materials containing easily polarizable atoms. Cochran [3] has shown that in order to describe the thermal motion of the atoms in these crystals it is necessary to assume that a shell of outer electrons moves with respect to the nucleus and the core electrons. This view has been substantiated by a number of experiments on phonon dispersion curves.

For liquids (both metallic and non-metallic) this effect should occur, although its magnitude is hard to calculate. A several % effect is likely at Q values corresponding to the size of an atom, i.e., $Q \sim 2Q_0$. Unfortunately, such an effect renders the usual X-ray theory invalid, but since the effect is small an approximation may be made to give

$$(d\sigma/d\Omega) \simeq P(Q) \cdot S(Q), \qquad (7)$$

where $P(Q)$ is the Fourier transform of an average electron distribution including perturbations due to effects (i)-(iii) above.

The function $S(Q)$ is measured by recording the intensity of scattered X-rays or neutrons as a function of the momentum transfer, i.e.,

$$\left. \begin{array}{l} \dfrac{1}{A}\left(\dfrac{d\sigma}{d\Omega}\right)_{\text{neutrons}} = S(Q) \\[1em] \dfrac{1}{B}\left(\dfrac{d\sigma}{d\Omega}\right)_{\text{X-rays}} = P(Q) \cdot S(Q) \end{array} \right\} \qquad (8)$$

By dividing the neutron result into the X-ray result it is possible to measure the function $P(Q)$. This requires measurements of high accuracy ($\sim 1\%$) which is just possible using modern techniques. In this way the positions of both the nuclei and the electrons can be studied.

4. GENERAL TRANSPORT COEFFICIENTS

The phenomena occurring in a liquid are both frequency (ω) and wave number (Q) dependent. In this section we define a transport coefficient which depends upon these parameters, and then discuss its relation to a measurable function (e.g., the scattering law) of the same parameters.

Chester [4] uses phenomenological equations to define the general transport coefficient as follows. We imagine a system in equilibrium which is disturbed by a number v of different driving forces $\mathbf{X}_v$, and then suppose this causes a number μ of currents $\mathbf{J}_\mu$ to flow in the system; in general all currents are assumed to be produced by each driving force. Now we assume a linear relation between the forces and the currents, and also, that the driving forces and the coefficients in this relation are position and time dependent. The general linear relationship is

$$\mathbf{J}_\mu(r,t) = \sum_v \int_{-\infty}^t dt' \int dr' Z_{\mu v}(r-r', t-t') \mathbf{X}_v(r',t'). \qquad (9)$$

Fourier transformation of this equation gives the general transport coefficient $Z_{\mu\nu}(Q,\omega)$, i.e.,

$$\mathbf{J}_\mu(Q,\omega) = \sum_\nu Z_{\mu\nu}(Q,\omega) \cdot \mathbf{X}_\nu(Q,\omega). \tag{10}$$

In order to measure this quantity it is necessary to relate it to $S(Q,\omega)$. For this purpose, matter transport modes u are defined by

$$u = A(Q,\omega) \exp[i(\mathbf{Q} \cdot \mathbf{r} - \omega\tau)] \text{ for } \tau > 0 \quad (a)$$

$$A(Q,\omega) = \frac{2kT}{\hbar} \int_0^\infty d\tau \int d\mathbf{r} \, \text{Imag } G(\mathbf{r},\tau) \exp[i(\mathbf{Q} \cdot \mathbf{r} - \omega\tau)] \quad (b) \tag{11}$$

It may be shown that for a classical liquid,

$$S(Q,\omega) = \tfrac{1}{2}\pi \int \exp[i(\mathbf{Q} \cdot \mathbf{r} - \omega\tau)] G(\mathbf{r},\tau) d\mathbf{r} d\tau$$

$$= \frac{1}{\pi} \frac{\text{Imag } A(Q,\omega)}{\omega}, \tag{12}$$

so that the amplitude of these modes may be calculated from measurements of $S(Q,\omega)$.

A further simplification is achieved if it is assumed that the matter transport mode satisfies a simple differential equation.[4] For the self term of $G(r,\tau)$ it is assumed that the diffusion equation is appropriate, i.e.,

$$\left(\frac{kT}{MD(Q,\omega)} \frac{\partial}{\partial t} - \frac{kT}{M} \nabla^2\right) u_s = Q^2 \frac{kT}{M} \exp[i(\mathbf{Q} \cdot \mathbf{r} - \omega\tau)], \tag{13}$$

where $D(Q,\omega)$ is a general diffusion coefficient. For the complete $G(r,\tau)$ it is assumed that the longitudinal wave equation is appropriate, or

$$\left(\frac{\partial^2}{\partial \tau^2} - \frac{V(Q,\omega)}{\rho} \frac{\partial}{\partial \tau} \nabla^2 - \frac{kT}{MS(Q)} \nabla^2\right) u = \frac{Q^2 kT}{M} \exp[i(\mathbf{Q} \cdot \mathbf{r} - \omega\tau)], \tag{14}$$

where $V(Q,\omega)$ is a general viscosity coefficient. Because of these definitions the macroscopic diffusion D and viscosity coefficients are given in terms of $D(Q,\omega)$ and $V(Q,\omega)$ by

$$D = \frac{2}{\pi} \{[\text{real } D(Q,\omega)]_{Q \to 0}\}_{\omega \to 0}, \tag{15}$$

$$\tfrac{4}{3}\eta + \zeta = \frac{2}{\pi} \{[\text{real } V(Q,\omega)]_{Q \to 0}\}_{\omega \to 0}, \tag{16}$$

where η and ζ are the shear and bulk viscosities respectively. If eqn. (11a) is substituted into (13) and (14) the relationships

$$A_s(Q,\omega) = \frac{Q^2 D(Q,\omega)}{Q^2 D(Q,\omega) - i\omega}, \tag{17a}$$

$$A(Q,\omega) = \frac{kTQ^2/M}{kTQ^2/MS(Q) - i\omega Q^2 V(Q,\omega) - \omega^2}, \tag{17b}$$

are found. These relationships when combined with (11) enable some experimental data on $D(Q,\omega)$ and $V(Q,\omega)$ to be obtained. In particular, the spectral density of the velocity correlation function is equal to $D(0,\omega)$ and the spectral density of the (z,z) stress correlation function is equal to $V(0,\omega)$.

5. COMPARISON OF DIFFERENT RADIATION SCATTERING METHODS

In the discussion leading to the formula in item 2(f) it has been implicitly assumed that the atomic positions are all determined at the same instant of time. If this were the case the cross-section would correspond to the intensity integrated over all possible values of the energy transfer (i.e., $S(Q)$). On the other hand, if elastic scattering only were measured the correlation function would give the time-averaged positions of the atoms. Thus there are three kinds of measurement which may be made. These are (a) the intensity as a function of the momentum and the energy transferred in the scattering process: this gives the most complete information on the positions and motions of the atoms in the scattering system. (b) The intensity

TABLE 1.—FUNCTIONS ACCESSIBLE BY RADIATION SCATTERING METHODS

self G-function	coherent G-function
incoherent neutron scattering	coherent neutron scattering
neutron absorption	electron scattering
γ-ray absorption/emission	X-ray or γ-ray scattering
	Raman or Brillouin scattering

as a function of the momentum transfer but integrated over all possible energy transfers: this gives the Fourier transform of a "snapshot" of the atomic positions. (c) The intensity as a function of the momentum transfer considering only elastic scattering: this gives the Fourier transformation of the time averaged atomic positions and is used to study crystal structures.

For liquids measurement, (c) is not strictly possible as there is no elastic scattering, but where a quasi-elastic peak is well defined it has some meaning. Only measurements (a) and (b) are considered here, and they may be subdivided into measurements of the self and coherent G-functions. Table 1 shows the functions accessible to the different techniques.

TABLE 2.—WAVELENGTH AND ENERGY OF VARIOUS TYPES OF RADIATION

radiation	wavelength Å	approximate momentum $= 2\pi/\lambda$ Å^{-1}	energy	approximate δE (expt.), e\
neutrons	1→10	2	100→1 meV	10^{-3}—10^{-1}
electrons	0·1	0·1	~50 keV	wide
X-rays	0·5→2	1	~10 keV	wide
γ-rays	1→2	1	~10 keV	~10^{-9}
light (Raman)	4,000	10^{-3}	~10 eV	~10^{-1}
light (Brillouin)	4,000	10^{-3}	~10 eV	~10^{-5}

δE (expt) indicates the energy transfer range which may be covered.

These different types of radiation may be compared through their wavelength and energy. Table 2 shows the typical values of wavelength and energy for neutrons, electrons and several kinds of electromagnetic radiation.

In order to measure the correlation function in detail it is necessary for the wavelengths to be of the order of magnitude of interatomic distances in condensed matter, and for the energy resolution to be of the order of the widths and spacings of the energy levels in condensed matter. From table 2, neutrons satisfy these requirements, while the other kinds of radiation satisfy either one or the other of the two requirements. This is further illustrated in fig. 1, which is a momentum-energy space diagram.

The range of the variables ($\omega - Q$) covered in typical measurements by each technique has been marked, and through the use of a logarithmic scale the axes have been placed at positions equal to the reciprocal spacing and energy levels of atoms in a typical liquid.

To conclude this section some of the difficulties which are met in measuring $d\sigma/d\Omega$ for X-rays and neutrons are discussed. First, there is the question of whether Q is constant in a measurement at constant angle. For neutrons suffering an energy transfer of $\hbar\omega$ the difference ΔQ in Q compared to elastic scattering is

$$\Delta Q/Q = -\hbar\omega/E_0 \qquad (17)$$

This ratio may be as high as $\frac{1}{2}$, (e.g., for scattering by molecular liquids) while for

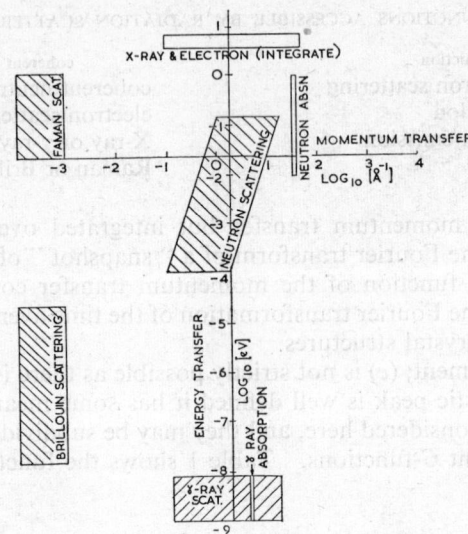

Fig. 1.—Momentum energy space diagram showing the regions covered by different types of radiation: the axes are drawn at values of the momentum corresponding to the reciprocal atomic spacing and the energy corresponding to room temperature. Broadly, the optical scattering experiments follow the energy axis. Scattering of X-rays and electrons involve an integration over the energy transfer and provides information as a function of one variable (momentum) only. Neutron absorption experiments occupy a very small region and involve relatively poor resolution. The only technique which covers the central portion of momentum and energy space is that of neutron scattering.

other cases it may be as low as 1/30, (e.g., liquid metals). In the former case a correction is necessary if the proper value for $S(Q)$ is to be derived by eqn. (6). Corrections of this kind have been considered by Placzek[6] and discussed in detail by Enderby,[7] while Ascarelli and Caglioti[8] suggest using a model in order to derive the correct value. Placzek's method consists of writing an expansion for the cross-section in terms of the energy moments of $S(Q,\omega)$. One difficulty is that his expansion converges rather slowly but if a model is used, as proposed by Ascarelli and Caglioti,[8] the correction obtained may depend upon the details of the model. Indeed, this method seems to lead to corrections which are too large. There is no real alternative to using a higher incident energy thereby making ΔQ small, and probably the incident energy normally employed (0·07 eV) is too low in some instances.

The second item to consider is the form factor for X-rays. This has been calculated for the elements, and tables are normally used giving its value (e.g., MacGillavry and Rieck [9] and Cromer.[10]) In addition these values may be checked by measurements of the scattering by crystals. The normal practice is to apply these $|F(Q)|^2$ values to each case without considering individual corrections. The error on this procedure is difficult to estimate (see §3) but may be of the order of 5 %. It is difficult to determine the X-ray scattered intensity at a large value of Q where the form factor is small and the corresponding intensity low. Several background effects occur which have to be calculated and subtracted (e.g., Compton scattering etc.). This introduces an intensity threshold and hence a limiting value of Q beyond which the data are unreliable.

Another problem is that of multiple scattering; this is more severe in neutron work than in X-rays because of the higher absorption cross-sections for X-rays. Vineyard [11] and by Cocking and Heard,[12] have shown that for successful neutron experiments it is necessary to use samples which are both thin and divided into segments. The correction for multiple scattering may then be readily calculated and accurate corrections made to the data. Absorption corrections, on the other hand, are large for X-rays but usually small for neutrons. Paalman and Pings [13] have discussed this correction for X-rays.

A problem in both kinds of experiments is that of low angle scattering, which is necessary in order to make observations at low values of Q. For X-rays this is particularly difficult, because the high absorption cross-sections means that a reflection geometry has to be used at glancing angles. Moreover, since the X-rays do not penetrate a liquid metal metal significantly the condition of the surface is important in that case. In contrast, low-angle scattering of neutrons is more straightforward because the neutrons can be transmitted through the body of the sample due to the low absorption cross-section. On the other hand, the corrections for multiple scattering are large because the probability of two large angle scatterings contributing to intensity in the forward direction is high.

The normalization of scattering data to give an absolute scale is important. Reference to eqn. (8) shows that it is the constants A and B which are required. One procedure with X-rays has been to use the fact that $S(Q) = 1$ at large values of Q. However, this method is difficult to carry out accurately because the X-ray intensity is small at high values of Q. Thus, where the assumption is most accurate the measurements are most inaccurate. Another method is to normalize to the density, but the integration cannot be done accurately. For these reasons, trial and error techniques are frequently used in X-ray work.

With neutrons the normalization procedure is more straightforward, because the scattering by a single nucleus is isotropic and, for incoherent neutron scattering, the intensity is uniform as a function of angle. Fortunately, vanadium is an almost purely incoherent scattering material and therefore forms an ideal calibration substance. By measuring the ratio of scattered intensities from the sample and from vanadium it is possible to obtain an accurate absolute scale for each measured point. This technique has been employed recently (e.g., Egelstaff et al.[14]) and the accuracy obtained was about 5 %. However, there is no reason, in principle, why accuracies of about 1 % should not be achieved using this method.

The above features are the major experimental problems met in X-ray and neutron scattering work. There are usually other problems associated with the particular equipment used for the experiment or with the particular sample and the temperature range employed. The overall accuracy which is now obtainable is several percent in each case, and it is just becoming feasible to make comparisons between the two kinds of data. The above discussion applies to measurements of $S(Q)$, but many of the points apply to the neutron measurements of $S(Q,\omega)$ also.

6. DISCUSSION

The radiation scattering data as a function of both momentum and energy transfer have been discussed, with the aim to bring out those features which are relevant to recent experiments and to indicate some of the directions which future research might take. By combining the neutron and X-ray data, it may be possible to obtain information on the electron distribution in the liquid. Such work may well form a valuable goal for high precision measurements. The limited data that are available at the present time suggest that a real effect may be observed.

In addition, the direct analysis of the function $S(Q)$ to test certain hypotheses, such as that of the uniform expansion of liquids, should be emphasized. With crystalline solids it is sometimes advantageous to discuss the behaviour of the Fourier components of the density (i.e., of $S(Q)$). Amongst the data which may be obtained in this way are the range of crystalline order, the spacing and number of atoms in a given direction, the expansion coefficient for the lattice itself and the size of the thermal cloud. A similar approach may be of value for liquids. For example, the temperature variation of the position of the first two peaks in $S(Q)$ may be compared to the change in the cube root of the density. For a perfect anharmonic lattice the expansion of $g(r)$ would be uniform and thus the contraction of $S(Q)$ would be proportional to $\rho^{\frac{1}{3}}$. Other models of interest include the harmonic lattice, where the positions are fixed but the peaks fall and the valleys rise to give a constant density, and the hard-sphere gas where the main peak position is fixed and the amplitude scales as the density to a first approximation. The experimental data show that the movements of the peak positions are neither proportional to $\rho^{\frac{1}{3}}$ nor independent of ρ, thereby indicating that the liquid differs from these extremes in that some spacings change at a different rate than others. More data on $S(Q)$ are needed over wider ranges of the parameter Q and over wider temperature ranges, and that these data should be measured to an accuracy of approximately 1 %.

An understanding of microscopic transport phenomena in liquids requires a theoretical and experimental examination of modes of motion over wide ranges of frequency and wave number. The background for discussing such effects has been developed in terms of correlation functions. With the aid of new radiation scattering techniques it is now possible to measure some parts of the correlation functions used in the theory. For temperatures near to the melting point temperature, such experiments have shown that the high-frequency behaviour of the liquid state is similar to the solid state in accordance with the visco-elastic theory of Frenkel and others.

Of the various functions now accessible experimentally the velocity correlation function has been studied in most detail, and in particular the shape of the spectral density has been determined. The time for a diffusive step has been measured for a number of systems and found to be fairly independent of material and temperature ($\sim 1\text{-}2 \times 10^{-12}$ sec). It seems to give one basic relaxation time in liquids. It is not the shortest time involved since the damping of high-frequency modes is necessarily faster and gives another basic relaxation time for energy reorganization of $\sim \frac{1}{3}$ of the former time. Thus, both these relaxation times (and the ordering time mentioned below) are $ca.$ 10^{-12} sec.

Experiments aimed at the study of the correlation functions used to discuss viscosity and heat conduction are limited so far. The spectral density of the correlation function for viscosity has the same general shape as that for diffusion, but the magnitude and detailed shape are different. High-frequency co-operative modes of motion have been observed in several liquids, the maximum frequency being similar to that for the corresponding solid. With present techniques it is difficult to identify the polarization of the mode, but significant evidence can be advanced for the existence of high-frequency transverse modes in simple liquids. A detailed theoretical discussion of all these points is awaited, since existing treatments are mainly phenomenological.

A simple picture of a dense liquid may be built up from recent structural and dynamic studies. It is postulated that a liquid is trying to be a structurally ordered material but that at any instant a significant number of atoms is in flight between ordered sites. The time in flight (i.e., the time to reach the ordered site) is relatively long so that by the time the " in-flight " atoms have completed their move some of the atoms previously ordered have started to diffuse to new sites. Atoms within the range of order in the liquid will contribute to the high-frequency vibrational modes, but atoms outside the range of order appear to be (relative to the local atoms) stationary. On this model, these are the atoms which are in flight, so that the flight time has to be longer than the time for a wave to propagate over the range of order; the role of the "on-site " and " in-flight " atoms can be interchanged. An equivalent argument is to say that the atoms outside the range of order appear stationary because many Fourier (frequency) components become important which from the central limit theorem leads to non-propagating motion. The lifetime for such motion can be measured and is found to be $\sim 10^{-12}$ sec; on this model this is the time it takes for an atom to move to an ordered site.

In the future it will be necessary to extend experimental measurements to wide ranges of temperature and pressure, essentially covering the whole of the liquid region of the condensed state. The complementary nature of the different radiation scattering techniques should be exploited and the results combined with measurements using the low-frequency techniques (ultrasonics, etc.). In this way, more detailed information on the correlation functions can be obtained and a more detailed understanding of the liquid state achieved.

[1] L. Van Hove, *Physic. Rev.*, 1954, **95**, 249.
[2] A. Sjolander, *Phonons and Phonon Interactions*, ed. T. A. Bak (W. A. Benjamin, New York, 1964), p. 76.
[3] W. Cochran, *Proc. Roy. Soc. A*, 1959, **253**, 260.
[4] G. Chester, *Reports Progr. Physics* 1963, **26**, 411.
[5] P. A. Egelstaff, *Reports Progr. Physics*, 1966, **29**, 333.
[6] G. Placzek, *Physic. Rev.*, 1952, **86**, 377.
[7] J. E. Enderby, *The Physics of Simple Liquids*, ed. J. S. Rowlinson, G. S. Rushbrooke and H. N. V. Temperley (North Holland Publishing Co., 1966).
[8] P. Ascarelli and G. Caglioti, *Nuovo. Cim.*, 1966, **X43**, 375.
[9] C. H. MacGillavry and G. D. Rieck, *International Tables for X-ray Crystallography, III. Physical and Chemical Tables* (The Kynoch Press, Birmingham, 1962).
[10] D. T. Cromer, *Acta Cryst.*, 1965, **19**, 224.
[11] G. Vineyard, *Physic. Rev.*, 1954, **96**, 93.
[12] S. J. Cocking and C. R. T. Heard, *AERE Report R* 5016, 1965 (H.M.S.O., London).
[13] H. H. Paalman and C. J. Pings, *J. Appl. Physics*, 1962, **33**, 2635.
[14] P. A. Egelstaff, C. Duffill, V. S. Rainey, J. E. Enderby and D. M. North, *Physics Letts.*, 1966, **21**, 286.

Brillouin Scattering of Neutrons from Liquids

By B. Dorner, Th. Plesser and H. Stiller

Kernforschungsanlage, Institut für Neutronenphysik, 517 Jülich, W.-Germany

Received 16th January, 1967

Inelastic coherent neutron scattering is called Brillouin scattering, if the momentum transferred to the scattering system is entirely taken up by collective particle motions. With this scattering, single excited states of such motions can be observed in polycrystals and in liquids in a similar way as in single crystals, provided the measurements are not too much contaminated by multiple scattering processes combining Bragg and inelastic scattering. Liquid and solid lead are investigated in this way. The comparison of the measured dispersion laws shows that at 340°C, for frequencies between 6.4×10^{11} and 2.3×10^{12} sec^{-1} and wavelengths between 7 and 21 Å, sound waves propagate in the liquid by the same mechanism as in the solid. The contaminating double scattering is predominantly determined by maxima in the distribution of frequencies of collective motions. The observed positions of such maxima indicate that transverse modes exist also in the liquid.

As in liquids the kinetic energy of the particles is comparable to the interactions, the liquid phase cannot be extrapolated to an ideal state, for which the N-particle-problem may be reduced to a number of one-particle-problems. As a consequence the liquid state can be described rigorously for two limiting regions of space and time only; for very small times and distances, where all systems behave like a gas, and for very large times and distances, where the equations of hydrodynamics are valid. For the intermediate region the most successful descriptions are based not on first principles but on models, which require experimental tests. As the region of interest extends from approximately 1 to, say, 100 Å and from approximately 10^{-14} to 10^{-10} sec, inelastic scattering of slow neutrons appears to be the most promising tool for such tests; neutron radiation taken from a reactor contains wavelengths between 0.5 and approximately 20 Å and frequencies between 10^{14} and 5×10^{10} sec^{-1}.* As has been shown by Van Hove [1] the most detailed information is obtained with coherent inelastic scattering. The measurable distribution, $S_{coh}(\mathbf{K},\omega)$, of momentum transfers $\hbar\mathbf{K}$ and energy transfers $\hbar\omega$ is related to a time-dependent correlation function $G(\mathbf{r},t) = G_s(\mathbf{r},t) + G_d(\mathbf{r},t)$ by

$$S_{coh}(\mathbf{K},\omega) = \frac{N}{2\pi} \int G(\mathbf{r},t) \exp\left[i(\mathbf{K}\mathbf{r} - \omega t)\right] d\mathbf{r} dt. \qquad (1)$$

$G_s(\mathbf{r},t)$ is the self-correlation, $G_d(\mathbf{r},t)$ is the pair-correlation,

$$\mathbf{K} = \mathbf{k}_0 - \mathbf{k}_1; \quad K^2 = k_0^2 + k_1^2 - 2k_0 k_1 \cos\phi, \qquad (2)$$

$$\pm\hbar\omega = \frac{\hbar^2}{2m}(k_0^2 - k_1^2), \qquad (3)$$

where $\mathbf{k}_0$ is the wave vector of the incoming, $\mathbf{k}_1$ the wave vector of the scattered neutrons, ϕ the scattering angle, m the neutron mass.

*In contrast, electromagnetic radiation of 10 Å wavelength has a frequency of 3×10^{17} sec^{-1}.

In general, a description of the space-time behaviour of a many-particle system can be tested in a direct way, if the relation, $\omega(\mathbf{q})$, between the frequencies ω and the wave vectors $\mathbf{q}$ of collective particle motions can be predicted from the description on the one hand and measured on the other hand. For instance, if the propagation of sound in a liquid is phenomenologically described by a wave equation for the imaginary part of $G(\mathbf{r},t)$,* one obtains [3]:

$$S_{\mathrm{coh}}^{(s)}(\mathbf{K},\omega) \alpha \frac{N\hbar^2 K^2}{4\pi 2m}\left(1+\coth\frac{\hbar\omega}{2k_B T}\right)\left\{\frac{1}{(\omega-\omega_s)^2+(2\tau_s)^{-2}}+\frac{1}{(\omega+\omega_s)^2+(2\tau_s)^{-2}}\right\}, \quad (4)$$

with

$$\omega_s(q) = \frac{1}{2\tau_s(q)}\{[2qc_s\tau_s(q)]^2-1\}^{\frac{1}{2}}. \quad (5)$$

The index s specifies the modes,† τ is a relaxation time, c the sound velocity. Under the assumption, that the dynamical behaviour of the liquid can be described by some single τ, the dependence of this quantity on q may be calculated from models.‡ The models then can be tested by experimental determinations of $\omega_s(q)$.

For the evaluation of corresponding experiments, the most difficult problem lies in the relation between $\mathbf{q}$ and $\mathbf{K}$. With single crystals such a relation is given by the interference condition $\mathbf{K} = 2\pi\mathbf{g} - \mathbf{q}$, where $2\pi\mathbf{g}$ is a reciprocal lattice vector and $\hbar\mathbf{g}$ is the momentum, which in the scattering process is taken up by the crystal without energy change. For liquid systems the question, which part of the momentum transfer $\hbar\mathbf{K}$ may be taken up by the system without energy change, is extremely complicated. To answer it, one needs a detailed knowledge of the liquid structure and also of the distribution of frequencies in the system.[6] These difficulties are avoided if the measurement is carried out within a region of reciprocal space where with certainty no momentum is transferred without energy change, i.e., in a region corresponding to the innermost Brillouin zone of a solid; we call this scattering Brillouin scattering.§ The interference condition is then

$$\mathbf{K} = -\mathbf{q}, \quad (6)$$

i.e., we have five equations, eqn. (3), (5) and (6), for five experimental variables, namely, ω, $\mathbf{q}$ and one quantity varied in the experiment, for instance $|\mathbf{k}_1|$; we obtain within $S_{\mathrm{coh}}(\mathbf{K},\omega)$ peaks at those values of the variables which satisfy those equations. By repeating the measurement with changed values for quantities kept constant within the single experiment, for instance with different ϕ, we can determine certain branches of $\omega_s(q)$, viz., those branches, where according to eqn. (6) $\mathbf{K}$ is parallel to $\mathbf{q}$ (for instance, the longitudinal mode for sound waves).

In contrast to experiments, in which the system takes up some average momentum without energy change, with Brillouin scattering each peak in $S_{\mathrm{coh}}(\mathbf{K},\omega)$ represents a single excited state of collective particle motions. Hence, with this method the only averaging, which enters the experiment, concerns a possible directional dependence

---

*Im$G(\mathbf{r},t)$ represents the density disturbance [2]; it is related to the real part of $G(\mathbf{r},t)$ by the fluctuation-dissipation theorem.

† The three values of s for acoustic motions are usually referred to as "longitudinal" and "transverse", respectively. A more precise meaning is discussed in ref. (4).

‡ From hydrodynamics one has [5]: $\tau^{-1} = Aq^2$, where A is a constant given by the transport coefficients. For a strict validity of hydrodynamics the transport coefficients should not depend on q or ω.

§ Because with inelastic interference scattering of light [7] one always measures within the innermost Brillouin-zone, since, in contrast to neutron scattering, the total momentum transfer is nearly zero compare the first footnote ref. (1)).

of $\omega_s(\mathbf{q})$, i.e., some possible short-range elastic anisotropy of the system. Even if such an anisotropy exists, this averaging is not very serious [4] from an experimental point of view, e.g. for the accuracy of frequency determinations or for the determina-

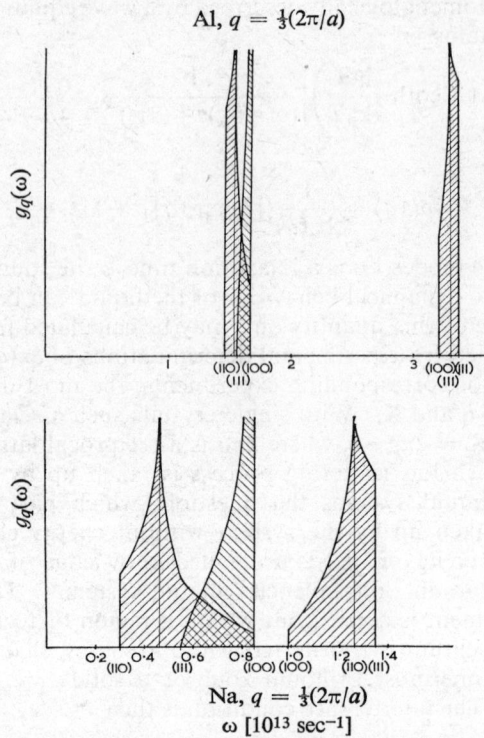

FIG. 1.—Directional distribution of sound wave frequencies for fixed wave number $|q|$, $g_q(\omega)$, for polycrystalline Al (small elastic anisotropy) and polycrystalline Na (large anisotropy). The second and the third peak fall into symmetry directions. The first peak contains a mixture of modes; from ref. (4).

tion of lifetimes, as long as the short range order is of sufficiently high symmetry, because then the directional distribution of frequencies is sharply peaked. This is shown in fig. 1.

EXPERIMENTAL

METHOD

Unfortunately, the simplicity of the experimental results obtained by measuring close to the origin of reciprocal space is paid for by small scattered intensities. The reasons are shown in fig. 2. The curves represent eqn. (2) and (3) after elimination of k_1 for several $E_0 = \hbar^2 k_0^2/2m$ and for scattering angles ϕ of 0 and 180°. The region, for which for liquid lead one may be certain that no momentum is taken up without energy change, is shaded in the figure. In order to stay within this region and to cross e.g., the line $\omega = cK$, one needs small k and large E_0 and, consequently, small ϕ. For small $|\mathbf{K}|$ the probability for excitation or de-excitation of collective motions is small (see e.g. ref. (8)). Small values of ϕ and large values of E_0 (with correspondingly small resolutions $\Delta E_0/E_0$) restrict the accessible solid angles.

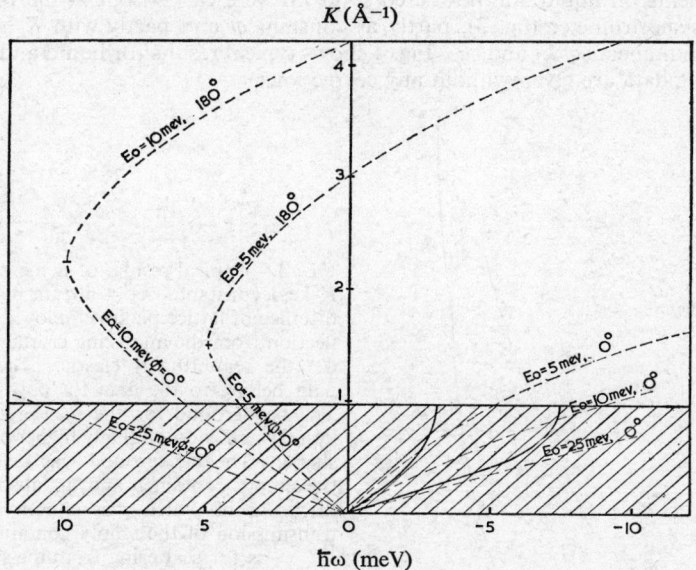

FIG. 2.—ω, K plane: the branches of the broken curves limit the regions accessible with fixed E_0. The shaded area is the region, where $2\pi g = 0$ in liquid lead. The solid curves represent dispersion branches for certain directions in crystalline lead. Values of ϕ are given on each curve.

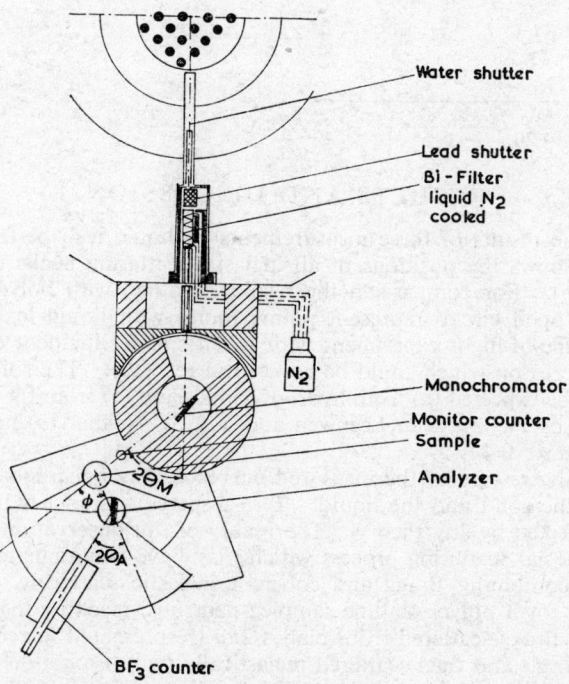

FIG. 3.—Schematic representation of the 3-axes-spectrometer at the FRJ-2 reactor. θ_M = Bragg angle of monochromizing single crystal, θ_A = Bragg angle analyzing crystal, ϕ = scattering angle. The three angles can be varied simultaneously and automatically.

Measurements on liquid and powdered solid Pb were carried out at the FRJ-2 reactor with a 3-axes-spectrometer (fig. 3), partly at constant ϕ and partly with K kept constant by varying simultaneously k_1 and ϕ. Fig. 4 shows typical results for liquid and polycrystalline lead. The data are given without any corrections.

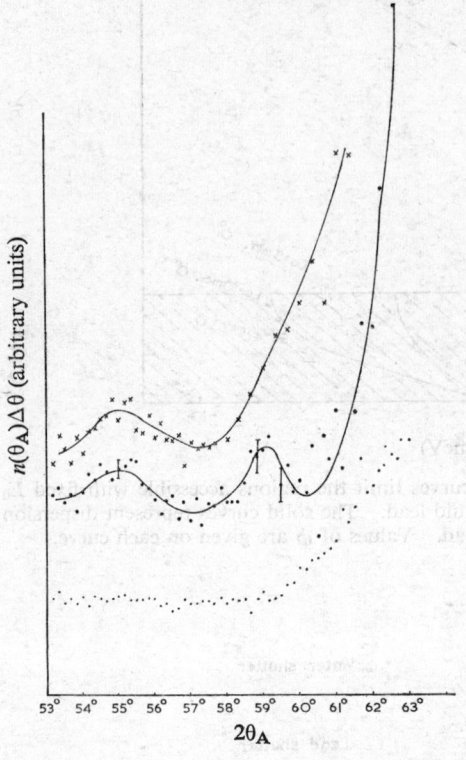

FIG. 4.—Typical results of a measurement with K kept constant. $k_1 = \pi(d \sin \theta_A)^{-1}$, with d = distance of lattice planes employed for Bragg reflection from the analyzing crystal. For $2\theta_A = 63°$ the scattering is elastic. The background data belong to the data for polycrystalline Pb. The background for the measurements on the liquid was correspondingly higher but of the same shape. The background was determined with the empty container and an absorber foil, the thickness of which was chosen such that the transmission of the empty container was 85 %, as for scattering from the sample.
$q = 0.6$ Å^{-1} $E_0 = 24.55$ meV
— ● — polycrystalline
— × — liquid
• background

RESULTS AND DISCUSSION

Fig. 5 shows the results of three measurements on liquid lead performed with K kept constant. Fig. 6 shows the positions of all inelastic scattering peaks observed,* i.e., the dispersion law $\omega_s(q)$. For comparison the results obtained with polycrystalline lead are also shown. The open circles represent points found with liquid lead by Cocking and Egelstaff [10] in a time-of-flight experiment with much smaller incident energy; the dotted curve indicates the region which could be covered in ref. (10). The solid curves represent dispersion laws to be expected (a) from hydrodynamics and (b) from the kinetic description of the liquid state by Nelkin, Van Leeuwen and Yip.[11] Neither (a) nor (b) can describe the observations for $q > 0.4$ Å^{-1}.

The most striking festure of the measured curves is the appearance of two dispersion branches in both the solid and the liquid. Two dispersion branches for sound waves in liquids are not expected by any theory. The reality of this observation was questioned by considering one special scattering process which may have contaminated the experiments, double scattering combining Bragg and coherent inelastic scattering. The possibility is illustrated in fig. 7 for a polycrystalline sample; neutrons, reaching the sample with wave vector $\mathbf{k}_0$, are first Bragg-scattered from planes $2\pi g$ (respresented in reciprocal space by a sphere of radius $|2\pi g|$) and then scattered inelastically (with excitation or de-excitation of

*Measurements not included in fig. 5 were done with different k_0 and with ϕ kept constant. Preliminary results, obtained with the same instrument at the BR-2 reactor in Mol, Belgium, have been reported already earlier.[9] They are included in fig. (6).

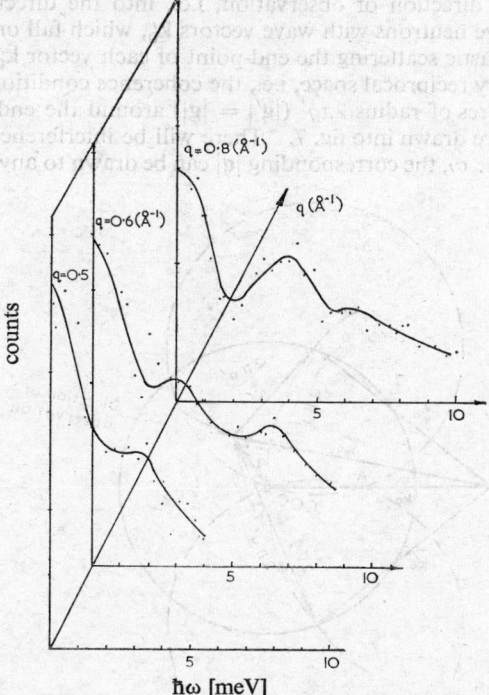

FIG. 5.—Results of three constant K measurements on liquid lead at $340(\pm 4)°C$. The background is subtracted. The intensity, $I(\hbar\omega)$, has been calculated from data, $n(\theta_A)$, as shown in fig. 4. The data are corrected for the reflectivity, $R(\theta_A)$, of the analyzing crystal.

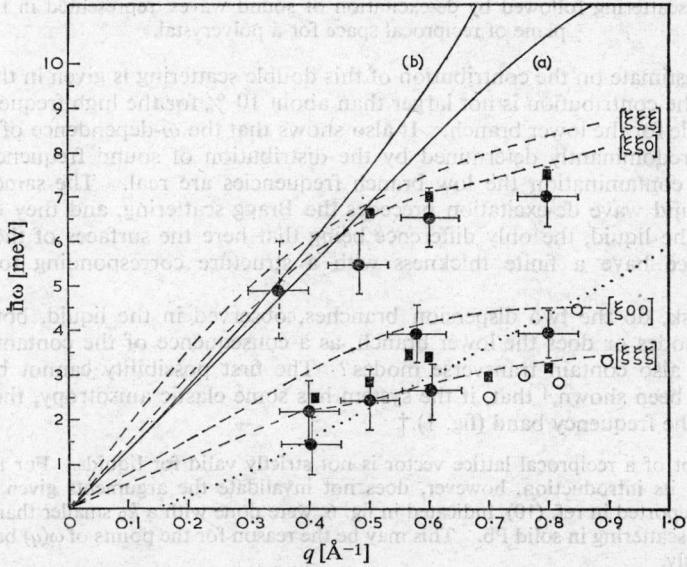

FIG. 6.—$\omega_s(q)$: ○, for liquid lead at 360°C (measured by Cocking and Egelstaff [10]; ●, for liquid lead at 340°C (present measurements); ■, for solid powdered lead at 20°C (present measurements); ----, measured in certain symmetry directions of a Pb single crystal [12]; ——, (a) from hydrodynamics: eqn. (5) with $c = 2100$ msec^{-1} and $1/\tau = (2\eta_1/3\rho)q^2$; $\eta_1 = 2.58$ centipoise; the terms involving η_2 and the heat conductivity are neglected, (b) from the gas-like model of Bhatnagar et al.[13] compare also ref. (11); .... limits the region, which could be covered with the measurements.[10]

sound waves) into the direction of observation, i.e., into the direction of k_1. After the Bragg scattering we have neutrons with wave vectors k'_0, which fall on to a cone around k_0. For the succeeding inelastic scattering the end-point of each vector k'_0 can be considered as the origin of a secondary reciprocal space, i.e., the coherence condition $K' = k'_0 - k_1 = 2\pi g' - q$ now refers to spheres of radius $2\pi g'$ ($|g'| = |g|$) around the end-points of the vectors k'_0; two such spheres are drawn into fig. 7. There will be interference scattering, whenever for some k_1, i.e. for some ω, the corresponding $|q|$ can be drawn to any one or several of such

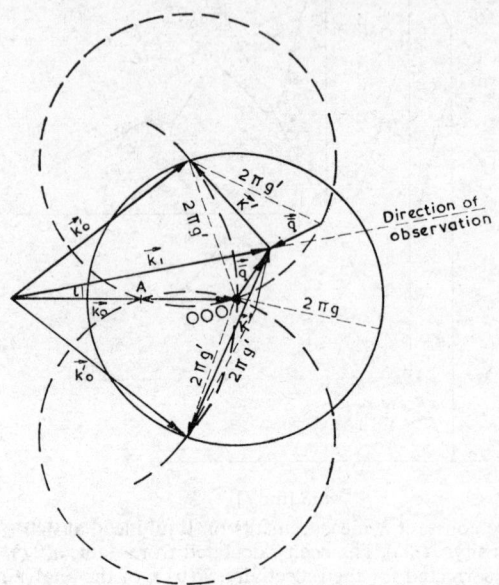

FIG. 7.—Bragg scattering followed by de-excitation of sound waves, represented in the scattering plane of reciprocal space for a polycrystal.

spheres. An estimate on the contribution of this double scattering is given in the appendix. It shows that the contribution is not larger than about 10 % for the high frequency branch, but considerable for the lower branch. It also shows that the ω-dependence of this double scattering is predominantly determined by the distribution of sound frequencies; hence, even with this contamination the low branch frequencies are real. The same arguments hold if the sound wave de-excitation precedes the Bragg scattering, and they qualitatively also hold for the liquid, the only difference being that here the surfaces of the spheres in reciprocal space have a finite thickness with a structure corresponding to diffraction patterns.*

We now ask, do the two dispersion branches, observed in the liquid, both represent longitudinal modes or does the lower branch, as a consequence of the contamination discussed above, also contain transverse modes? The first possibility cannot be excluded, because it has been shown,[4] that, if the system has some elastic anisotropy, the modes are mixed within the frequency band (fig. 1).†

*The concept of a reciprocal lattice vector is not strictly valid for liquids. For the q-ω-range here considered its introduction, however, does not invalidate the arguments given above. The measurements reported in ref. (10), indicated in fig. 6, were done with a k_0 smaller than the limiting value for Bragg scattering in solid Pb. This may be the reason for the points of $\omega(q)$ being observed for liquid Pb only.

†Another explanation for a low-frequency branch has been suggested by Egelstaff [14]: strong interactions among sound waves might give rise to secondary interference maxima called "pseudo-phonons". For the present case, however, we believe this explanation to be unlikely, because the lower branch covers too high frequency values, and because it does not exhibit strong temperature dependence.

The intensity of scattering with sound wave excitation or de-excitation is proportional to c^{-2}, if c is the phase velocity of the sound wave (see e.g. ref. (8)). If L_1 is the relative amount of longitudinal modes on the upper branch, L_2 the relative amount on the lower branch ($L_1+L_2 = 1$), D_1 the relative contribution of double scattering on the upper, D_2 on the lower branch, then the ratio of scattered intensity for the lower branch to scattered intensity for the upper branch should be

(a) if only longitudinal modes exist

$$\left(\frac{I_2}{I_1}\right)_a = \left(\frac{C_1}{C_2}\right)^2 \frac{L_2}{L_1},$$

(b) if both modes exist

$$\left(\frac{I_2}{I_1}\right)_b = \left(\frac{C_1}{C_2}\right)^2 \frac{L_2(1-D_2)+D_2}{(1-L_2)(1-D_1)+D_1}.$$

As $L_2 \ll 1$,* we expect $(I_2/I_1)_a < 1$, and $(I_2/I_1)_b \simeq (C_1/C_2)^2 D_2 \simeq 2.5$, with $D_2 = 0.65$ as estimated in the appendix. Since experimentally I_2/I_1 was always found to be greater than 1 (compare fig. 5), we conclude that transverse modes are contributing.†

The comparison of the dispersion of sound waves in liquid and in solid powdered lead thus shows, that at 340°C for frequencies between 6.4×10^{11} and 2.3×10^{12} sec^{-1} and wavelengths between 7 and 21 Å, liquid lead behaves much like a solid. The relaxation times for all modes are considerably longer than 5×10^{-11} sec. $q \simeq 0.4$ Å^{-1} ($\lambda \simeq 16$ Å) is certainly an upper limit for the validity of hydrodynamics. Unfortunately the experimental results cannot yet be compared to the most detailed solid-like model for the liquid state suggested so far, the model of Singwi,[16] because the dependence of $\omega_s(q)$ or of τ on the parameter R, which in this model characterizes the mean extension of regions of solid-like dynamics, has not yet been worked out.

The authors thank Dr T. Springer and Mr K. Mika for helpful discussions, Mr F. Fredel for his continuous assistance with the experiments and Mr K. W. Kutzbach for his help with the computer calculations.

APPENDIX

The relative amount of double scattering, combining Bragg scattering from a set of planes $2\pi g$ and de-excitation of sound waves of frequency ω, is

$$D_{K,g}(\omega) = \frac{P_B(g)P_2(g',q,\omega)}{P_B(g)P_2(g',q,\omega)+P_1(K,\omega)}, \quad (A.1)$$

where $P_B(g)$ is the probability for Bragg reflection from planes $2\pi g$, $P_1(K,\omega)$ is the probability for de-excitation of sound waves with $g = 0$, $P_2(g',q,\omega)$ the probability for sound wave de-excitation following Bragg scattering. For a liquid, $P_B(g)$ is to be replaced by the relative intensity of a diffraction peak. We have (see ref. (8) and (17))

$$P_1(K,\omega) = Nda^2 \frac{k_1}{k_0} \frac{k_B T}{2Mc^2} \exp(-u^2 K^2), \quad (A.2)$$

and (see ref. (6)),

$$P_2(g',q,\omega) = Nda^2 \frac{k_1}{k_0} \frac{\pi k_B T}{4MV} \frac{F_{g'}}{g'q} \sum_{i,s} \frac{f(\omega_s)}{\omega_s^2} \frac{(\mathbf{e}_s \cdot \mathbf{K}'_i)^2}{K'_i} \exp(-u^2 K_i'^2). \quad (A.3)$$

N is the density of scattering atoms, d is the sample thickness, a the coherent scattering amplitude, c the phase velocity of sound waves, M the mass of the scattering atoms, V the volume of the unit cell, $F_{g'}$ the multiplicity of planes $2\pi g'$, $f(\omega_s)$ the spectrum of sound wave

*For $q < 0.4$ Å^{-1}, L_2 has been estimated to be approximately 0.16.
†An indication for transverse modes also has been found [15] in liquid Al.

frequencies, e_s a unit vector in the direction of the wave polarization, u^2 the mean square displacement of the atoms. The summation goes over all spheres, for which $2\pi g' - q = K'_i$ is fulfilled (see fig. 7). As P_2 must go to zero for $q \to 0$ (elastic scattering), $K'_i = 2\pi g'$ must be excluded from the summation.

Since the origins of the K'_i are uniformly distributed on the base circle of the cone around k_0, the sum over i in (A.3) can be written as an integral. We write

$$K'^2 = k_0^2 + k_1^2 - 2k_0 k_1 \cos \phi_0 (\cos \phi + \sin \phi \tan \eta),$$

where ϕ_0 is the angle between k_0 and k'_0, ϕ the scattering angle, η the angle between k_0 and the projection of k'_0 on the plane of fig. 7 (the scattering plane). Thus

$$\frac{1}{q} \sum_{i,s} \ldots \to 2 \sum_s \frac{f(\omega_s)}{\omega_s^2 q} \frac{1}{2\pi} \int_{\eta(K'_{min})}^{\eta(K'_{max})} \frac{(\tan^2 \phi_0 - \tan^2 \eta)^{-\frac{1}{2}}}{\cos^2 \eta} \frac{(e_s \cdot K'(\eta))^2}{K'(\eta)}$$
$$\times \exp[-u^2 K'^2(\eta)] d\eta, \qquad (A.4)$$

where $K'_{min} = 2\pi g' - q$, as long as $K'(\phi_0) > 2\pi g' - q$, and $K'_{min} = K'(\phi_0)$, if $K'_{min} \leqslant 2\pi g' - q$, and correspondingly $K'_{max} = 2\pi g' + q$, as long as $K'(-\phi_0) < 2\pi g' + q$, and $K'_{max} = K'(-\phi_0)$ otherwise. The expression (A.4) has been evaluated numerically, with $e_s = q/q$ for the high frequency branch, which is entirely longitudinal, and with $(e_s \cdot K')^2 = K'^2 \{1 - (q \cdot K')^2/q^2 K'^2\}$ for the lower branch, i.e., neglecting the small contribution of longitudinal modes to the lower branches (compare ref. (4)), and with $f(\omega_s)$ and $q(\omega_s)$ taken from an approximate isotropic dispersion $\omega_s = c_s(q + b_s q^2)$. As a function of ω, (A.4) is predominantly determined by $f(\omega_s)$.

$P_B(g)$ was determined experimentally as the elastic scattering density per sterradian on the base circle of the cone around k_0, $\frac{2\pi g'}{k_0} \frac{1}{I_0} \frac{\Delta I(g)}{\Delta \psi}$, where $\Delta \psi$ is the vertical collimator divergence. For $2\pi g = 2.18 \text{ Å}^{-1}$ it was found $P_B = 1.6 \times 10^{-3}$. After summing with appropriate weights over all sets of planes, from which reflectioas are possible with the incident wave length, we obtain for $K = 0.6 \text{ Å}^{-1}$: for the high frequency branch ($\hbar \omega = 7 \text{ meV}$), $D_1 \lesssim 0.1$, and for the low frequency branch ($\hbar \omega = 3.2 \text{ meV}$) $D_2 \lesssim 0.65$.

[1] L. Van Hove, *Physic. Rev.*, 1954, **95**, 249.
[2] L. Van Hove, *Physica*, 1958, **24**, 404.
[3] T. Ruijgrok, *Physica*, 1963, **29**, 617.
[4] K. Mika, to be published.
[5] L. Kadanoff and P. Martin, *Ann. Physics.*, 1963, **24**, 419.
[6] P. Egelstaff, *A.E.R.E. N/R 1164* (1953).
[7] see e.g., J. Frenkel, *Kinetische Theorie der Flüssigkeiten* (VEB 1957), chap. VI, 9.
[8] A. Sjoelander, *Arkiv Fysik*, 1958, **14**, 315.
[9] B. Dorner, Th. Plesser and H. Stiller, *Physica*, 1965, **31**, 1537.
[10] S. Cocking and P. Egelstaff, *Physic. Letters*, 1965, **16**, 130.
[11] M. Nelkin, J. Van Leeuwen and S. Yip, *Inel. Scatt. of Neutrons*, 1965, vol. II, p. 35.
[12] B. Brockhouse, T. Arase, G. Caglioti, K. Rao and A. Woods, *Physic. Rev.* 1962, **128**, 1099.
[13] P. Bhatnagar, E. Gross and M. Krook, *Physic Rev.*, 1954, **94**, 511.
[14] P. Egelstaff, *Lattice Dynamics* (Pergamon Press 1964), p. 699.
[15] K. Larsson, U. Dahlborg and D. Jovic, *Inel. Scatt. of Neutrons*, 1965, vol. II, p. 117.
[16] K. Singwi, *Physic. Rev.*, A, 1964, **136**, 969; *Physica*, 1965, **31**, 1257.
[17] B. Dorner, *Report Jül.-412-NP*, 1966.

Neutron Scattering Spectroscopy of Liquids

By B. K. Aldred, R. C. Eden and J. W. White

Physical Chemistry Laboratory, South Parks Road, Oxford

Received 3rd March 1967

This paper reports the use of atomic substitution techiques in some preliminary studies by neutron scattering spectroscopy of the microscopic transport properties of acetic acid and methanol. By making selective substitution of deuterium and fluorine for the hydrogens in the CH_3 and OH groups of these molecules, the separate contributions to the quantized and diffusive motions of each have been analyzed. This is possible because the substitution of fluorine or deuterium for hydrogen in a particular group reduces the scattering cross-section of that group by at least an order of magnitude. The contributions of the group motions to the neutron scattering spectrum are then correspondingly reduced. In the inelastic scattering region of the spectrum we have been able to make vibrational assignments as a result. In the quasi-elastic region the intensity and angular dependence of the scattering show a marked dependency on the nature of the protons substituted. In this region the results have been analyzed by determining an effective molecular diffusion coefficient and by comparing this with values from bulk-phase studies. Particular attention has been devoted to the question of the extent to which intra-molecular hindered rotation contributes to the quasi-elastic scattering.

In neutron scattering spectroscopy a beam of thermal neutrons, which has been made almost monoenergetic by velocity selection, is allowed to fall on the sample. Neutrons in the beam are scattered, often through large angles, in collisions with moving atomic nuclei in the sample. The scattering collisions may be either elastic or inelastic. Elastic scattering alone would occur for a perfectly rigid scattering centre; inelastic processes follow when energy can be exchanged between the neutron and the scattering nucleus which is in motion. For molecules, this inelastic exchange of energy can occur with quantized motions, such as molecular vibrations and rotations, or with non-quantized diffusional motion in the liquid and gaseous states. Experimentally, neutron scattering spectra are recorded by analyzing the energies of all neutrons scattered over a particular angle by some method such as time of flight. In general, the spectra are recorded at several different angles of scattering (which correspond to different momentum transfers for the scattered neutron) and they may by divided up into a quasi-elastic and an inelastic region.

The technique thus resembles Raman scattering except that a beam of monoenergetic neutrons rather than photons is scattered by the moving molecules. There are some important differences, however, which make neutron studies, especially on liquids, of unique interest. These stem from the fundamental difference in mechanism between neutron and photon excitation of molecular motion and from the greatly different time scales involved in the neutron and in the photon "collision" with the scattering centre. In molecules, photon excitation of molecular vibrations occurs via the electrons in the molecules which transmit the electric disturbance to the charged nuclei and cause them to vibrate. Thus optical excitation invariably involves dipole and induced dipole selection rules. Neutron excitation by contrast occurs by the direct impact of the neutron and the scattering nucleus in the bond suffering excitation. A consequence of this direct method of stimulation is that not only can vibrational and rotational frequencies be determined as by optical means, but the absolute intensities of the bands concerned can be measured. Further deductions may follow this about the mean square amplitude of the motions concerned. Again, because the neutron velocity is much lower than that of light, its interaction time with the molecule during scattering is about 10^{-11} sec. This time is long enough for some liquid molecules to move so that Doppler broadening of the energy spectrum, even for elastically scattered neutrons occurs. This quasi-elastic scattering often leads to lines in the elastic region which are considerably broader than the energy spread of the incident neutron beam. The broadening is greatest the faster the relative motion between the scattering molecule and the neutron during the time of the scattering event. It is thus greatest at highest angles of scattering (largest momentum transfers) and for the most mobile liquids. As discussed below, the broadening is directly related to microdiffusion of the molecule and can sometimes be related to the bulk diffusion constant.

In the inelastic region information about molecular vibration and rotation frequencies (although not necessarily about their intensities) should be complementary to that from optical spectra. In some cases difficulties have been encountered [1] in achieving a synthesis between these two different sets of results. This has been partly because of difficulty in making unambiguous assignments of bands in the neutron spectrum to particular vibrating groups as the resolution in neutron spectroscopy is still lower than that in optical spectroscopy. The atomic substitution technique, reviewed for two groups of molecules in this paper, suggests a method of making more confident assignments. Secondly, there has been a considerable discussion [2,3] about whether the diffusion constants measured by neutron scattering observations in the quasi-elastic region are the same as those determined by tracer studies in the bulk phase. In general, the diffusion constants measured by neutrons have been greater than those measured in the bulk, and it has been suggested that since the neutron method measures diffusion over a very small distance (typically 1-2 Å) microdiffusional processes, such as hindered internal rotation, contribute to the transport of scattering nuclei during the "event". The atomic substitution technique for a molecule which contains two scattering centres, one susceptible to internal rotation and the other not, provides an experimental method of testing these views.

The time development of the displacement of a representative incoherent scattering centre in a moving molecule may be described by the space-time correlation function $G(r,t)$.[4] This function may be made sufficiently general to include both oscillatory and diffusive motions of the scattering atom. The time Fourier transform of this function gives the spectral density of the atomic motions as a function of frequency. This is the same spectral density function which is used to discuss the frequency dependence of nuclear and electron magnetic relaxation probabilities. The way in which the spectral density can be obtained from neutron measurements is illustrated below.

For an incident neutron spectrum with a narrow energy spread, the observed intensity distribution of the scattered neutrons as a function of the energy transfer ω and the solid angle of scatter Ω is identical to the differential scattering cross section $\partial^2\sigma/\partial\Omega\partial\omega$:

$$\frac{\partial^2\sigma}{\partial\Omega\partial\omega} = b^2 \frac{k}{k_0} \frac{1}{2\pi} \iint \exp\left(i(Q \cdot r - \omega t)\right) . G(r,t) dr dt. \tag{1}$$

Here b is the scattering length of the nucleus; k, k_0 are the scattered and incident wave vectors of the neutron respectively, $Q = k - k_0$ and is the momentum transfer in the collision, ω is the energy transferred in the collision, expressed in radians/sec, and $G(r,t)$ is the space-time correlation function describing the motion of the atom containing the scattering nucleus. It is a correlation function and is defined by eqn. (2):

$$G(r,t) = \frac{1}{N} \sum_{n,m} \langle \delta(r+r_n(0)-r_m(t)) \rangle \qquad (2)$$

In this expression, $r_n(t)$ is the position of the atom m at time t. The functional relationship between r and t may be simply sinusoidal as for a vibrator, or it may have a complicated form as for diffusive motions in liquids. Suitable expressions for $G(r,t)$ have been discussed by Larsson.[5] For convenience, the concept of a scattering law $S(Q,\omega)$ is introduced to describe the distribution of the intensity of scattering as a function of momentum transfer and energy transfer. This is defined from eqn. (1) in eqn. (3).

$$\partial^2 \sigma / \partial \Omega \partial \omega = b^2 k S(Q,\omega)/k_0 \qquad (3)$$

The scattering law defined in eqn. (3) is not symmetrical because the anti-Stokes scattering is more probable than the Stokes scattering of cold neutrons from samples at room temperature. The intensities of the Stokes and anti-Stokes regions are connected by a Boltzmann factor and so $S(Q,\omega)$ can be modified to a symmetrical scattering law, $\tilde{S}(Q,\omega)$ independent of populations, by extracting an exponential as in eqn. (4).

$$\frac{\partial^2 \sigma}{\partial \Omega \partial \omega} = b^2 \frac{k}{k_0} \exp -\left(\frac{\hbar \omega}{2kT}\right) \cdot \tilde{S}(Q,\omega). \qquad (4)$$

Each of the parent molecules considered in this paper has two incoherent scattering centres. If these centres have scattering lengths b_1 and b_2 then the differential scattering cross-section can be written as

$$\partial^2 \sigma / \partial \Omega \partial \omega = (k/k_0)[b_1^2 S_1(Q,\omega) + b_2^2 S_2(Q,\omega)]. \qquad (5)$$

There are no cross-terms so long as the scattering from each centre is incoherent and so long as ortho and para states for the two centre system have sufficiently close energies. Since the neutron scattering spectrum is the simple sum of the effects due to two independent scattering laws, whose relative importance is determined by the values of the b_1 and b_2, it is possible to make clear assignments by isotopic and atomic substitution. In our case we have been able to change the relative values of b_1 and b_2 (which are proportional to the square-root of the scattering cross-section) so that the substituted spectrum is largely derived from one or other of the two scattering laws. The changes produced by this device not only occur in the inelastic scattering region of the spectrum but also in the quasi-elastic region since the scattering law describes this as well.

The spectral density of the atomic motional frequencies as a function of frequency is a most suitable function for comparisons of neutron scattering, magnetic resonance and infra-red data since the neutron data overlap the regions of interest in both techniques. This function may be obtained from values of the reduced scattering law defined in eqn. (4), by finding the limit defined in eqn. (6):

$$f(\omega) = \text{const.} \, \omega^2 \lim_{Q \to 0} (S(Q,\omega)/Q^2) \qquad (6)$$

The limit chosen in this expression is the optical limit of zero momentum transfer.

For liquids a number of models have been proposed to describe the molecular motions and hence to provide values of $S(Q\omega)$. Using these it is possible to analyze the shape and angular dependence of the quasi-elastic region of the spectrum to obtain the diffusion coefficients associated with a particular scattering centre. The various models have been discussed by Larsson [5, 6] and Sjolander.[7] For a molecule undergoing simple diffusion the differential scattering cross section is given by eqn. (7):

$$\frac{\partial^2 \sigma}{\partial \Omega \partial \omega} = \text{const.} \frac{\exp(-x^2 Q^2) D Q^2}{(DQ^2)^2 + \omega^2}, \tag{7}$$

where Q^2 is the momentum transfer squared, ω^2 is the energy transfer squared, D is the diffusion constant defined by Fick's law and x^2 is a Debye-Waller factor from which it is possible to obtain the amplitude of the motion giving rise to diffusion.[5] The energy width of the quasi-elastic region for a liquid which obeys simple diffusion (eqn. (7)), should increase linearly with momentum transfer squared, as shown by eqn. (8):

$$\Delta E = 2\hbar D Q^2 \tag{8}$$

where $\hbar$ is Planck's constant divided by 2π.

EXPERIMENTAL

The experiments were carried out using the cold neutron time-of-flight spectrometer on the DIDO reactor at A.E.R.E. Harwell. This has been described by Harris et al.[8] and is shown diagramatically in fig. 1. Thermal neutrons from the moderator of the reactor are passed into a liquid hydrogen moderator, 3 in. diam. and 2 in. long, which reduced their

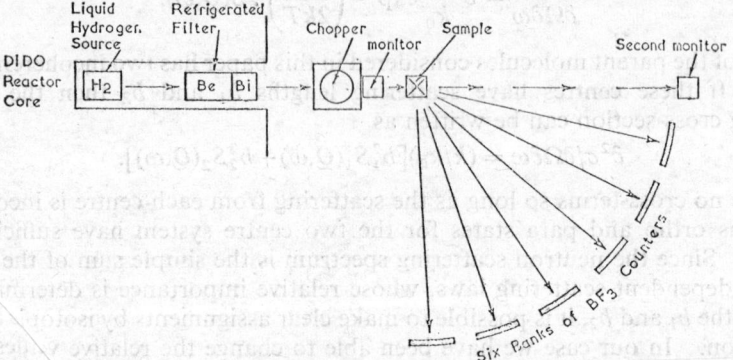

FIG. 1.—Schematic diagram of the cold neutron scattering spectrometer on the DIDO reactor at Harwell. For the experiments described here the chopper was set to pass 5·3 Å neutrons.

energy to a Maxwell-Boltzmann distribution about 30°K. Any fast neutrons unchanged by this process are removed from the beam by passing it through a filter of beryllium and bismuth cooled in liquid-nitrogen. The beam then passes to a rotating chopper which has the dual function of pulsing the beam and also transmitting only neutrons which have a defined small range of velocities. The velocities of the neutrons passed are determined by the curvature of the slots in the rotor and by its spinning speed. The sample is inclined at 45° to the neutron beam and the scattered neutrons are collected in boron trifluoride counters placed at distances of 1·2 m from the sample and at 8 angles ranging from 5 to 90° of inclination from the incident neutron beam. In these experiments the time of flight of the scattered neutrons from the sample to each of the detectors is measured. The neutron scattering spectrum built up from each counter is therefore a plot of the number of neutrons arriving at the counter as a function of their time of flight from the sample.

The chopper was set to deliver bursts of monokinetic neutrons every 2,760 μsec. The energy of these neutrons was such that they had a wavelength of 5·3 Å. The incident neutrons had a wavelength spread of 0·6 Å, which corresponds to a resolution for the experiment of about 6 cm⁻¹. All spectra were normalized to a run using vanadium. A typical run consisted of two samples and the vanadium standard being cycled through the beam with counting periods of 20 min per sample. The total running time for good counting statistics over the whole neutron scattering spectrum was generally 1-2 days. Care was taken to use thin samples so that at no time did the scattering exceed 15 %. This procedure minimizes double scattering of the same neutron and so all peaks in the spectra may be attributed to single scattering processes.

The acetic acids used in these experiments were carefully distilled several times to give the correct boiling point. The deuterated compounds were obtained from Merck, Sharp and Dohme Limited, and their nuclear magnetic resonance spectra were run to make sure that the deuteration was complete. As no peaks due to mixed deuteration were visible in any of the samples, it was concluded that deuteration was at least 99·5 % complete.

RESULTS

ACETIC ACIDS

The neutron scattering spectra from carefully dried and purified acetic and trifluoro-acetic acid were recorded using the spectrometer described above. The spectra for the two materials at 20°C and at scattering angles of 20 and 90° to the

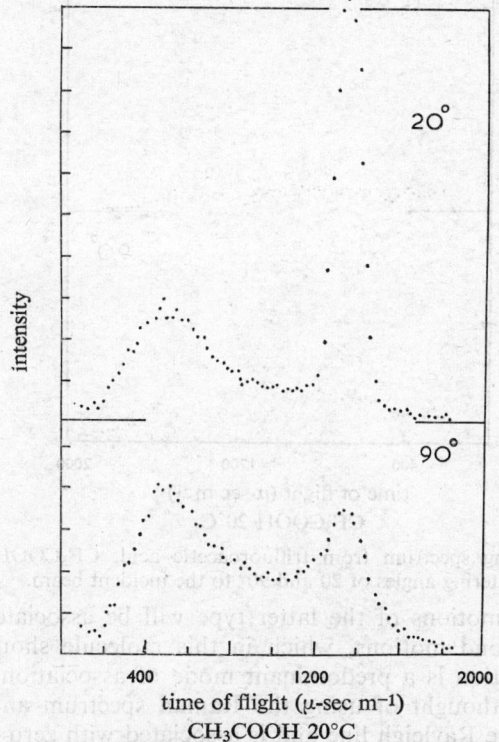

FIG. 2.—Neutron scattering spectrum from acetic acid, CH_3COOH, at 290°K and at scattering angles of 20 and 90° to the incident beam.

incident neutron beam, are shown in fig. 2 and 3. The substitution of fluorine (scattering cross-section 4 barns) for hydrogen (scattering cross-section approximately 80 barns) produces marked changes in both the inelastic region of the spectrum at short times of flight, and also in the elastic region.

INELASTIC REGION

Since the sample temperature is 20°C, the dominant inelastic scattering process is one whereby the neutrons gain energy in collisions with the molecules. The inelastic scattering region then appears at shorter times of flight than the elastic region. In the spectra shown in fig. 2 and 3 little energy loss spectrum is observed because the incident neutrons have such low energies.

Acetic acid shows a broad maximum at about 500 μsec/m in the inelastic region. This has a long tail to lower energy transfers which extends right into the quasi-elastic region at about 1,350 μsec/m. In this general region there are bands corresponding to quantized motions of both the CH_3 group and OH group in the molecule.

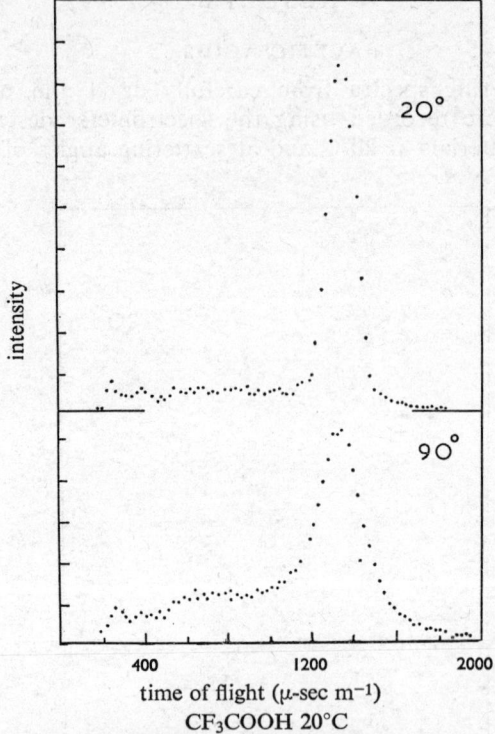

FIG. 3.—Neutron scattering spectrum from trifluoroacetic acid, CF_3COOH, at 290°K and at scattering angles of 20 and 90° to the incident beam.

The lowest frequency motions of the latter type will be associated with the intermolecular hydrogen bond motions, which in this molecule should be reasonably simple as dimer formation is a predominant mode of association. For simplicity, the spectrum may be thought of using the Raman spectrum analogy; the elastic peak corresponds to the Rayleigh line and is associated with zero energy transfer in the scattering process. The large inelastic feature at about 500 μsec/m corresponds to an optical excitation frequency of about 155 cm^{-1}. The present experiment therefore measures the lowest energy motions of acetic acid. The spectrum cuts off at about 800 cm^{-1}, where thermal population of excited vibrational states becomes inadequate to provide enough scattering intensity in these energy gain experiments. The angular dependence of the intensity in the inelastic region is characteristic of solid-like behaviour. Treating the vibrational motion associated with the 155 cm^{-1}

peak as harmonic in the one phonon approximation, the observed increase in intensity with increased scattering angle can be described as the effect of a Q^2 term and a single exponential containing a Debye-Waller factor. This procedure allows the root mean square vibrational amplitude, $\sqrt{\langle r^2 \rangle}$ to be determined as 0·6 Å. Also as a result, at all angles of scattering in our experiments the momentum transfers associated with this peak are sufficiently large that the "observation time" associated with the neutron molecule scattering is short compared to the time for gas like diffusive motions to set in.

QUASI-ELASTIC REGION

The quasi-elastic region of scattering for acetic acid falls between about 1200 and 1600 μsec/m on the time-of-flight scale. The strong angular dependence shown by the spectrum is the result of a fall-off in area with increasing momentum transfer and an increase in the peak breadth due to Doppler broadening during diffusive steps. The logarithm of the area of the quasi-elastic peak is shown plotted as a function of the square of the momentum transfer in fig. 4. The dependence is almost exponential

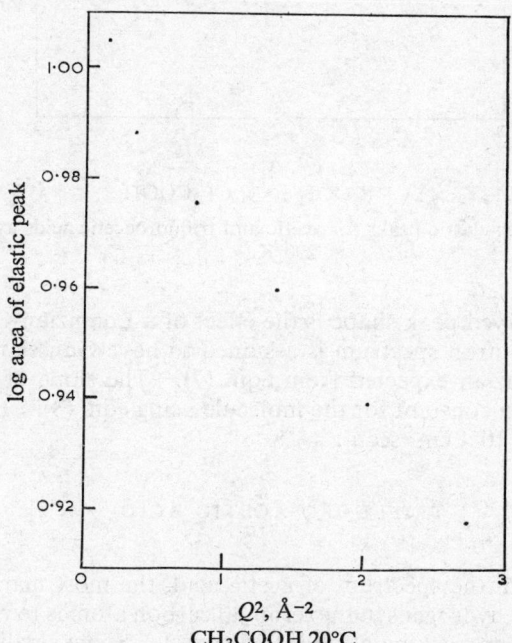

FIG. 4.—Debye-Waller plot of the log quasi-elastic area against momentum transfer squared, Q^2, for acetic acid.

and can be described by an effective Debye-Waller factor from which it is possible to calculate [5, 9] the mean amplitude of the thermal cloud developed by the diffusive motions associated with this region to be 1·2 Å.

The other feature in the quasi-elastic region is the dependence of the peak width on momentum transfer squared. Because it is difficult to subtract the inelastic contribution at high angles of scattering, measurements of this width are uncertain at these angles. Nevertheless, since measurements at the lowest angles are the most important for measuring molecular diffusion coefficients, the difficulties are not insuperable. Fig. 5 summarizes the results for both acetic acid and trifluoro-acetic acid. To determine the diffusion constant the peak broadening is measured relative to the width of a vanadium peak at the same angle of scattering, and is calculated on

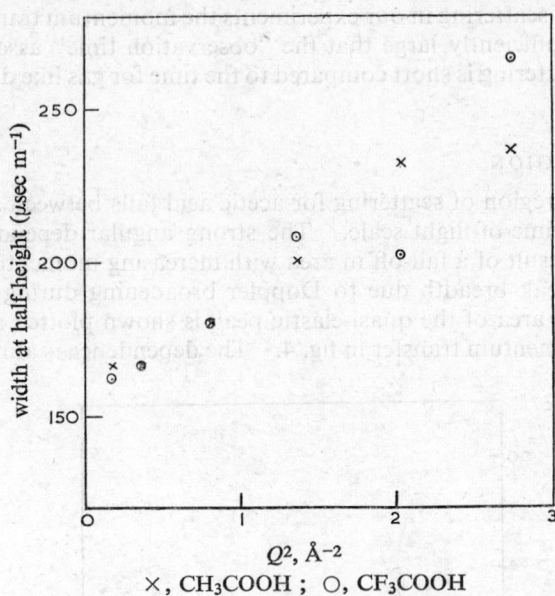

FIG. 5.—Width of the quasi-elastic peaks for acetic and trifluoroacetic acids as a function of Q^2 at 290°K.

the basis that the observed peak shape is the effect of a Lorenzian-Gaussian convolution. The incident neutron spectrum is assumed to have Gaussian form and this is broadened by a Lorenzian expected from eqn. (7). The slope of the curve can be converted to a diffusion constant for the molecule using eqn. (8). For acetic acid the tentative value is $2 \cdot 1 \times 10^{-5}$ cm^2 sec^{-1}.

TRIFLUORO-ACETIC ACID

INELASTIC REGION

By comparison with the spectrum of acetic acid, the most marked effect of substituting 3 fluorines for hydrogens in the terminal carbon atom is to remove completely the large inelastic feature peaking at about 155 cm^{-1}. Some small inelastic features of low intensity remain, but these will not be discussed. Fluorine substitution therefore allows us to assign the high intensity peak in the acetic acid spectrum to a CH_3 motion, most probably the torsional vibration. At 90° scattering angle, where the inelastic processes are more important compared to elastic ones, the small features just visible in the spectrum of trifluoro-acetic acid at 20° angle of scattering, are more apparent. The dominant feature in the 90° spectrum is the band between 500 and 800 μsec/m, which also extends on the low-energy side into the quasi-elastic region. We assign this band to the OH motion, most probably the intermolecular hydrogen bond stretching frequency. This band corresponds, in approximate position, to a discontinuity in the acetic acid spectrum. We note that the OH band fuses with the quasi-elastic region at high angles of scattering.

QUASI-ELASTIC REGION

The quasi-elastic region for trifluoro-acetic acid has sharply contrasting features from that in acetic acid. At a scattering angle of 20° the scattering intensity between the elastic peak and the inelastic region is almost down to background level, a feature only commonly encountered with solids. Again the quasi-elastic area show a much less marked dependence on momentum transfer than does the corresponding area for the acetic acid. This is also a feature reminiscent of scattering from solids. The effective Debye-Waller factor is less easy to determine than for acetic acid because of some Bragg scattering particularly in the 60 and 75° counters, which arises from the relatively greater proportion of coherent scattering in this system. Despite this, an estimate has been made leading to a mean amplitude for the diffusion thermal cloud of 1·2 Å. This is surprisingly close to the acetic acid value. The agreement may be fortuitous, however, due to different mechanisms for diffusion of the OH protons and so it cannot be discussed without more information on the angular dependence of the inelastic scattering in CF_3COOH. The qualitative differences between the CH_3COOH and CF_3COOH spectra remain, however, and suggest that the OH protons are part of a relatively well-defined "lattice" which vibrates during the time scale of the neutron molecule scattering "event". This situation contrasts with the alternative picture of a "gas-like" liquid of freely diffusing molecules with a continuum of state at low energies.

The dependence of the width of the quasi-elastic peak, on momentum transfer squared, is given in fig. 5.

The dependence on momentum transfer shown by the width of the quasi-elastic peak in trifluoroacetic acid is almost identical with that in acetic acid suggesting that their diffusion coefficients as measured by neutrons are also equal. An alternative suggestion is that the motion of the OH hydrogen in both of these systems is the dominant contribution to the quasi-elastic broadening. In either case, a paradox arises so that theories of broadening in similar systems where hindered internal rotation has been taken as an essential contribution to explain discrepancies between the higher diffusion constants observed by neutron scattering and those observed by tracer elements must be reconsidered.[5] A model system to explore these effects further is the methanols which are discussed below.

METHYL ALCOHOLS

The neutron scattering spectrum of methyl alcohol H_4 has been measured over an extensive range of momentum transfers by Saunderson and Rainey.[1] The spectrum and its angular dependence superficially resemble those of acetic acid shown in fig. 2, although the details of band positions and broadenings, differ. This resemblance arises, however, because the scattering centres in the two molecules, the CH_3 group and the OH group, are the same. The spectra of the two deuterated analogues of methyl alcohol, CD_3OH and CH_3OD may therefore be compared with fig. 2 in a rough quantitative way to see the large changes in intensity produced by deuteration, especially in the inelastic region of the spectrum. In these molecules the deuteration techniques seems extremely powerful as the contributions from each of the scattering centres may be evaluated separately with a minimal change in the total mass of the molecule. Although deuterium is a coherent scattering nucleus, the present preliminary appraisal of the data shows that Bragg peaks and other coherent scattering intrude only to a minor extent to mar the simplicity of the spectral changes. The coherent effects are noticed in the elastic peak and these only at high angles of scattering. When they are present the area/Q^2 plot deviates from linearity.

METHANOL-$d3$

The neutron scattering spectrum for liquid methanol $d3$ CD_3OH, at 290°K and at scattering angles of 20 and 90° to the incident neutron beam is shown in fig. 6. The effect of deuterating the methyl group is to produce changes in both the inelastic and in the quasi-elastic region of the spectrum which are reminiscent of the changes produced by fluorination of the methyl group in acetic acid.

In the inelastic region the large peak in methanol at about 160 cm^{-1} is almost absent from the spectrum recorded at the 20° angle of scattering. At 90° this peak is slightly apparent. This is the most noticeable qualitative change. The spectral

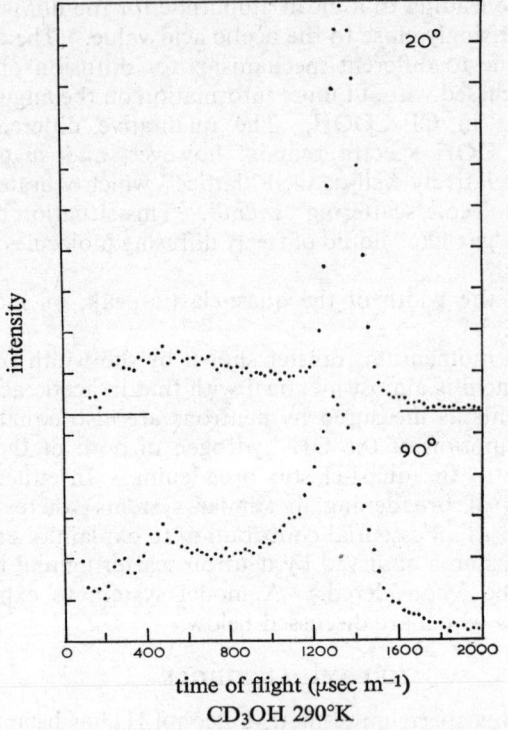

FIG. 6.—Neutron scattering spectrum of CD_3OH at 290°K and at scattering angles of 20 and 90° to the incident beam.

distribution in the inelastic region is, however, quite different from that observed in the acetic acids; there are, for instance, many more low frequency motions excited between 800 and 1200 μsec/m time of flight. These probably correspond to quasi-acoustic modes of the liquid. There is also strong evidence of fine structure in the spectral distribution, from the number of spectra which have been recorded.

Associated with the changes in the inelastic region of the spectrum there are marked differences between CD_3OH and CH_3OH for quasi-elastic scattering. Whereas in methanol itself the quasi-elastic region has a strongly angular dependent intensity and width, this is much less noticeable for CD_3OH. In fig. 6, even at 90° of scattering, the quasi-elastic region is well-resolved and of greater intensity than the inelastic region, at shorter times of flight than 1,000 μsec/m. The intensity of the scattering in the quasi-elastic for CD_3OH falls off almost exactly linearly as $\exp(-x^2Q^2)$, where x^2 is a Debye-Waller factor and Q^2 is the momentum transfer squared. The Debye-Waller factor is 0·14 which corresponds to a mean amplitude for the thermal cloud generated by the motion of 0·9 Å.

The width of the quasi-elastic peak, obtained after subtraction of a reasonable inelastic background, is also a simple function of momentum transfer squared. The simple diffusion model seems to hold over the momentum transfer range of our measurements as is shown by fig. 7, where the width at half-height in μsec/m is plotted as a function of Q^2. After deconvoluting this width it is possible to determine the value for the diffusion coefficient associated with the motion of the OH group.

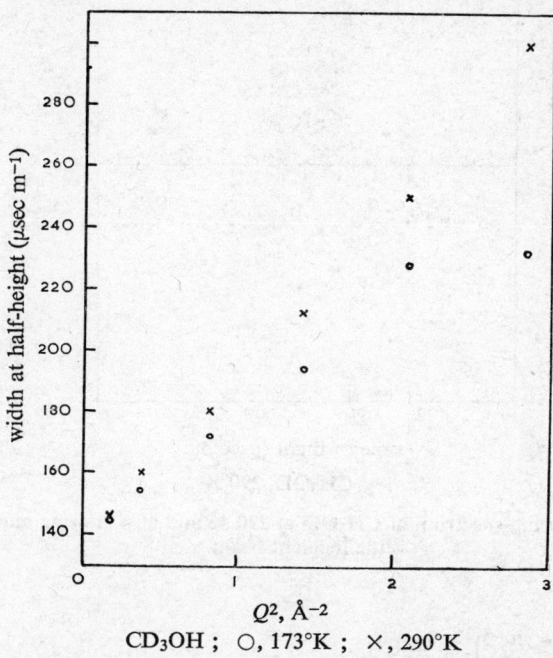

FIG. 7.—Energy width of the quasi-elastic peaks in CD_3OH at 290 and 173°K as a function of Q^2 showing the jump diffusion behaviour at low temperatures.

At 290°K this has the value of $1·9 \times 10^{-5}$ cm² sec⁻¹. Measurements have also been made at 170°K near the freezing point of the liquid. At this temperature the free diffusion model seems to break down about 2 Å⁻² but below this a diffusion constant can be found which is approximately $1·2 \times 10^{-5}$ cm² sec⁻¹.

Since great care was taken in preparing these samples to ensure that the materials were extremely dry and free of any traces of acid or alkaline catalysts which might promote hydrogen exchange between molecules, we assume that the diffusion constants measured here are characteristic not only of the OH but also of the whole molecular diffusion since the residence time of the OH proton in this case is much longer than the time of observation in any of these neutron scattering experiments.

METHANOL $d1$

In the inelastic region the reappearance of a strong band at an energy transfer corresponding to 160 cm⁻¹ provides confirmation of the assignment of this region of the spectrum to the methyl group motions. The peak height of this band shows a strong dependence on the momentum transfer associated with the scattering and this

180 NEUTRON SCATTERING SPECTROSCOPY

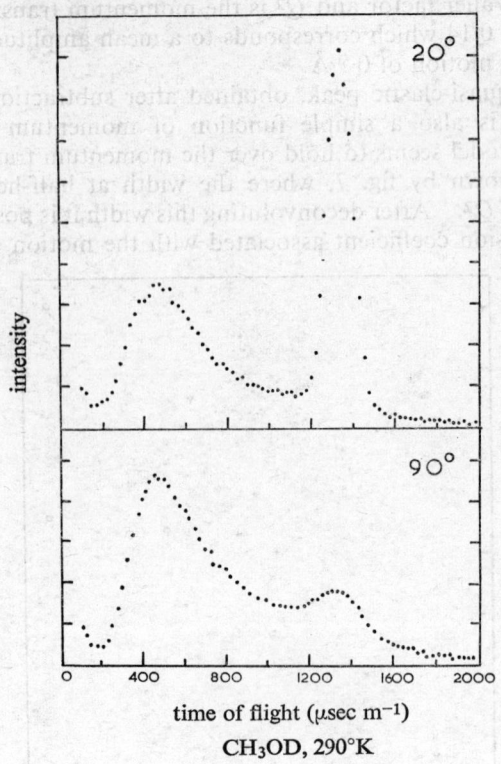

FIG. 8.—Neutron scattering spectrum of CH$_3$OD at 290°K and at scattering angles of 20 and 90° to the incident beam.

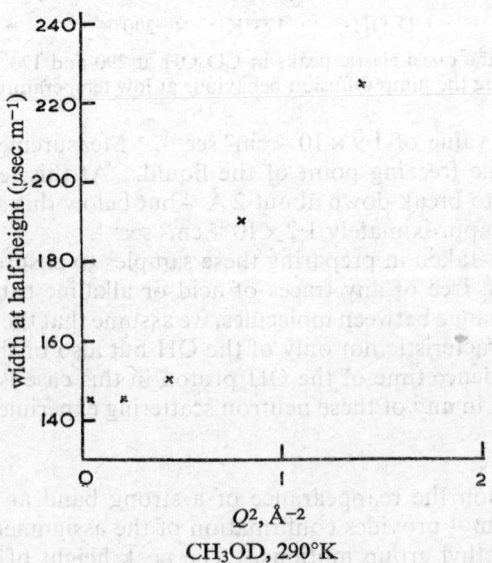

FIG. 9.—Energy width of the quasi-elastic peak in CH$_3$OD as a function of Q^2 at 290°K.

appears to obey the scattering law in the one phonon harmonic approximation. Fig. 8 shows the scattering spectrum of CH_3OD at scattering angles of 20 and 90° for the sample temperature 290°K. At the highest momentum transfers used, a shoulder appeared on the peak at 800 $\mu sec/m$. This may also correspond to a methyl group motional frequency.

Not only are there large changes in the inelastic region between CD_3OH and CH_3OD, but so also are there associated changes in the quasi-elastic region. Fig. 8 shows the extremely sensitive variation of the quasi-elastic area with momentum transfer. The peak height changes by almost a factor of 10 in going from the 20° angle of scattering to 90° angle of scattering. The intensity change obeys a Debye-Waller expression with a factor of 0.6 corresponding to a mean amplitude of motion of 1.9 Å.

The quasi-elastic peak widths have a linear dependence on Q^2 and some results are shown in fig. 9. Because the strong inelastic scattering band makes width measurements above 45° scattering angle difficult, only the results for lower angles are shown. An inelastic background was subtracted before calculating the deconvoluted peak widths. Fig. 9 indicates that the molecular diffusion studied through the methyl group also fits the simple diffusion law and gives a diffusion constant of 2.1×10^{-5} cm^2 sec^{-1} which is approximately equal to that for CD_3OH at 290°K. The behaviour parallels the results for the acetic acids although again there are clear qualitative differences between the substituted and unsubstituted spectra.

DISCUSSION

These new experimental results are intended as a preliminary review of the power of substitution methods in studying neutron scattering spectroscopy of liquids. One application is the assignment of particular parts of the inelastic scattering spectrum to particular atomic motions. The unique virtue in the neutron method is that a band associated with the vibration of any chosen atom can be almost completely removed from the spectrum rather than moved to lower frequencies where it could increase the complexity as in infra-red spectrometry. It has been possible to assign both the CH_3 and OH motions in acetic acid and in methanol by this technique. The frequencies of the band motions are listed in table 1, which also shows the available infra-red data.

TABLE 1.—FREQUENCIES (cm^{-1}) OF PROMINENT BANDS IN THE INELASTIC NEUTRON SCATTERING SPECTRA

CH_3COOH	155				
CF_3COOH	255	155	114	65	44
(infra-red)		176		75	40
CH_3OD	160	50			
CD_3OH (290°K)	550	150 (broad)			
CD_3OH (173°K)	550	100			

The second contribution that the atomic substitution studies have made is that changes produced in the inelastic region on substitution are accompanied by corresponding changes in the quasi-elastic scattering. Both the acetic acid and the methanol systems show this. In particular, the spectra show that where there is strong scattering in the inelastic region from a methyl group so also there will be a strong and highly angular-dependent scattering in the quasi-elastic region. When only the scattering from the hydroxyl hydrogens in these hydrogen-bonded systems is recorded, the quasi-elastic region is sharp and well defined even at high angles of scattering. These liquids therefore show solid-like behaviour, the hydrogen-bonded protons effectively remaining fixed in their positions during the observation time. This particular view is corroborated for the methanols by the relatively high Debye temperatures and small amplitudes associated with the motion in this region.

The third interesting observation which has come from the atomic substitution studies (most particularly from the isotopic substitution experiments) is that the neutron scattering measurements of molecular diffusion constants do not seem to depend on which proton in the molecule is chosen as the scattering centre for the measurement. In acetic acid and trifluoroacetic acid the diffusion constants are almost equal. This may mean that the dominant motional process is that associated with some intermolecular exchange of hydrogens rather than with the motion of the molecule as a whole. Exchange is very unlikely in our systems since scrupulous care was taken to avoid any catalysts for this process, and so the equality of the two diffusion constants may mean that all protons in acetic acid are participating in the same diffusive process as the single proton in trifluoroacetic acid. Under these circumstances the neutron measures, in acetic acid, the mean diffusion constant of all the four protons and this is no different from the diffusion constant that would be measured from any one of them separately. Although this view is unexpected because the molecular masses of trifluoroacetic acid and acetic acid differ considerably, it does fit with the observations on the substituted methanol. There again, especially for CH_3OD, we find diffusion constants associated with the CH_3 motion and the OH motion to be almost equal. Both values also agree closely with the value found for CH_3OH by Saunderson and Rainey ($2 \cdot 1 \times 10^{-5}$ cm^2 sec^{-1}).

If the methyl group in the molecule were rotating freely so that internal rotation with respect to an oncoming neutron could give rise to preferential Doppler broadening for methyl protons, we should expect that the diffusion constant measured for CH_3 groups would be greater than that measured for either the molecule as a whole or for the OH groups separately. The present analysis does not support this view and so for the molecules studied and at the temperatures at which the experiments were done, the physical process of intramolecular rotation does not contribute appreciably to the diffusive kinetic processes seen by a neutron. On the time scale of the neutron observation range, the OH groups are relatively localized in the liquid. If free rotation is not important, then the predominant motion for the CH_3 group is a torsional vibration around an equilibrium position.

The problems posed by invoking free rotation in some systems to explain the higher values for molecular diffusion constants obtained by neutron scattering measurements, compared to those obtained for bulk phase tracer studies, have been discussed by Egelstaff.[3] Fig. 10 shows how the neutron scattering data at the lowest momentum transfers must theoretically fit the values predicted by a simple diffusion theory. That they do not, e.g. for glycerol, at the normal momentum transfers used in neutron scattering experiments, must mean a simple Gaussian is no longer a suitable correlation function. Associated with the point of inflection needed to join the neutron data to the bulk diffusion data there must come in the time Fourier transform of the correlation function (the spectral density of eqn. (6)) a maximum shown in fig. 10 as BCD. This maximum can only be associated with physical processes such as a quantized internal rotation. In our systems the only feature in the spectrum which could correspond to this is a vibration associated with the OH measurement, which under conditions of chemical exchange could easily merge into the quasi-elastic region. As particular care has been taken to avoid this exchange in our experiments, the OH peak appears separately (energy transfer is approximately equal to 65 cm^{-1}). And so the spectral density as a function of frequency probably does not show the feature. It is possible that selective isotopic substitution experiments on glycerol and other liquids, which do not show the simple diffusion behaviour, would reveal these effects.

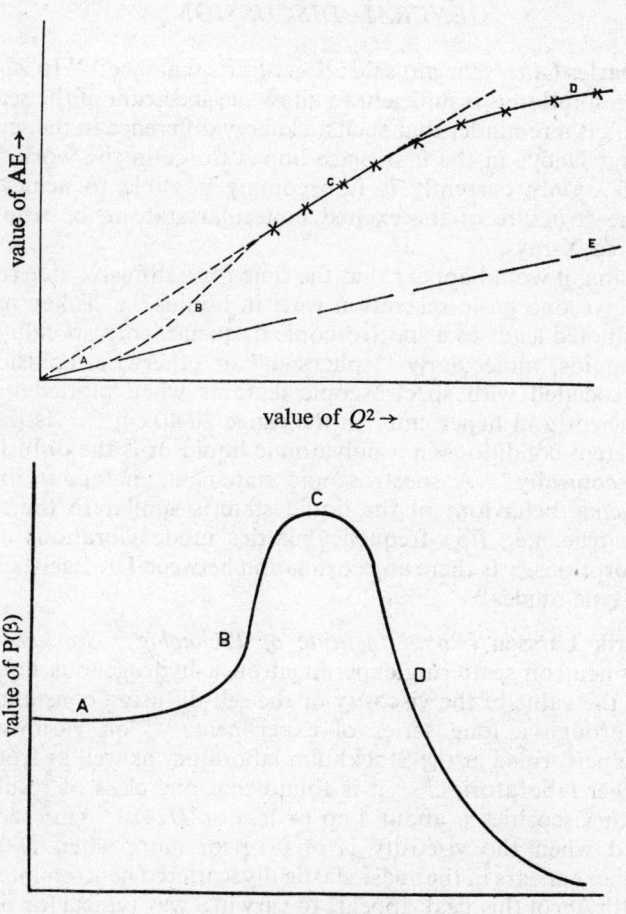

FIG. 10.—(i) Relationship between experimental neutron scattering results on the momentum transfer dependence of the quasi-elastic peak width and the theoretical line predicted for some liquids using bulk diffusion constant data. The experimental region is shown with points.

(ii) Possible spectral density for a system showing the above width dependence.

[1] D. H. Saunderson and V. S. Rainey, *Inelastic Scattering of Neutrons* (I.A.E.A. Vienna), 1963, vol. 1. p. 413.
[2] K. E. Larsson in *Thermal Neutron Scattering*, ed. P. A. Egelstaff, 1965, p. 378.
[3] P. A. Egelstaff, *Inelastic Scattering of Neutrons* (I.A.E.A.), 1965, vol. 2, p. 553.
[4] L. Van Hove, *Physic. Rev.*, 1954, **95**, 249.
[5] K. E. Larsson *Inelastic Scattering of Neutrons* (I.A.E.A. Vienna) 1965, vol. 2. p. 3.
[6] K. E. Larsson in *Thermal Neutron Scattering* (ed. P. A. Egelstaff) (Academic Press, 1965), p. 347.
[7] A. Sjolander *Thermal Neutron Scattering* (ref. 6) p. 291.
[8] D. H. C. Harris, S. J. Cocking, P. A. Egelstaff and F. J. Webb, *Inelastic Scattering of Neutrons*, (I.A.E.A. Vienna), 1963, vol. 1, p. 107.
[9] J. S. Downes, P. A. Egelstaff and J. W. White, *Chem. and Ind.*, 1967.

GENERAL DISCUSSION

Dr. Mansel Davies (*Aberystwyth*) said: Egelstaff's sentence: " In X-ray scattering work the energy resolution is insufficient to allow the spectrum of the scattered X-rays to be determined," is a reminder that such an energy difference in the scattered X-rays was precisely what Debye in the first place hoped to see in the work with Scherrer, initiated in 1915. Only currently is it becoming possible to achieve a sufficient resolution for the structure of the excited molecular state to be seen from the inelastically scattered X-rays.

In the discussion, it would appear that the time for a diffusive step (*ca.* $1\text{-}2 \times 10^{-12}$ sec) " seems to give one basic relaxation time in liquids ". Taken as a relaxation time, the factor quoted leads to a spectroscopic frequency corresponding to 2-5 cm^{-1}. In polyatomic liquids, molecularly " spherical " or otherwise, collisional processes appear to be associated with spectroscopic features when plotted in terms of an absorption coefficient α in néper cm^{-1} in the range 20-40 cm^{-1}. Is this difference a result of the different conditions in a polyatomic liquid or is the diffusive step not to be seen spectroscopically? A spectroscopic statement analogous to Egelstaff's— " the high frequency behaviour of the liquid state is similar to the solid state "— is also probably true, i.e., (low-frequency) lattice mode vibrations appear also in liquid-phase absorptions. Is there any correlation between Dr. Egelstaff's frequencies and such lattice-type modes?

Prof. Karl-Erik Larsson (*Royal Institute of Technology, Stockholm*) said: The results of a slow neutron scattering experiment on a hydrogenous liquid is strongly dependent upon the value of the viscosity or the self-diffusion constant for the liquid in question. Through a long series of experiments [1-4] on various hydrogenous liquids that were performed at the Stockholm laboratory as well as from experiments performed at other laboratories [5,6] it is found that one class of results is obtained from liquids with viscosities η about 1 cp or less or $D \geqslant 10^{-5}$ cm^2/sec, and another class is obtained when the viscosity is of 0·1 p or more when $D < 10^{-6}$ cm^2/sec. The main difference appears in the quasi-elastically scattered neutron intensity in such a way that the width $\Delta\omega$ of this peak appears to vary in a way typical for simple diffusion

$$\Delta\omega = 2D\kappa^2 \tag{1}$$

when η is small ($\hbar\kappa$ is the momentum change in the scattering process) and in a way typical for solid behaviour

$$\Delta\omega \underset{\kappa \text{ large}}{\longrightarrow} 2/\tau \quad \text{(only approximately)} \tag{2}$$

when η is large. Here τ is some relaxation time. The approach to the almost constant or slowly rising value of $\Delta\omega$ occurs differently for different liquids. Intermediate

---

[1] K. E. Larsson and U. Dahlborg, *Physica*, 1964, **30**, 1561.
[2] K. E. Larsson, *Proc. IAEA* (Bombay, December, 1964) (Vienna, 1965), vol. 2, p. 3.
[3] K. E. Larsson and L. Bergstedt, *Physic. Rev.*, 1966, **151**, 117.
[4] K. E. Larsson, L. Queiroz do Amaral, N. Ivantchev, S. Ripeanu, L. Bergstedt and U. Dahlborg, *Physic. Rev.*, 1966, **151**, 126.
[5] *Proc. Symp. Inelastic Scattering of Neutrons in Solids and Liquids* (Vienna, 1960, Chalk River, 1962 and Bombay, 1964). (The International Atomic Energy Agency, Vienna, 1961, 1963 and 1965).
[6] *Thermal Neutron Scattering*, ed. P. A. Egelstaff (Academic Press, 1965), chap. 7 and 8.

behaviours of $\Delta\omega$ as a function of κ are also observed most often when $100 > \eta > 1$ cp. The high viscosities are reached only in liquids with strong intermolecular bonds like the hydrogen bonds. Examples are glycerol and n-propanol at temperatures below room temperature. Examples of low viscosity liquids are methane, pentane, methyl- and ethyl-alcohol, etc. The details of the experimentally observed line widths may be understood if a neutron cross-section is formulated on the basis of the van Hove [1] formalism.

The molecules considered consist of carbon chains with protons and hydroxyl groups hooked on to the chain at selected positions. The motion of this " line " molecule with respect to the centre of gravity is described (fig. 1) in the following way. At time $t = 0$ the molecule has the direction in space given by N_1. A proton at r_1 vibrates round a quasi-equilibrium position, which in itself performs simple diffusive motion. The diffusive motion which gradually changes the molecular direction in

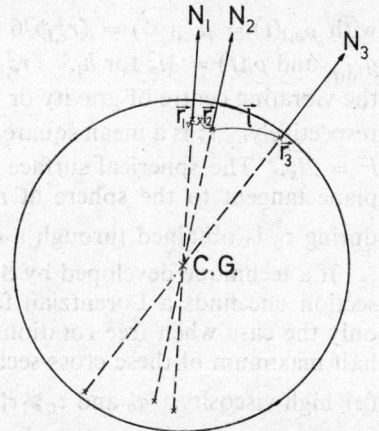

FIG. 1.—The motion of the molecule relative to its centre of gravity: N_1 is molecular direction at time $t = 0$; N_2 is molecular direction at time $t = \tau_0$. In between these positions the direction diffuses randomly. A proton at r_1 at time $t = 0$ diffuses and vibrates until it reaches position r_2. N_3 is molecular direction after jump. A proton starting at r_1 is dragged with the molecule in its directional change to the position r_3. The jump length l is covered in time τ_1.

space is described by a diffusion coefficient D_p and continues until the average time $t = \tau_0$ when the molecular direction has changed from N_1 to N_2, resulting in a displacement of the equilibrium position of the regarded proton from r_1 to r_2. The physical cause for these small displacements is small changes in the orientations of neighbour molecules. After the elapse of τ_0 the molecular direction in space changes abruptly from N_2 to N_3 in a short time τ_1. This large change of molecular orientation transfers the proton from r_2 to r_3, a distance l, the jump length, and results from a larger change of the position or orientation of neighbour molecules. The equivalent to a sudden change of molecular orientation would be a partial rotation to form an isomeric molecular form. After the average time $\tau_0 + \tau_1$ the whole procedure is repeated. The motion of the centre of gravity is described as *either* a vibrational state when the molecule is bound to neighbours for the time τ'_0, which should be long in the solid state, *or* as a diffusive state for the time τ'_1. The displacement of the centre of gravity is then described by $\Delta x^2_{c.g} = 2D\tau'_1$. A mixture of the two cases might occur even in hydrogen bonded liquids of high temperatures. At the end of the average time τ'_0, which might be much longer than $\tau_0 + \tau_1$, the molecular configuration round the regarded molecule has changed so much that the molecule is free to diffuse for the time τ'_1 to another position where it is again caught in a quasi-stable position. The same discussion can be carried through for each proton in the complex molecule.

[1] L. Van Hove, *Physic. Rev.*, 1954, **95**, 249.

In order to calculate the cross-section,[1] five different partial self-correlation functions are needed describing respectively: the diffusion of the centre of gravity $h_e(r,t)$, the vibration of the centre of gravity $g_e(r,t)$, the vibration of the proton with respect to the centre of gravity $g_{i_{\text{vib}}}(r,t)$ the diffusion of the vibrating proton $g_{i_{\text{diff}}}(r,t)$ and the jump of the proton $h_i(r,t)$. It is first assumed that all five functions are Gaussian functions of the form:

centre of gravity motion
three dimensional motion

$$\begin{Bmatrix} g_e(r,t) \\ h_e(r,t) \end{Bmatrix} = \frac{1}{(4\pi\rho_e(t))^{\frac{3}{2}}} \exp\left(-\frac{r^2}{4\rho_e(t)}\right)$$

relative motion
three dimensional motion

$$g_{i_{\text{vib}}}(r,t) = \frac{1}{(4\pi\rho_i(t))^{\frac{3}{2}}} \exp\left(-\frac{r^2}{4\rho_i(t)}\right)$$

approximated as motions in a plane

$$\begin{Bmatrix} g_{i_{\text{diff}}}(r,t) \\ h_i(r,t) \end{Bmatrix} = \frac{1}{4\pi\rho_i(t)} \exp\left(-\frac{r^2}{4\rho_i(t)}\right)$$

with $\rho_{e,i}(t) = \rho_{e,i}(\infty) = \langle r_{e,i}^2 \rangle/6$ for g_e and $g_{i_{\text{vib}}}$, $\rho_e(t) = Dt$ for h_e, $\rho_i(t) = D_p t$ for $g_{i_{\text{diff}}}$ and $\rho_i(t) = \frac{1}{2}\overline{l_x^2}$ for h_i. $\langle r_{e,i}^2 \rangle$ is the mean square of the thermal cloud set up by the vibrating centre of gravity or the vibrating proton relative to the centre of gravity respectively. $\overline{l_x^2}$ is a mean square component of the jump length l. It is assumed that $\overline{l^2} = 2\overline{l_x^2}$. The spherical surface on which the proton moves is approximated by a plane tangent to the sphere at r_2. It is assumed that the relative proton motion during τ_0 is obtained through a folding $g_i(r,t) = \int g_{i_{\text{diff}}}(r',t) g_{i_{\text{vib}}}(r'-r,t) dr'$.

If a technique developed by Singwi and Sjölander[2] is used to calculate the cross-section one finds a Lorentzian form for the quasi-elastic peak. We shall consider only the case when free rotations are hindered such that $\tau_0 \gg \tau_1$. The full width at half maximum of these cross-sections are:

(a) high viscosity. τ_0' and $\tau_0 \gg \tau_1'$ and τ_1

$$\Delta\omega = \frac{2}{\tau_{00}}\left(1 + \frac{2}{3}D_p\tau_{00}\kappa^2 - \frac{\tau_{00}}{\tau_0}\exp(-2W_i - 4W_e) - \frac{1}{6}\overline{l^2}\kappa^2 - \frac{\tau_{00}}{\tau_0'}\frac{\exp(-4W_i - 2W_e)}{1 + D\tau_0'\kappa^2}\right). \quad (4a)$$

Here

$$\tau_{00}^{-1} = \tau_0^{-1} + \tau_0'^{-1}.$$

If the molecular mass is much larger than the proton mass, $W_e \ll W_i$. For large κ-values the line width asymptotically approaches

$$\Delta\omega = 2(1/\tau_{00} + D_p\kappa^2). \quad (4b)$$

There is no horizontal tangent to the curve $\Delta\omega = f(\kappa^2)$ unless $D_p = 0$ (solid state).
As κ approaches zero one obtains

$$\Delta\omega = 2\left[D + \frac{2}{3}D_p + \frac{\overline{r_i^2}}{6\tau_0} + \frac{\overline{l^2}/6}{\tau_0} + \frac{\overline{r_i^2}}{3\tau_0'}\right]\kappa^2 = 2[D_{\text{c.g.}} + D_{\text{rel}} + D_{\text{mix}}]\kappa^2 = 2''D''\kappa^2, \quad (4c)$$

where $D_{\text{c.g.}} = D$, $D_{\text{rel}} = \frac{2}{3}D_p + \frac{\overline{r_i^2}}{6\tau_0} + \frac{\overline{l^2}/6}{\tau_0}$ and $D_{\text{mix}} = \frac{\overline{r_i^2}}{3\tau_0'}$;

(b) $\tau_1' \gg \tau_0'$ and $\tau_0 \gg \tau_1$.

[1] K. E. Larsson and L. Bergstedt, *Physic. Rev.*, 1966, **151**, 117.
[2] K. S. Singwi and A. Sjölander, *Physic. Rev.*, 1960, **119**, 863.

GENERAL DISCUSSION 187

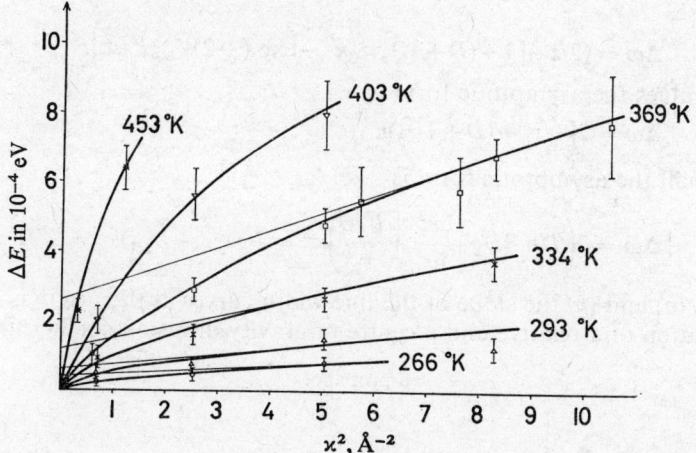

FIG. 2.—Observed line width data on glycerol together with fitted theoretical line width forms given at solid lines. The best fit to the asymptotic behaviour is shown for 266, 293, 334 and 369°K. The intercept on the ΔE axis is $2\hbar/\tau_{00}$. The slope of the asymptote is $2\hbar D\varepsilon$.

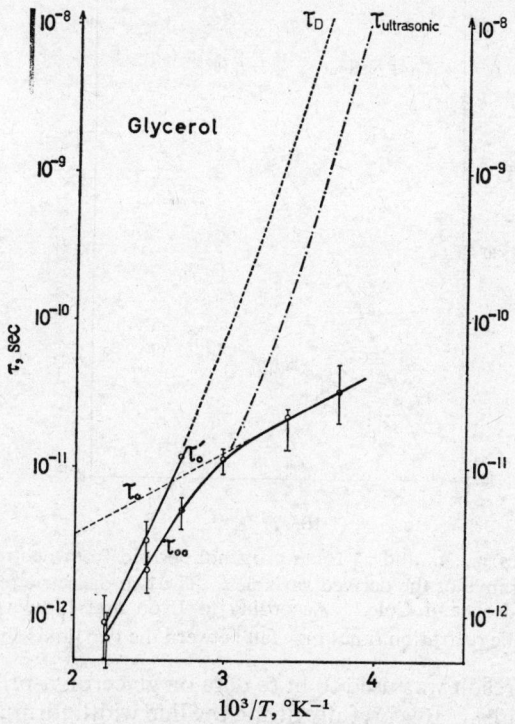

FIG. 3.—Relaxation times τ_{00}, τ_0 and τ'_0 for glycerol derived from neutron data. Measured dielectric relaxation time τ_D ranges from lower temperatures up to 285°K. Thereafter an extrapolation is made according to a formula given by McDuffie and Litowitz.[1] Ultrasonic data from Piccirelli and Litowitz.[2]

[1] G. E. McDuffie, Jr. and T. A. Litowitz, *J. Chem. Physics*, 1962, **37**, 1699.
[2] R. Piccirelli and T. A. Litowitz, *J. Acoust. Soc. Amer.*, 1957, **29**, 1009.

In this case,
$$\Delta\omega = (2/\tau_0)[1+(D+\tfrac{2}{3}D_p)\tau_0\kappa^2 - \exp(-2W_i)\tfrac{1}{6}\overline{l^2}\kappa^2]. \tag{5a}$$

For large κ-values the asymptotic form is
$$\Delta\omega = 2[1/\tau_0+(D+\tfrac{2}{3}D_p)\kappa^2]. \tag{5b}$$

When κ is small the asymptotic form is
$$\Delta\omega = 2\left(D+\tfrac{2}{3}D_p+\frac{\overline{r_i^2}}{6\tau_0}+\frac{\overline{l^2}/6}{\tau_0}\right)\kappa^2 = 2(D_{\text{c.g.}}+D_{\text{rel}})\kappa^2 = 2''D''\kappa^2. \tag{5c}$$

In both cases (a) and (b) the slope of the line width curves at the origin is determined by a combination of a relative and a centre of gravity diffusion coefficient.

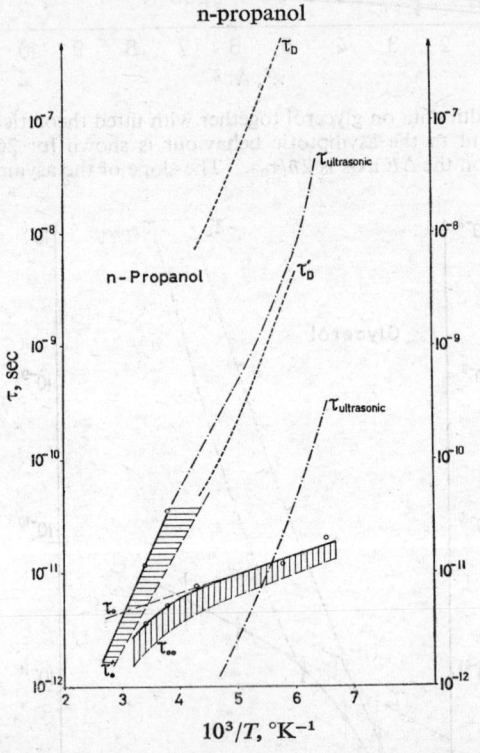

FIG. 4.—Relaxation times τ_{00}, τ_0 and τ_0' for n-propanol derived from neutron data. The shaded areas show the possible range of the derived variables. The two dielectric relaxation times τ_D and τ_D' are taken from Davidson and Cole.[1] According to Lyon and Litowitz[2] the distribution of ultrasonic relaxation times may fall between the two limits shown.

The cross-section result was used to fit to data on glycerol, n-propanol and pentane for various temperatures. By carefully fitting the line width formulas to experimental values were obtained for l^2, D_p, τ_0 and τ_0'. An example of the line width data and fit for glycerol is given in fig. 2. Similar results were obtained for n-propanol. In both cases l^2 is temperature-independent for each substance and $l^2 = 2 \cdot 6 \text{ Å}^2$ for

[1] D. W. Davidson and R. H. Cole, *J. Chem. Physics*, 1951, **19**, 1484.
R. H. Cole and D. W. Davidson, *J. Chem. Physics*, 1952, **20**, 1389.
[2] T. Lyon and T. A. Litowitz, *J. Appl. Physics*, 1955, **27**, 179.

glycerol and 8·0 Å² for n-propanol. All the other quantities vary with temperature. The product $2D_p\tau_0$ describing the change in molecular direction in the time τ_0 remains about constant for each substance and is about 0·7 Å² for glycerol and 0·3 Å² for n-propanol.

Of particular interest are the temperature variation of the relaxation times τ_0 and τ_0'. These are given for glycerol and n-propanol in fig. 3 and 4, where a comparison is made with experimental data on dielectric and ultrasonic relaxation times. In both cases the time τ_0' and the dielectric—or some component thereof—relaxation times agree relatively well. The mechanical relaxation time is not in disagreement with τ_0' but may be a mixture of τ_0' and τ_0. Since τ_0' is identified with the mean lifetime of a hydrogen bond, the agreement is gratifying. An example of how well the

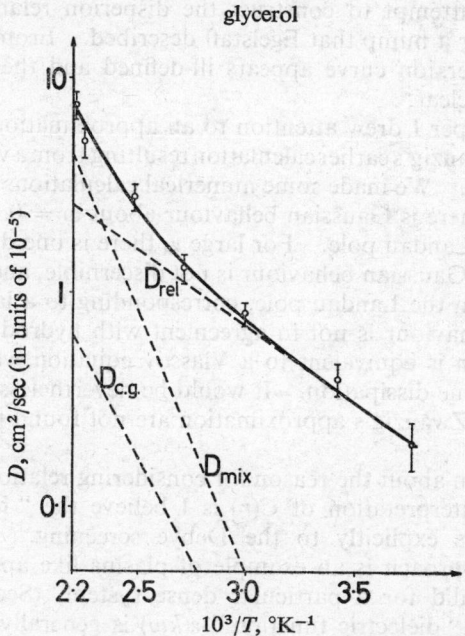

FIG. 5.—Observed diffusion coefficient "D". The various theoretical components D, D_{mix} and D_{rel} are shown as dashed lines. The full line is the sum of these components.

components of D when summed up describe the directly observed D is given in fig. 5. Both glycerol and n-propanol are non-Arrhenius, i.e., high-viscosity liquids.

For pentane the viscosity is in the range 1 cp and no solid-like behaviour is observed. Unfortunately the experimental accuracy is poor but it seems that an application of formula (5a) for the line width would fit the data. The observed slope at the origin is about twice the value of the self-diffusion coefficient indicating contributions from the terms D_p and $\overline{l^2}/6\tau_0$. In general it is expected that for liquids in or near the Arrhenius region simple diffusion will dominate and rotational effects are difficult to observe in the width of the quasi-elastic peak.

Using the present model the neutron data on several hydrogenous liquids are understood. The fact that the motion relative to the centre of gravity is divided into small and large fluctuations represented by two Gaussian functions indicate that this motion—sum of two Gaussians—in non-Gaussian. The present analysis also permits a direct connection between the neutron data and dielectric and ultrasonic data.

Prof. J. Stecki (*Warsaw*) said: In Pings' paper, the question arises of the physical significance of the direct correlation function experimentally determined. One simple and straightforward interpretation is that $-kTC(r)$ is an effective potential. The relation between $g(r)$ and $-kTC(r)$ is the same as between $g(r)$ and the true potential in a dilute (Debye) plasma. Thus $C(r)$ is the effective potential to use if relations valid for a plasma are forced to fit any other system, i.e., if actual screening is described by the Debye screening.

Am I correct in supposing that the dispersion relation $\omega(k)$ in Stiller and Dorner's paper is determined by choosing a sharp peak in the $S(k,\omega)$ against ω plot and then following the shift of the peak maximum with k? What is the criterion of sharpness? Surely one would not attempt to construct the disperion relation by following a strongly damped peak or a hump that Egelstaff described. From this point of view, the concept of the dispersion curve appears ill-defined and the significance of the plots thus obtained not clear.

At the end of my paper I drew attention to an approximation to $v(k,\omega)$ which is exactly equivalent to Zwanzig's earlier calculation resulting from a variational treatment of the Liouville equation. We made some numerical calculations of $S(k,\omega)$ at fixed k. For low values of βv_k, there is Gaussian behaviour about $\omega = 0$ and a damped peak near the corresponding Landau pole. For large v_k there is one damped peak not far from $\omega = 0$, so that the Gaussian behaviour is not discernible, and another peak with negligible damping, from the Landau pole, corresponding to a large sound velocity. Thus the qualitative behaviour is not in agreement with hydrodynamical behaviour since this approximation is equivalent to a Vlassov equation which is a short-time equation involving no true dissipation. It would be nevertheless interesting to see if some of the features of Zwanzig's approximation are not found in what is called the " kinetic regime ".

In reply to Rowlinson about the reason for considering relations that are valid for a plasma. First, the interpretation of $C(r)$ is I believe the " right one ", i.e., the effective potential refers explicitly to the Debye screening. In particular, also, the Ornstein-Zernike approach is an example of plasma-like approximations found (or assumed!) to be valid for a particular dense system. Secondly, the relation between $S(k\omega)$ and the " dielectric function " $\varepsilon(k\omega)$ is generally valid for a slightly generalized definition of ε and it is fortuitous that these relations were derived first for a quantum or classical electron gas.

Dr. A. Levi (*Rijksuniversiteit te Leiden*) said: The velocity self-correlation function $F(t) = \langle \dot{x}(0)\dot{x}(t) \rangle$ has acquired an increasing importance in the dynamical description of liquids. It is useful to find a simple analytic form for it, containing a few parameters which can be fitted from experiments or theories, and incorporating some of the interesting properties of that function. Simple forms of this kind are afforded by stochastic processes, if one makes convenient assumptions about the atomic motions.

It has often been assumed, by analogy with Brownian motion theory, that the velocity vector contains a term behaving as a Gaussian, Markovian process. This, however, is in contrast to the short-time properties of the correlation function, which can be studied by Taylor expansion. A Markovian process is non-differentiable and would correspond to infinite mean square force, while the mean square force is a finite quantity, well known from both theory and experiments. On the other hand, it is much more reasonable to assume Gaussian and Markovian properties for the stochastic pair formed by velocity and acceleration together, taking into account explicitly the above information about the mean square force. In this case the velocity self-correlation is

$$F(t) = \frac{kT}{m}(1-z^2)^{-1}\left[\exp(-z\omega t) - z^2 \exp\left(-\frac{\omega t}{z}\right)\right]$$

where k is Boltzmann's constant, T the temperature, m the molecular mass, ω is given by $\omega^2 = \langle V^2 u \rangle / 3m$ while the mean square force is $kT\langle V^2 u \rangle$, and z is related to the self-diffusion coefficient by $D = (kT/m\omega)(z+z^{-1})$. Similarly, under more general conditions, one can assume Gaussian and Markovian properties for the triplet formed by velocity, acceleration and time derivative of the acceleration; one gets a definite analytic form again, although slightly more complicated. One can even devise a general approximation scheme where in the nth approximation a stochastic vector formed by the first n time-derivatives of displacement is assumed to perform a Gaussian, Markovian process. This is described by the matrix equation

$$R(t) = \exp(Qt)R(0), \qquad (2)$$

where $R(t)$ is the correlation matrix and $Q = \dot{R}(0)R^{-1}(0)$. This equation becomes exact when the full set of derivatives is considered ($n \to \infty$), but in general it is an approximation. The situation is still simple, however, since the velocity self-correlation function is a sum of n exponentials, with coefficients and exponents connected with the initial correlations, except for one parameter which is left free in order to get damping at long times. The n time factors are the eigenvalues of Q. The correlation functions obtained by this method have a clear mathematical meaning, so that they are perhaps suited for an approximate description of the true correlation functions.

These models were applied to liquid argon at the triple point. The parameter ω was taken from the isotopic separation factor and the experimental diffusion coefficient D (from neutron scattering) was also used. The velocity correlation function was computed in the second and third approximations, and the results were compared to Rahman's molecular dynamics correlation functions. They agree before the first zero, but at later times the amplitude of the oscillations is too large, nor does the third approximation improve over the second.

Presumably, a smoothing due to three-dimensional effects has been neglected. To be more precise, any coupling between motions in different directions has been ignored; since the components of velocity are actually uncorrelated, any such coupling disappears in the Gaussian approximation. The latter should therefore be dropped in a more exact treatment, while the Markov property can still be expected to hold to a reasonable extent. The correlation function (1) is the same as is obtained from the equation of the kind

$$\dot{F}(t) = -\int_0^t \alpha(\tau)F(t-\tau)d\tau \qquad (3)$$

provided $\alpha(t)$ has an exponential form.

Nuclear Magnetic Resonance in the Study of Liquids

By J. A. Pople

Carnegie Institute of Technology and Mellon Institute

Received 7th February, 1967

Mechanisms of nuclear spin relaxation in liquids are listed and discussed. It is pointed out that measurements of spin relaxation times (and also dielectric relaxation times) give information about different aspects of the process of molecular rotation and re-orientation in liquids. Comparative studies of different mechanisms should lead to a more detailed understanding of these movements.

1. INTRODUCTION

Nuclear magnetic resonance experiments are most directly affected by the structure and behaviour of the surrounding medium through the process of nuclear spin relaxation. This is the process whereby a set of nuclear spins tends to re-orient towards a random distribution competing with the orienting forces due to the externally applied magnetic fields. It can be studied experimentally [1] by measurements of the spin-lattice relaxation time T_1 which is the time constant for approach of nuclear spins to thermal equilibrium in the presence of a strong external magnetic field H. The subject of this review is the relationship between T_1 and the properties of the liquid medium, particularly the rotation and re-orientation of molecules.

One important way in which nuclear spin relaxation differs from other molecular relaxation processes is that the time scale is much longer. Proton spins in an organic liquid may take many seconds to achieve equilibrium compared with perhaps 10^{-10} sec for dielectric relaxation. This is because the nuclear spins are only very weakly coupled to the other motions of the system (translations, rotations and vibrations, usually inaccurately called lattice motions), so that any particular molecule undergoes many rotations and other movements in the liquid before the direction of its nuclear spins are significantly changed. However, nuclear spin relaxation only occurs because of these weak interactions and the interpretation of experimental data has to be in terms of them. As with the theory of any relaxation process, two main features are involved : (i) the nature and magnitude of the interaction energy ; (ii) the way in which the interaction changes with time due to the random motions of the molecules in the liquid. If there is sufficient understanding of the first item, nuclear spin relaxation experiments can provide useful information about the second and hence about the molecular dynamics.

There is a number of mechanisms by which nuclear spins may be coupled to the lattice motions. It is useful to begin by listing them before proceeding to more detailed considerations.

(1) The interaction between the electric quadrupole moment of the nucleus and the electric field gradient produced by the surrounding electrons and nuclei. Nuclear quadrupole moments only exist for nuclei with spins greater than $1/2$ (N^{14}, O^{17}, etc.), but, if present, this mechanism is usually dominant.

(2) The interaction between the magnetic moment of the nucleus and magnetic fields due to the dipoles of other magnetic nuclei. As the molecules move about

in the liquid, the local magnetic field at one particular nucleus will fluctuate and relaxation may occur. This process may be subdivided into intramolecular and intermolecular contributions. The intramolecular parts involve molecular re-orientation and the intermolecular parts relative diffusion of neighbours.

(3) The interaction between a nuclear magnetic moment and the magnetic fields generated by the orbital motion of the nuclei and electrons as charged particles. As the molecule moves in the liquid, it generates a fluctuating magnetic field which will be experienced by each nuclear spin. This mechanism is frequently referred to as a spin-rotation interaction, but similar effects can arise from fluctuations of relative translational motion.

(4) Another magnetic mechanism arises from fluctuating magnetic fields produced by anisotropic chemical shifts. As the molecules rotate, the screening field, produced by the diamagnetic electronic currents induced by the primary external field will fluctuate and may cause relaxation. This mechanism can only be significant if the external field is large.

(5) Finally, relaxation may occur by interaction of nuclear spins with the unpaired electron spins of paramagnetic species present in the system. This may be by means of long-range dipolar interactions or by a contact mechanism if the unpaired electron density becomes significant at the positions of the nucleus under investigation.

2. RELAXATION IN FLUCTUATING FIELDS

The general theory of the relaxation of nuclear spins in liquids involves time-dependent perturbation theory where the perturbation is the Hamiltonian $\mathcal{H}'(t)$ representing the interaction between the nuclear spin and the other (lattice) degrees of freedom. As noted in the introduction, this perturbation may arise by several mechanisms, but the quantum mechanical treatment of the relaxation process is similar in all cases. The perturbation, which will fluctuate with the time because of molecular motion, will have a matrix element between initial and final spin states 1 and 2 which may be written

$$(2|\mathcal{H}'(t)|1) = \{[|(2|\mathcal{H}'|1)|^2]_{av}\}^{\frac{1}{2}} u(t), \qquad (2.1)$$

where the root-mean-square value should be calculable from equilibrium statistical mechanics and $u(t)$ is a fluctuating function with mean-square modulus unity.

In time-dependent perturbation theory [2] the transition probability per unit time is given by

$$P_{1 \to 2} = \hbar^{-2}[|(2|\mathcal{H}'|1)|^2]_{av} \int_{-\infty}^{\infty} \exp(i\omega\tau) \cdot \rho(\tau) d\tau, \qquad (2.2)$$

where $\hbar\omega$ is the energy difference between states 1 and 2 and $\rho(\tau)$ is the autocorrelation function of $(2|\mathcal{H}'|1)$ defined as

$$\rho(\tau) = [u(t)u(t+\tau)]_{av}. \qquad (2.3)$$

If $\rho(\tau)$ is supposed to decay exponentially,

$$\rho(\tau) = \exp(-\tau/\tau_c), \qquad (2.4)$$

where τ_c is a correlation time, (2.2) becomes

$$P_{1 \to 2} = 2\hbar^{-2}[|(2|\mathcal{H}'|1)|^2]_{av} \tau_c/(1+\omega^2\tau_c^2). \qquad (2.5)$$

These results are of general validity and may be applied to any type of relaxation by using appropriate expressions for the coupling Hamiltonian $\mathcal{H}'$.

3. RELAXATION BY ELECTRON FIELD GRADIENTS

For nuclei with a spin of 1 or higher, relaxation occurs principally by means of the interaction between the electric field gradient and the nuclear position and the nuclear electric quadrupole moment eQ. If the electric field gradient is axially symmetric and has the value eq, the full expression for the spin-lattice relaxation time is

$$T_1^{-1} = e^4 q^2 Q^2 \hbar^2 \left[\frac{3}{80} \int \exp(i\omega_0 \tau) \cdot \rho_2(\tau) d\tau + \frac{3}{40p} \int \exp(2i\omega_0 \tau) \cdot \rho_2(\tau) d\tau \right], \quad (3.1)$$

where ω_0 is the (angular) Larmor frequency and $\rho_2(\tau)$ is the autocorrelation function for $P_2(\cos\theta)$, that is the average value of $P_2(\cos\theta)$, θ being the angle between the axis of the electric field gradient at times zero and τ. With the exponential form (2.4) for $\rho(\tau)$, this gives

$$T_1^{-1} = \tfrac{3}{8} e^4 q^2 Q^2 \hbar^2 \tau_c \quad (3.2)$$

for $\omega_0 \tau_c \ll 1$.

4. RELAXATION BY NUCLEAR DIPOLE-DIPOLE INTERACTION

This mechanism arises because the magnetic field at one nuclear position fluctuates because of the re-orientation of the line joining the two particles. If the second nucleus is of a different species (or has a large chemical shift with respect to the nucleus undergoing transitions), T_1 is given by

$$T_1^{-1} = \tfrac{1}{2} \hbar^2 \gamma^2 \gamma'^2 b^{-6} \rho_2(\tau), \quad (4.1)$$

where $\rho_2(\tau)$ is again the autocorrelation function of $P_2(\cos\theta)$, θ now being the angle between new and old positions of the line joining the two nuclei. γ and γ' are the magnetogyric ratios of the two nuclei and b is the distance separating them. Clearly, the re-orientation function $\rho_2(\tau)$ in (4 1) is very similar to that used in the theory of electric quadrupole relaxation (eqn. (3.1)). Eqn. (4.1) is explicitly for intramolecular relaxation where the intervening distance b is constant. Relaxation can also occur by interactions with spins in other neighbouring molecules.

The theory of nuclear dipole-dipole relaxation has the considerable advantage that the mean square of fluctuating Hamiltonian is known (if b, γ and γ' are known) so direct information can be obtained about the correlation function $\rho_2(\tau)$ if this mechanism is dominant.

5. RELAXATION BY MOLECULAR MOTION

The theory of spin relaxation by the magnetic fields produced by the relative motion of other electrons and nuclei in the same and neighbouring molecules differs from the previous treatment because the strength of the fluctuating fields depends on the *velocities* (linear and angular) of the molecules rather than their positions. If we consider only intramolecular contributions to the local magnetic field, the coupling Hamiltonian will be proportional to the angular momentum $\mathbf{J}$ and may be written

$$\mathcal{H}' = C_{\alpha\beta} I_\alpha J_\beta \quad (5.1)$$

(In this equation a summation convention is used for tensor suffixes.) C is usually referred to as the spin-rotation interaction tensor. It may, in principle, be calculated quantum-mechanically from a knowledge of molecular wave functions, but such calculations have only been carried through so far for small molecules. It can also be measured directly by microwave methods for small molecules. For example, there have been recent studies of formaldehyde.[3]

The general discussion is simplified if the full expression (5.1) is replaced by a scalar interaction,

$$\mathcal{H}' = C\mathbf{I} \cdot \mathbf{J}. \quad (5.2)$$

Clearly, the interaction (5.2) gives a magnetic field at the nucleus which is proportional to the angular momentum. The general equation (2.2) then involves the angular momentum autocorrelation function $\rho_J(\tau)$, which describes the average rate at which a molecule changes its rotational velocity.

$$\rho_J(\tau) = [\mathbf{J}(0) \cdot \mathbf{J}(\tau)]_{av}/[\mathbf{J}^2(0)]_{av}. \tag{5.3}$$

6. RE-ORIENTATION OF MOLECULES IN LIQUIDS

From the preceding discussion, all intramolecular nuclear spin relaxation processes are related to the way in which molecules re-orient in the liquid phase. Dielectric relaxation times of polar molecules are also determined by re-orientation rates, so it should be possible to probe the details of such movements by careful comparison of the various physical measurements.

In the theory of dielectric relaxation, the loss (or imaginary part of the complex dielectric constant) at angular frequency ω is proportional to

$$\int_{-\infty}^{\infty} \exp(i\omega\tau) \cdot \rho_1(\tau) d\tau, \tag{6.1}$$

where ρ_1 is the autocorrelation function for the dipole moment,

$$\rho_1(\tau) = [\boldsymbol{\mu}(0) \cdot \boldsymbol{\mu}(\tau)]_{av}/[\boldsymbol{\mu}^2(0)]_{av}. \tag{6.2}$$

This is clearly the autocorrelation function of $\cos\theta$, where θ is the angle between orientations of the dipolar axis at times 0 and t.

This means that experimental information should be available on the Fourier component (at angular frequency ω) of the autocorrelation functions of both $\rho_1(\cos\theta)$ and $\rho_2(\cos\theta)$ and also of the angular momentum $\mathbf{J}$. These three quantities are strongly interrelated since the angle change θ occurs only through the rotation associated with the angular momentum. Comparison of these quantities should provide a powerful test of any detailed model for re-orientation.

The most widely used model is that of Brownian rotation motion which has been applied in theories of dielectric and nuclear spin relaxation. This leads to exponential decay functions of the type (2.4) for both ρ_1 and ρ_2. Using a model of a rough sphere of radius a rotating in a viscous fluid, Bloembergen, Purcell and Pound [1] found

$$\tau_c = 4\pi\eta a^3/3kT \tag{6.3}$$

where η is the viscosity. This is the same model as was previously used by Debye [4] for dielectric dispersion.

Although the agreement with experimental nuclear spin relaxation times was quite good using (6.3), the underlying assumptions of the Brownian motion theory are unrealistic for the rotational motion. In brief, they are that the molecules moves as if in a viscous liquid except for short intervals of time during which strong random torques act to maintain the equilibrium thermal distribution of angular momentum. In a real liquid, the motion is more continuous and it should be possible to set up other models connecting the decay rates of angles and angular moments. Such a theory should give more direct information on molecular re-orientation by avoiding appeal to a semi-macroscopic description as in (6.3).

---

[1] N. Bloembergen, E. M. Purcell and R. V. Pound, *Phys. Rev.*, 1948, **73**, 679.
[2] J. A. Pople, W. G. Schneider and H. J. Bernstein, *High Resolution Nuclear Magnetic Resonance* (McGraw-Hill, New York, 1959).
[3] W. H. Flygare, V. W. Weiss, *J. Chem. Physics*, 1966, **45**, 2785.
[4] P. Debye, *Polar Molecules* (Dover Publications, New York, 1945).

Study of Molecular Motion in Liquids by Measurement of Nuclear Relaxation

By R. A. Dwek and R. E. Richards

Physical Chemistry Laboratory, Oxford

Received 23rd January, 1967

Nuclear magnetic relaxation times depend on the strengths of the magnetic components of random molecular motion at nuclear or electron resonance frequencies. The methods by which these spectral densities can be obtained are outlined. Measurements of correlation times for different types of molecular motion and their dependence on temperature are reviewed.

Magnetic resonance methods may be used to study molecular motion in liquids and in suitable cases can provide detailed information about specific interactions between molecules in the liquid phase. In this paper the principles involved in such studies are set out in an attempt to illustrate the scope and limitations of the method.

Molecular motion in liquids directly affects the nuclear relaxation times T_1 and T_2. The spin lattice relaxation time T_1 is a measure of the time taken for the nuclei to achieve an equilibrium population among the allowed energy levels in the applied magnetic field H_0; it is sometimes referred to as the longitudinal relaxation time as it is concerned with the relaxation of the nuclear magnetization along the direction of the applied field H_0, usually called the z direction. T_1 is a measure of the time required for the nuclei to exchange energy with their surroundings. The spin-spin relaxation time T_2 measures the time taken for nuclei to exchange energy among themselves by an adiabatic process; it is sometimes referred to as the transverse relaxation time because it is concerned with the relaxation of the nuclear magnetization in the transverse (xy) plane at right angles to H_0. In liquids, T_1 and T_2 are usually nearly equal, but in some special cases their differences can give valuable information.

It is convenient to consider first the mechanism of spin lattice relaxation for a system of nuclei of spin $\tfrac{1}{2}$. In an applied magnetic field H_0 these nuclei are distributed between two energy levels, which by convention we label +(lower) and −(higher), and which correspond to the two allowed orientations of the nuclear magnets in H_0. When radiation of angular frequency ω_n is applied to the system in the appropriate way, transitions are induced among the energy levels; the probability of a quantum of radiation inducing an upward transition is the same as for a downward transition, so a net exchange of energy between the nuclear spins and the radiation can only occur if the populations of the two nuclear energy levels are unequal. If the lower energy level has an excess population (as it would have at thermal equilibrium) then energy is absorbed from the radiation, but if the upper energy level were more highly populated for some reason, then an emission spectrum would be induced.

The angular frequency ω_n is equal to $\gamma_n H_0$, where γ_n is the nuclear magnetogyric ratio, and H_0 is the magnetic field actually experienced by the nucleus. For magnetic fields of the order of 10^4 gauss, ω_n is near 10^7 c/sec. The probability that a nucleus will make a spontaneous jump from one energy level to another is vanishingly small, and for nuclei of spin $\frac{1}{2}$, there is no mechanism other than the oscillating field at ω_n for the particular applied field H_0, which can cause transitions.

When a sample of nuclei of spin $\frac{1}{2}$ is placed suddenly in H_0, the initial population of the two nuclear energy levels must be equal because the nuclei have random orientations in zero field. The nuclei then relax to the populations corresponding to thermal equilibrium with the characteristic time T_1. The oscillating magnetic fields at ω_n, needed to induce the transitions, are derived from the random motion of the molecules in the liquid.

The magnetic moments of the nuclei in the liquid set up local fields in their environment which are proportional to μ/d^3, where μ is the nuclear magnetic moment and d is the distance from it to the point at which the field is measured. The proportionality constant depends on the angle between H_0 and the vector joining the nucleus to the point considered.

These local magnetic fields fluctuate according to the molecular motion. Rotation of a molecule will cause the local field at one nucleus due to another in the same molecule to fluctuate at the rotational frequency. Relative diffusion of molecules causes the local fields at the nuclei of one molecule, due to those of another, to change. The frequency of the molecular motion is usually characterized by a correlation time, τ_r for rotation and τ_d for diffusion. For any random motion there is the whole spectrum of frequencies and the variation of the intensity of the fluctuations with frequency must depend on the type of motion concerned. However in all cases, the variation of the "spectral density" $J(\omega)$ with ω has a similar form which is roughly represented in fig. 1. $J(\omega)$ is independent of ω until $\omega\tau$ approaches unity, when the intensity falls to zero as ω increases. When τ is small, $J(\omega)$ is low and extends to high values of ω; when τ is large, $J(\omega)$ is greater but falls to zero at a lower frequency.

The relaxation times are therefore dependent on the values of $J(\omega)$ at the particular value of ω_n. $J(\omega)$ may be written

$$J(\omega) = \int_{-\infty}^{\infty} g(\tau) \exp(-i\omega\tau) \, d\tau, \tag{1}$$

where $g(\tau)$ is the correlation function. The form of this function must be known if correlation times are to be calculated from relaxation data. It is common to use an exponential function, which is physically reasonable for some types of motion and for which the Fourier transform is particularly simple. If we write $j(\omega) = J(\omega)/J(0)$ then

$$j(\omega) = 1/(1+\omega^2\tau^2) \tag{2}$$

and in several cases, this has been shown to be a good approximation.

However, more precise correlation functions can only be calculated on the assumption of a suitable molecular model, and Abragam [1] has dealt with several cases in some detail. Two further examples, however, are given to illustrate the type of progress that is being made towards our understanding of molecular motion. The first is that of Hubbard [2] who has considered the dipolar interactions between spins positioned off the centre of spheres. He assumed that both relative translation and rotation of the spheres could be described by a diffusion equation and has shown that to a first approximation, it is valid to neglect the contribution of the rotational motion to the relaxation rates, and to treat the spins as being at the centre of the spheres. $j_d(\omega)$ is then given by

$$j_d(\omega) = (15/2)I(u),$$

where

$$u = |\omega\tau|^{\frac{1}{2}}, \quad \tau = d^2/D,$$

and

$$I(u) = u^{-5}\{u^2 - 2 + e^{-u}[(u^2-2)\sin u + (u^2+4u+2)\cos u]\}.$$

d is the distance of closest approach of the two spins, and D is the diffusion coefficient in the equation describing the translational diffusion of the spheres. Although the form of $j(\omega)$ appears to be quite different from eqn. (2), it still has a shape similar to those of fig. 1.

The second example is simpler, and invokes the concept of a distribution of correlation times. It is often found that discrepancies between theory and experiment can be removed by such a postulate. A recent paper concerned with the hydration of keratin [3] shows this well. It is assumed that the water molecules can exist in a range of different environments, each characterized by its own correlation time, and proton exchange occurs between these sites in a time short compared with T_2. A log-normal distribution of correlation times was used in this case, implying that for rotation of the water molecules, there is a Gaussian distribution of free energies of activation, and the experimental measurements could be reproduced well. On the other hand, there may be a quite different correlation function with a single value of τ_c. A recent paper by Waugh [4] is concerned with the nature of the correlation

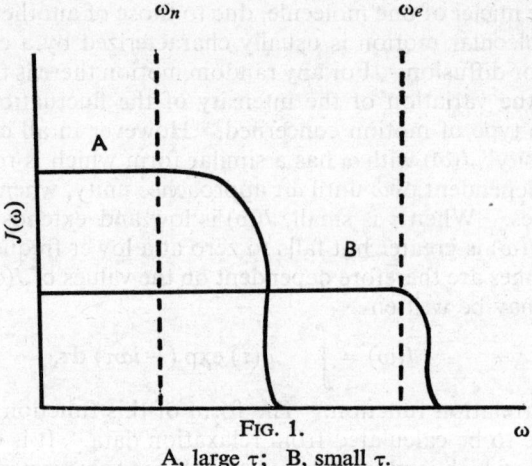

FIG. 1.
A, large τ; B, small τ.

function for rotation in liquids and gases, and points out how in certain special cases additional information about the form of the correlation function may be obtained.

For most liquids, τ_c is near 10^{-10} sec, and ω_n usually lies near 10^7 sec^{-1}. $\omega_n \tau_c$ is therefore much less than 1 (fig. 1) and we are well back on the flat part of the correlation spectrum, in the so-called "white spectrum". The relaxation time is therefore independent of ω_n and hence of H_0. In special cases, such as rotationally relaxed nuclei in molecules at infinite dilution in a non-magnetic solvent, the theory of relaxation allows τ_r to be obtained from measurements of T_1.[5] Usually, however, we are not able to do this, but the effect of changing conditions on τ can often be followed directly by measuring the change of T_1. For example, when the temperature is changed, τ changes and this is reflected by a corresponding change of T_1. From such measurements, activation energies for molecular motions can be obtained directly. For example, in benzene, the nuclear relaxation rate is determined by modulation of the dipole-dipole interactions. These may be either inter- or intramolecular, and we may write

$$1/T_1 = 1/T_{1\text{ inter}} + 1/T_{1\text{ intra}}.$$

$1/T_{1\text{ intra}}$ depends only on the rotation of the molecules while $1/T_{1\text{ inter}}$ depends primarily on translation. By measuring the proton T_1 for mixtures of benzene with a non-magnetic diluent such as carbon disulphide, or better, with fully deuterated benzene, and extrapolation to zero proton concentration, these two contributions can be separated.[6] The activation energies obtained from relaxation measurements for these processes have been compared with those corresponding to various physical properties [6] and are listed in table 1.

TABLE 1.—APPARENT ACTIVATION ENERGIES FOR LIQUID BENZENE IN kcal mole^{-1} AT ROOM TEMPERATURE

self diffusion	3·1 kcal mole^{-1}
viscosity/absolute temperature	3·2
$T_{1\ \text{inter}}$	3·0
Rayleigh light scattering	1·35
deuteron T_1	1·86
$T_{1\ \text{intra}}$	1·2
$T_{1\ \text{intra}(d)}$	1·86

One might expect agreement between the activation energies of $T_{1\ \text{inter}}$ and those of self-diffusion and viscosity, as all three depend mainly on translational motion. Similarly, those of Rayleigh light-scattering, deuteron T_1, and $T_{1\ \text{intra}}$ agree reasonably well, since all depend principally on rotation.

The rotation of a group or molecule may give rise to a group or molecular magnetic moment, and interaction of the nuclear magnetic moment with this may provide an additional relaxation mechanism. This interaction is termed the spin-rotation interaction and contributes to $1/T_{1\ \text{intra}}$. By considering the two contributions to $T_{1\ \text{intra}}$ the dipolar one, $T_{1\ \text{intra}\ (d)}$ and the spin rotation $T_{1\text{SR}}$, we can write

$$1/T_{1\ \text{intra}} = 1/T_{1\ \text{intra}\ (d)} + 1/T_{1\text{SR}},$$

The apparent activation energy for $T_{1\ \text{intra}\ (d)}$ is then found to be 1·86 kcal/mole^{-1} in excellent agreement with that found from the deuteron T_1.[6] It may be that a redetermination from Rayleigh light-scattering is desirable.

The nuclear relaxation times in a diamagnetic liquid are often reduced remarkably when very small concentrations of paramagnetic solutes are added. The presence of dissolved oxygen, for example, in benzene, reduces the proton relaxation time by a factor of 5. The reason for this is that the magnetic moments of unpaired electrons are about three orders of magnitude greater than nuclear moments, so that the local fields generated by them are correspondingly greater; the increased intensity of the fluctuating fields induce more efficient nuclear spin relaxation. The situation is more complicated than this, however, and can lead to more important information about molecular motion in the liquid.

In a dilute solution of a paramagnetic solute, the nuclear relaxation is often entirely dominated by pairwise interactions between an unpaired electron, S, and nucleus, I; the rapid diffusion of the solute through the solvent ensures that all the nuclei are equally affected so that the relaxation is shared among them all. The strong local fields produced by the electron can be coupled to the nuclei by simple dipole-dipole interaction, or sometimes by a scalar coupling transmitted through a chemical bond, which may be transient, by the same mechanism which is responsible for the hyperfine structure of e.s.r. spectra or the spin-spin multiplets in n.m.r. spectra.

For purely dipole-dipole coupling, the pairwise interaction of a nucleus and an electron can induce three types of transition involving the nuclei, which are illustrated in fig. 2. There are four energy levels, corresponding to the combinations of the

S and I spin quantum numbers. The lowest nuclear energy level is by convention labelled $+$, and because the magnetic moment of the electron has the opposite sign to that of the proton, we label the lower electronic energy levels negative. The random magnetic field fluctuations can induce nuclear transitions which may be denoted conveniently by the shorthand I_- and I_+, which represent nuclear transitions *from* the $-$ and from the $+$ levels respectively. As well as these transitions, the dipolar coupling can introduce the coupled transitions $S_+I_+(S_-I_-)$ and $S_+I_-(S_-I_+)$ (fig. 2) in which the electron and nucleus make simultaneous flips, and these terms have larger coefficients than the I_+ or I_- terms. The frequency involved in the I_+, I_- transitions is ω_n, but the coupled transitions involve frequencies $(\omega_e - \omega_n)$ and $(\omega_e + \omega_n)$ which, because ω_e is so much larger than ω_n, can both be taken to be ω_e, the electronic Larmor frequency. The expression for the effect of the paramagnetic solute on the

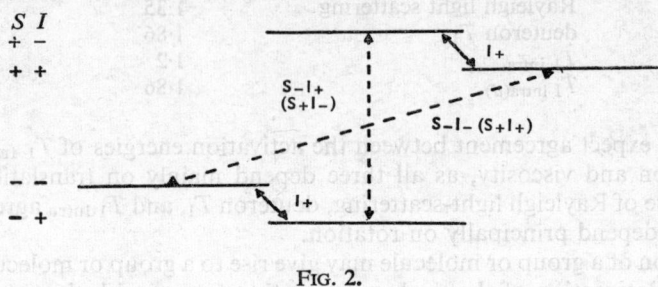

FIG. 2.

nuclear relaxation time therefore contains two terms, one involving ω_n and the other ω_e. If there is also a scalar interaction between the nuclei and electrons, this will add a further term, and since scalar coupling can induce only the coupled transitions $S_+I_-(S_-I_+)$, it also will involve ω_e. The resulting equation may be written:

$$\frac{1}{T_1} = \frac{N_e}{N_n} p \frac{2}{15} \frac{s(s+1)g^2\beta^2\gamma_n^2}{d^6}\left[\frac{3\tau_c}{1+\omega_n^2\tau_c^2} + \frac{7\tau_c}{1+\omega_e^2\tau_c^2}\right] + \frac{N_e}{N_n} p \frac{2}{3}s(s+1)\frac{A^2}{\hbar^2}\left[\frac{\tau_e}{1+\omega_e^2\tau_e^2}\right], \quad (4)$$

where N_e and N_n are the molar concentrations of unpaired electrons and of nuclei respectively, p is the number of nuclei affected at each encounter, s is the electron spin quantum number, g is the electronic g factor, β the Bohr magneton, A the scalar coupling constant and τ_e is the correlation time for the modulation of the scalar coupling.

Whereas $\omega_n^2\tau_c^2$ in liquids is usually much smaller than 1, this is not necessarily so for $\omega_e^2\tau_c^2$. For example, if τ_c is 10^{-10} sec, then at 10^4 gauss, ω_e is about $1\cdot 8 \times 10^{10}$ sec^{-1} and $\omega_e^2\tau_c^2$ is 3·24. It therefore follows that an important term in eqn. (4) will be magnetic-field-dependent, and a study of the variation of T_1 with magnetic field can allow τ_c to be measured if the scalar contribution to T_1 is unimportant. This value of τ_c will be the correlation time for relative motion of nuclei and electrons; it may be a measure of the rate of rotation of a weak complex of solvent and solute molecules or it may be the diffusional correlation time of solute molecules with respect to solvent molecules. An example of the former would be the relaxation of nuclei in a large ligand bound to a paramagnetic metal atom; the latter situation arises when there is no significant binding between solute and solvent as in the case of a free radical dissolved in an inert solvent.

Several measurements of molecular correlation times in liquids by this method have been performed. Hausser, Kruger and Noack [7] have measured the frequency and temperature dependence of the relaxation times of several protonic systems containing various free radicals. The experimental results agree with the theoretical predictions based on the translational diffusion of spheres with only dipole-dipole interactions between radical and solvent molecules. The correlation times were found to depend on the diffusion constant of the solvent and on the temperature. However, for solutions of free radicals in toluene, discrepancies between this theory and experiment were apparent at low temperatures.[7] Reinvestigation of toluene solutions over an extended temperature and frequency range [8] showed that the experimental results could be interpreted in terms of purely dipolar interactions, the time dependence of which arises from the relative translational motions and also the rotational tumbling of an associated complex. The activation energies for these processes were found to be 3·1 and 7·8 kcal mole^{-1} respectively. The activation energy calculated in previous work [7] assuming only translational motion to be contributing to T_1, was 4·4 kcal mole^{-1}. Thus it is essential to analyze relaxation data in some detail, if meaningful activation energies for molecular motions are to be calculated.

Kramer, Muller-Warmuth and Schindler [9] have also investigated the temperature dependence of the correlation times of several protonic systems containing free radicals. Since translational diffusion had been shown to be the main mechanism of relaxation, the activation energies for viscosity should be similar to those of the correlation times, and indeed this was the case. On the other hand, the activation energies from dielectric relaxation measurements would be expected to be different, since the molecular motion in this case is rotation. This has been illustrated for diethyl ether, for which the activation energies for the viscosity and those of the translational correlation times are about 1·8 kcal mole^{-1}. This value can be contrasted with that of 1·3 kcal mole^{-1} obtained from dielectric relaxation.

If scalar interaction makes an important contribution to the nuclear relaxation, there are two correlation times to contend with and it is also of interest to be able to measure the value of the scalar coupling constant. For this purpose, additional information can be obtained from the field and temperature dependence of the nuclear T_2. Any mechanism of interaction between nucleus and electron which can affect T_1 must also affect T_2, but scalar coupling can also shorten T_2 by a mechanism which cannot affect T_1. T_2 measures the time taken for the nuclear magnetization in the xy plane to decay by a gradual loss of phase of the precessing nuclei. This phase loss can be induced by any static component of a local field which can cause some nuclei to precess at different frequencies from others; scalar interaction produces such a component which does not vary as the complex rotates. The longer the component is applied the more the nuclei lose phase, so the effect will be proportional to τ_e, the lifetime of the scalar coupling. The expression for T_2 is therefore similar to that for T_1 but contains an additional term in τ_e in the scalar part:

$$\frac{1}{T_2} = \frac{N_e}{N_n} p \frac{1}{15} \frac{s(s+1)g^2\beta^2\gamma_n^2}{d^6}\left[\frac{7\tau_c}{1+\omega_n^2\tau_c^2} + \frac{13\tau_c}{1+\omega_e^2\tau_c^2}\right] + \frac{N_e}{N_n} p \frac{1}{3} s(s+1) \frac{A^2}{\hbar^2}\left[\tau_e + \frac{\tau_e}{1+\omega_e^2\tau_c^2}\right]. \quad (5)$$

Note that $T_1/T_2 = 1$ except when scalar coupling becomes important, when $T_1 > T_2$. The importance of the scalar term for relaxation depends not only on A but also on τ_e and ω_e and hence on temperature and applied field strength. The detailed study of systems to evaluate all these parameters has been carried out only in a few cases; a recent paper by Pfeifer et al.[10] describes some interesting examples and gives many references.

Further information about molecular correlation times for diffusion may be obtained from nuclear electron double resonance experiments. If the electron resonance of the free radical dissolved at low concentration in a diamagnetic liquid is saturated, remarkable changes in the nuclear resonance intensities often occur. This phenomenon depends on the spin-lattice relaxation processes already described.

When the electron resonance of the radical is strongly irradiated, the populations of the electron energy levels $(+-$ and $-+)$ may be equalized; the resonance is saturated. The spin-lattice relaxation processes attempt to restore the populations of the energy levels to the thermal equilibrium values in which more spins are in the lower two levels than in the upper two (fig. 2). For dipolar coupling, the processes are S_+I_+ and S_+I_-, but the first has the greater importance. The electronic transition is from the $(-+)$ to the $(++)$ level, and from the $(--)$ to the $(+-)$ levels (fig. 2). The dominant relaxation is from $(++)$ to $(--)$ by the S_+I_+ process, so that nuclei initially in the lowest $(-+)$ energy level are transferred to the $(--)$ upper nuclear level. Under optimum conditions the populations of the two nuclear levels can be changed by a fraction $\frac{1}{2}\gamma_e/\gamma_n$, which for protons is -330; the population of the upper nuclear level becomes 330 times greater than that of the lower level is greater in the upper at thermal equilibrium. The nuclear resonance becomes an *emission* instead of an absorption spectrum and is greatly increased in intensity.

The theory of the effect is well understood [2] and depends entirely on the spin-lattice relaxation of the nuclei and of the electrons. Since this mechanism depends on the spectral density of the thermal motion in the liquid at ω_e as described above, so the enhancement of the nuclear resonance must also depend on this spectral density; when ω_e is small enough to lie on the flat part of the correlation spectrum (fig. 1), the maximum enhancement (of -330 for protons) may be obtained, but at higher values of ω_e the spectral density decreases and the nuclear resonance enhancement becomes smaller. Measurements of the enhancement of the nuclear resonance at different magnetic field strengths (and hence of ω_e) can often be satisfactorily interpreted by a model of diffusing spheres with a single translation correlation time [9, 11, 12]

If there is also scalar coupling between the electrons and the nuclei, there is an additional relaxation mechanism of the S_+I_- type (see above). If this relaxation mechanism is stronger than the dipolar mechanism, saturation of the electron resonance equalizes the population of the two electronic energy levels, and the S_+I_- relaxation returns nuclei to the lower $(-+)$ nuclear energy level. Under optimum conditions the population of the lower level is increased by a fraction $-\gamma_e/\gamma_n$, which is about $+660$ for protons; the nuclear resonance *absorption* is *increased* in intensity. There is thus a striking and qualititative difference in the results for dipolar and scalar coupling. If the scalar coupling is weak and comparable with the dipolar coupling, the nuclear resonance intensity lies somewhere between -330 and $+660$.

Various attempts have been made to interpret quantitative measurements of these nuclear electron double resonance experiments in terms of simple models for the scalar coupling.[11, 13] These studies give values for correlation times and coupling constants which are in approximate agreement with other measurements, but unfortunately none of them have so far proved entirely satisfactory.[13, 14] When scalar coupling is present, therefore, double resonance experiments provide an extremely sensitive indication of its importance, although the correlation times derived may not be accurate. On the other hand, when scalar coupling is absent, the double resonance measurements provide a useful addition to direct measurements of T_1, and the values of translational correlation times and their field dependence, as obtained from both these methods are often in excellent agreement.[9]

For nuclei with spin quantum numbers greater than $\frac{1}{2}$, the distribution of positive charge over the nucleus may be aspherical, and this situation may be described in terms of a nuclear electric-quadrupole moment. If the electron distribution about the nucleus has less than cubic symmetry, the resulting electric field gradient can couple with the nuclear electric quadrupole moment.[1] This nuclear quadrupole coupling provides a further mechanism in addition to the nuclear magnetic moment by which the nucleus can relate its orientation to that of other particles around it. Thus fluctuation of the electric field gradient coupled to the quadrupole moment can provide an additional mechanism for nuclear relaxation; the relaxation rate $1/T_1 = 1/T_2$ is proportional to the square of the electric quadrupole coupling constant.[1] Because the relaxation is governed by fluctuations of the quadrupole interaction at the nuclear resonance frequency ω_n, the relaxation rate is also proportional to τ in the "white spectrum" approximation, where τ is the correlation time for the motion which modulates the quadrupole interaction.

The electric field gradients produced by chemical bonds are often very strong and the electric quadrupole interaction often completely dominates the relaxation times of the nuclei. The quadrupole relaxation is often so strong that nuclear resonances become very broad and difficult to detect.

The relevant correlation time may be rotational or diffusional in a liquid. In a molecule such as carbon tetrachloride, the quadrupole coupling arises from the electric field produced by the C—Cl bond, so that relaxation is produced by rotation of the molecule. On the other hand, the electron distribution about the bromine nucleus in the bromide ion in solution is symmetrical, but the symmetry is momentarily reduced by collisions with solvent molecules or with other ions. In this case the transient quadrupole coupling is associated mainly with a diffusional correlation time.[15]

TABLE 2

molecule	ΔE expt. (kcal mole^{-1})	ΔE viscosity (kcal mole^{-1})
CCl_4	1·3 ±0·1	2·3
$HCCl_3$	1·4 ±0·1	1·8
ClC_6H_5	1·6 ±0·2	2·3
$TiCl_4$	1·0 ±0·1	2·1
ClO_3^- (in H_2O)	1·5 ±0·4	3·7

If the quadrupole coupling constant is known from other measurements, the experimental values of T_1 or T_2 can be used to obtain a value for τ. Herbison-Evans and Richards made such measurements on some nitrogen compounds [16] and found that their results supported the theory of Wirtz which relates the correlation time to the microviscosity.

The temperature dependence of correlation times of some chlorine compounds have also been determined from measurements of T_2 of the ^{35}Cl resonances.[17] This temperature dependence is quite different from that of the bulk viscosity as is evident from the activation energies in table 2. In this case the motion involved is molecular rotation so the activation energies are different from those for viscosity which depend on translation. The authors suggest that the correct temperature dependence of the correlation time would be obtained from considerations of the microviscosity temperature dependence. This would also seem to be the case for the results of Herbison-Evans and Richards. It will be interesting to compare the activation energies for the quadrupole relaxation of halide ions in solutions of electrolytes, which depend on translational motion, with the appropriate energies for bulk viscosity.

Moniz and Gutowsky [18] have studied the relaxation times of ^{14}N in different types of groups and again using known values of ^{14}N quadrupole coupling constants, correlation times for the molecular reorientation were calculated. The temperature dependence of T_1 was also measured for several compounds, and the range of activation energies was found to lie between 1·4 and 3·2 kcal mole^{-1}, the differences generally reflecting the relative sizes and shapes of the molecules. The temperature dependence of the proton and ^{14}N spin lattice relaxation times in methyl cyanide were found to be 1·4 kcal mole^{-1} and 1·9 kcal mole^{-1} respectively. This reflects the different types of motion contributing to the T_1 in each case; rotation for the ^{14}N, rotation and translation for protons. The relaxation time of the nitrogen nucleus is determined mainly by rotation about the axes perpendicular to the C—CN bond, while rotation about all axes could contribute to the relaxation rate of the protons. Zeidler [19] has found the rotational correlation time for the protons to be in good agreement with that obtained by the nitrogen T_1. This could be understood if rotation about the C—CN axis makes little contribution to the proton T_1 because of very fast reorientation about the C_3 axis of the molecule, as would seem reasonable. Thus rotation about this bond would have an extremely short correlation time and would not make much contribution to T_1.

In conclusion, it must be emphasized that from measurements of nuclear relaxation times or of the enhancement of the nuclear resonance in a nuclear electron double resonance experiment, we are measuring the spectral density of the molecular interaction at particular frequencies, ω_n or ω_e. We can measure how these functions vary with ω by making measurements at different magnetic field strengths; their temperature dependence at each frequency can also be measured. It is therefore possible in principle to plot out the correlation spectrum at any temperature from purely experimental results. If a model for the molecular motion is assumed, the correlation function can be obtained and the experimental results expressed in terms of one or more correlation times. These can then be compared with values measured in other ways.

When there are specific intermolecular interactions during a collision between two molecules in the liquid, these can often be detected in the nuclear resonance spectrum. If one of the molecules is paramagnetic, measurements of T_1 and T_2 and especially of the enhancement of the nuclear resonance in a nuclear electron double resonance experiment, can give sensitive indications of scalar coupling formed by weak transient chemical binding.

[1] A. Abragam, *The Principles of Nuclear Magnetism*, chap. VII, (Clarendon Press, Oxford, 1961)
[2] P. S. Hubbard, *Proc. Roy. Soc. A*, 1966, **291**, 537.
[3] B. Sheard and J. Clifford, *Biopolymers*, 1966, **4**, 1057.
[4] J. S. Waugh, *Molecular Relaxation Processes*, (Chem. Soc. Spec. Publ. no. 20), p. 113. (Academic Press, 1966).
[5] see e.g., A. M. Pritchard and R. E. Richards, *Trans. Faraday Soc.*, 1966, **62**, 1388.
[6] J. G. Powles and R. Figgins, *Mol. Physics*, 1966, **10**, 155.
[7] K. H. Hausser, G. J. Kruger and F. Noack, *Z. Naturforsch*, 1965, 20a, 91.
[8] G. J. Kruger, W. Muller-Warmuth and R. Van Steenwinkel, *Z. Naturforsch.* 1966, 21a, 1224.
[9] K. D. Kramer, W. Muller-Warmuth and J. Schindler, *J. Chem. Physics*, 1965, **43**, 31.
[10] H. Pfeifer, D. Michel, D. Sames and H. Spring, *Mol. Physics*, 1966, **11**, 591.
[11] K. D. Kramer, W. Muller-Warmuth, and N. Roth, *Z. Naturforsch.*, 1965, 20a, 1391.
[12] R. A. Dwek, J. G. Kenworthy, D. F. S. Natusch, D. J. Shields and R. E. Richards, *Proc. Roy. Soc. A*, 1966, **291**, 487.
[13] W. Muller-Warmuth, *Z. Naturforsch.*, 1966, **21**, 153.
[14] R. A. Dwek, J. G. Kenworthy, J. A. Ladd and R. E. Richards, *Mol. Physics*, 1966, **11**, 287.
[15] C. Deverell, D. J. Frost and R. E. Richards, *Mol. Physics*, 1965, **9**, 565.
[16] D. Herbison-Evans and R. E. Richards, *Mol. Physics*, 1964, **1**, 515.
[17] D. E. O'Reilly and G. E. Schacher, *J. Chem. Physics*, 1963, **39**, 1768.
[18] W. B. Moniz and H. S. Gutowsky, *J. Chem. Physics*, 1963, **38**, 1155.
[19] M. D. Zeidler, *Ber. Bunsenges. Physik. Chem.*, 1965, **69**, 659.

Angular Correlation in Liquids

By A. D. Buckingham

School of Chemistry, The University of Bristol

Received 16th January 1967

Distribution functions describing the correlation between the positions and orientations of groups of one, two, three, ..., molecules are defined and discussed. The one-particle distribution function of an anisotropic fluid—such as a liquid in a uniform field—is expanded in orthogonal functions S that are simply related to the mean values of the Legendre polynomials describing its orientation. A variety of observables, including dielectric polarization, optical birefringence, Rayleigh and harmonic scattering, and magnetic resonance spectra, are described in terms of the appropriate S-coefficients and the orientation distribution functions.

The microscopic structure and the bulk equilibrium properties of fluids are expressible in terms of *distribution functions*, which give the probability of finding molecules in various configurations.[1,2] The pair distribution function is by far the most important, and is adequate for the description of the equilibrium properties of imperfect gases at low pressure, and of dense fluids, if the configurational energy is a sum of pair potentials.

The distribution function $n^{(h)}(\mathbf{r}_1;\mathbf{r}_2;\ldots;\mathbf{r}_h)$ is defined so that

$$n^{(h)}(\mathbf{r}_1;\mathbf{r}_2;\ldots;\mathbf{r}_h)d\mathbf{r}_1 d\mathbf{r}_2 \ldots d\mathbf{r}_h$$

is the probability of finding one molecule in each of the h volume elements $d\mathbf{r}_1, \ldots, d\mathbf{r}_h$ at $\mathbf{r}_1, \ldots, \mathbf{r}_h$. Thus, the singlet distribution function $n^{(1)}(\mathbf{r}_1)$ is the number density; in a fluid it is independent of the position $\mathbf{r}_1$ and equal to $n = N/V$, where N molecules are confined to the volume V. The pair distribution function $n^{(2)}(\mathbf{r}_1;\mathbf{r}_2)$ in a fluid is a function only of the difference of $\mathbf{r}_1$ and $\mathbf{r}_2$ and may be written $n^{(2)}(\mathbf{r})$.

The distribution function $n^{(h)}$ for a system at equilibrium obeying the laws of classical statistical mechanics may be expressed in terms of the configurational energy $U(\mathbf{r}_1;\mathbf{r}_2;\ldots;\mathbf{r}_N) = U$:

$$n^{(h)}(\mathbf{r}_1;\mathbf{r}_2;\ldots;\mathbf{r}_h) = \frac{N!}{(N-h)!} \frac{\int\ldots\int \exp(-U/kT)d\mathbf{r}_{h+1}\ldots d\mathbf{r}_N}{\int\ldots\int \exp(-U/kT)d\mathbf{r}_1 d\mathbf{r}_2 \ldots d\mathbf{r}_N}. \quad (1)$$

The factor $N!/(N-h)!$ is the number of ways h objects may be chosen in order from N objects. The denominator in eqn. (1) may be expressed in terms of the configurational partition function Q, where

$$Q = \frac{1}{N!}\int\ldots\int \exp(-U/kT)d\mathbf{r}_1 d\mathbf{r}_2 \ldots d\mathbf{r}_N \quad (2)$$

determines the bulk properties of a system at equilibrium. Hence these properties may also be related to the distribution functions.

The radial distribution function $g(r)$ is proportional to the probability of finding molecule 2 at a distance r from the molecule 1, and is defined by the equation

$$n^{(2)}(\mathbf{r}) = [N(N-1)/V^2]g(r). \quad (3)$$

For large N, $g(r) = n^{(2)}(r)/n^2$. This function is equal to zero for small r because of the repulsion between overlapping molecules, and in a fluid is unity for large r; it rises to a maximum at the most favoured separation where the configurational energy is a minimum. For a dilute gas of spherical molecules

$$g(r) = \exp(-u_{12}/kT) \qquad (4)$$

where u_{12} is the interaction energy of molecules 1 and 2.

ANGLE-DEPENDENT DISTRIBUTION FUNCTIONS

The concept of *radial* correlation can be extended to *angular* correlation. Thus, the distribution function $n^{(h)}(\mathbf{r}_1,\omega_1;\mathbf{r}_2,\omega_2;\ldots;\mathbf{r}_h,\omega_h)$ is defined so that

$$n^{(h)}(\mathbf{r}_1,\omega_1;\mathbf{r}_2,\omega_2;\ldots;\mathbf{r}_h,\omega_h)d\mathbf{r}_1 d\omega_1 d\mathbf{r}_2 d\omega_2 \ldots d\mathbf{r}_h d\omega_h$$

is the probability of finding a molecule in each of the h volume elements $d\mathbf{r}_1$, $d\mathbf{r}_2$, ..., $d\mathbf{r}_h$ at $\mathbf{r}_1, \mathbf{r}_2, \ldots, \mathbf{r}_h$ and in the orientational elements $d\omega_1, d\omega_2, \ldots, d\omega_h$ at $\omega_1, \omega_2, \ldots, \omega_h$. The minimum number of coordinates needed to specify ω_h depends on the symmetry of the molecules comprising the medium—it is two if the molecules are linear, and three if they are non-linear and rigid. Also

$$\int \ldots \int n^{(h)}(\mathbf{r}_1,\omega_1;\mathbf{r}_2,\omega_2;\ldots;\mathbf{r}_h,\omega_h)d\omega_1 d\omega_2 \ldots d\omega_h = n^{(h)}(\mathbf{r}_1;\mathbf{r}_2;\ldots;\mathbf{r}_h). \qquad (5)$$

In an isotropic fluid, the distribution functions are

$$n^{(1)}(\mathbf{r}_1,\omega_1) = n/\Omega_1 \qquad (6)$$

$$n^{(2)}(\mathbf{r}_1,\omega_1;\mathbf{r}_2,\omega_2) = n^{(2)}(\mathbf{r},\omega), \qquad (7)$$

where $\mathbf{r},\omega$ are coordinates relative to $\mathbf{r}_1$, ω_1 and $\Omega_1 = \int d\omega_1$.

The mean value of some function $f(\omega_1)$ of the orientation of a molecule is given by

$$\overline{f(\omega_1)} = \int f(\omega_1)\mathscr{P}(\omega_1)d\omega_1 \qquad (8)$$

where $\mathscr{P}(\omega_1)d\omega_1 = n^{-1}n^{(1)}(\mathbf{r}_1,\omega_1)d\omega_1$ is the probability a molecule has an orientation between ω_1 and $\omega_1+d\omega_1$, and may be called the singlet orientation distribution function. If one direction is favoured over others in a fluid (as when a uniform field is applied), $\mathscr{P}(\omega)$ gives the mean orientation of the molecule and may conveniently be described in terms of the direction cosines $a_i = \cos\theta_i$ ($i = 1,2,3$) of the favoured direction in a cartesian frame, 1,2,3 fixed in the molecule. Thus

$$\mathscr{P}(\omega) = n^{-1}n^{(1)}(\mathbf{r},\omega) = \Omega^{-1}[1+3\sum_i S_i a_i +5\sum_{i,j} a_i a_j S_{ij}+7\sum_{i,j,k} a_i a_j a_k S_{ijk}+$$

$$9\sum_{ijkl} a_i a_j a_k a_l S_{ijkl}+ \ldots], \qquad (9)$$

where the S-coefficients describe the ordering and, if $\delta_{ij} = 1$ if $i = j$ and $= 0$ if $i \neq j$,

$$\overline{a_i} = \overline{P_1(\cos\theta_i)} = \int a_i \mathscr{P}(\omega)d\omega = S_i, \qquad (10)$$

$$\tfrac{3}{2}\overline{a_i a_j} - \tfrac{1}{2}\delta_{ij} = S_{ij}, \qquad (11)$$

$$\tfrac{5}{2}\overline{a_i a_j a_k} - \tfrac{1}{2}(\overline{a_i}\delta_{jk}+\overline{a_j}\delta_{ki}+\overline{a_k}\delta_{ij}) = S_{ijk}, \qquad (12)$$

$$\tfrac{35}{8}\overline{a_i a_j a_k a_l} - \tfrac{5}{8}(\overline{a_i a_j}\delta_{kl}+\overline{a_i a_k}\delta_{jl}+\overline{a_i a_l}\delta_{jk}+\overline{a_j a_k}\delta_{il}+\overline{a_j a_l}\delta_{ik}+\overline{a_k a_l}\delta_{ij})+$$

$$\tfrac{1}{8}(\delta_{ij}\delta_{kl}+\delta_{ik}\delta_{jl}+\delta_{il}\delta_{jk}) = S_{ijkl}. \qquad (13)$$

In general there are three independent coefficients S_i (viz., S_1, S_2, S_3), five independent coefficients S_{ij} (S_{11}, S_{22}, S_{12}, S_{23}, S_{31}) (for $S_{11}+S_{22}+S_{33} = 0$), seven independent coefficients S_{ijk} (S_{111}, S_{112}, S_{113}, S_{122}, S_{123}, S_{222}, S_{223}), nine independent coefficients S_{ijkl}, etc. However, if the molecule possesses elements of symmetry, these numbers are reduced. Thus, just one coefficient of any order (S_1; S_{11}; S_{111}; S_{1111}; ...) is sufficient to describe the mean orientation of a linear molecule in space. For a molecule with C_{3v} symmetry (e.g., NH_3, CH_3Cl), the following are independent: S_1; S_{11}; S_{111}, S_{222}; S_{1111}, S_{2221}; for D_{6h} (e.g., C_6H_6) there are S_{11}; S_{1111}; and for C_{2v} (e.g. H_2O, CH_2O, CH_2Cl_2) S_1; S_{11}, S_{22}; S_{111}, S_{221}; S_{1111}, S_{1122}, S_{2222}.

The five P_2 coefficients S_{ij} were introduced by Saupe [3] to describe the average alignment of molecules dissolved in liquid crystal solvents in a uniform magnetic field. In isotropic fluids every S is zero, and in a completely oriented arrangement of linear molecules, $S_1 = S_{11} = S_{111} = S_{1111} = 1$. The coefficients have the following limits:

$$-1 \leqslant S_1, S_2, S_3 \leqslant 1;$$

$$-\tfrac{1}{2} \leqslant S_{11}, S_{22}, S_{33} \leqslant 1, \quad -\tfrac{3}{4} \leqslant S_{12}, S_{13}, S_{23} \leqslant \tfrac{3}{4};$$

$$-1 \leqslant S_{111} \leqslant 1, \quad -\frac{8}{3\sqrt{15}} \leqslant S_{112} \leqslant \frac{8}{3\sqrt{15}}, \quad -\frac{5}{6\sqrt{3}} \leqslant S_{123} \leqslant \frac{5}{6\sqrt{3}};$$

$$-\tfrac{3}{7} \leqslant S_{1111} \leqslant 1.$$

In an isotropic fluid, the orientation distribution function $g(\mathbf{r},\omega)$ is defined as

$$g(\mathbf{r},\omega) = \Omega^2 n^{-2} n^{(2)}(\mathbf{r},\omega) \tag{14}$$

so that $(V\Omega)^{-1} g(\mathbf{r},\omega) d\mathbf{r} d\omega$ is the probability molecule 2 is centred at a point between $\mathbf{r}$ and $\mathbf{r}+d\mathbf{r}$ from molecule 1 and at a relative orientation between ω and $\omega+d\omega$. For a dilute gas

$$g(\mathbf{r},\omega) = \exp(-u_{12}/kT), \tag{15}$$

where u_{12} is now dependent on orientation as well as separation.

In a mixture of species a and b, there are two singlet distribution functions $n^{(1)}$, such that $n_a^{(1)}(\mathbf{r}_1,\omega_1) = n_a/\Omega_1$, and $n_b^{(1)}(\mathbf{r}_1,\omega_1) = n_b/\Omega_1$, where $n_a = N_a/V$, $n_b = N_b/V$. However, there are now three pair distribution functions, $n_{aa}^{(2)}(\mathbf{r},\omega)$, $n_{ab}^{(2)}(\mathbf{r},\omega)$ and $n_{bb}^{(2)}(\mathbf{r},\omega)$; these functions give rise to the pair orientation distribution functions:

$$\begin{aligned} g_{aa}(\mathbf{r},\omega) &= \Omega^2 n_a^{-2} n_{aa}^{(2)}(\mathbf{r},\omega), \\ g_{ab}(\mathbf{r},\omega) &= \Omega^2 n_a^{-1} n_b^{-1} n_{ab}^{(2)}(\mathbf{r},\omega), \\ g_{bb}(\mathbf{r},\omega) &= \Omega^2 n_b^{-2} n_{bb}^{(2)}(\mathbf{r},\omega), \end{aligned} \tag{16}$$

defined so that $(V\Omega)^{-1} g_{ab}(\mathbf{r},\omega) d\mathbf{r} d\omega$, for example, is the probability a particular molecule of species b is at a point between $\mathbf{r}$ and $\mathbf{r}+d\mathbf{r}$ from molecule 1 of species a, and at a relative orientation between ω and $\omega+d\omega$.

MOLECULES IN AN ELECTRIC FIELD

Using the method of Kirkwood,[4] it is possible to derive a rigorous expression for S_1, the mean value of the cosine of the angle between μ_1, the permanent dipole moment of molecule 1, and the electric field $\mathbf{E}$;

$$S_1 = \frac{3\varepsilon}{2\varepsilon+1} \frac{\overline{m_1} E}{3kT} \tag{17}$$

where ε is the static dielectric constant and where $\overline{m_1}$ is the mean dipole moment, in the direction of μ_1, of molecule 1 and its neighbours in a small macroscopic sphere centred on molecule 1.

If the molecules are not polarizable, $\overline{m_1} = g\mu$, where

$$g = 1 + n\Omega^{-1} \int\int \cos\gamma\, g(\mathbf{r},\omega) d\mathbf{r} d\omega \tag{18}$$

is the *angular correlation function*,[5] γ being the angle between the dipole moments of molecules 1 and 2; the integration over **r** is limited to this sphere inside the fluid. Hence $\overline{\cos \theta_1}$ is determined by $\langle \cos \gamma \rangle$. In polar liquids in electric fields ~ 100 e.s.u., $S_1 \sim 10^{-3} - 10^{-2}$.

Distortions of molecules through interactions with neighbours lead to difficulties in the general theory of dielectric polarization. However, if the actual dipole m_1 is related to the permanent moment μ by the Onsager relation [6]

$$m = \frac{(2\varepsilon+1)(\varepsilon+2)}{3(2\varepsilon+\varepsilon_\infty)}\mu \tag{19}$$

where ε_∞ is the high-frequency dielectric constant, then [7, 8]

$$\frac{\varepsilon-1}{\varepsilon+2} - \frac{\varepsilon_\infty-1}{\varepsilon_\infty+2} = \frac{4\pi n \mu^2 g}{9kT} \frac{3\varepsilon(\varepsilon_\infty+2)}{(\varepsilon+2)(2\varepsilon+\varepsilon_\infty)}. \tag{20}$$

Table 1 shows correlation parameters g derived from eqn. (20) for a variety of polar liquids. It is clear that $g>1$ for molecules whose dipole axis is the short axis (chloroform, paraldehyde, trimethylamine), and $g<1$ if the dipole axis is the long axis (acetonitrile, chlorobenzene, nitrobenzene). In water, the strong hydrogen bonds linking a molecule to its four neighbours produce an abnormally large value of g which decreases at T increases.[9]

TABLE 1.—DIELECTRIC DATA AND MOLAR VOLUMES V_m AND DERIVED ANGULAR CORRELATION FUNCTIONS, g

substance	T(°C)	V_m(cm³)	ε	ε_∞	μ(D)	g
CH₃Cl	25	57·47	9·68	1·93	1·86	0·90
CH₂Cl₂	25	64·47	8·93	2·35	1·57	1·01
CHCl₃	25	80·72	4·72	2·37	1·01	1·19
CH₃CN	25	52·82	36·7	1·8	3·96	0·82
(CH₃)₂CO	25	73·86	19·11	2·0	2·89	0·97
paraldehyde	25	133·5	12·93	2·5	1·44	3·56
N(CH₃)₃	25	94·3	2·44	1·8	0·61	1·5
C₆H₅Cl	25	102·2	5·612	2·55	1·73	0·61
C₆H₅NO₂	25	102·7	34·89	2·63	4·24	0·87
C₆H₅NO₂	200	121	15·95	2·29	4·24	0·83
p-CH₃.C₆H₄.NO₂	58	120·4	22·2	2·4	4·5	0·70
H₂O	0	18·02	88·2	1·79₇	1·84	2·89
H₂O	25	18·07	78·5	1·79₅	1·84	2·81
H₂O	83	18·58	60·4	1·76₇	1·84	2·69
NH₃	−33	25·4	22·4	1·47	1·47	1·66
NH₃	25	28·3	16·9	1·53	1·47	1·65

OPTICAL BIREFRINGENCE IN FLUIDS

In optical birefringence experiments, the observable is generally the difference between the index of refraction in the x and y directions, $n_x - n_y$. In a fluid this difference may be induced by a strong electric field (the Kerr effect), a strong magnetic field (the Cotton-Mouton effect), an electric field gradient, or the field of an intense light beam.

$$n_x - n_y = \frac{1}{9n}(n^2+2)^2 2\pi \frac{N}{V}(\overline{\alpha_{xx} - \alpha_{yy}}) \tag{21}$$

where α is the polarizability in the presence of the external field, and the bars denote statistical averages. If the molecules are anisotropically polarizable, the effect of the fields on the polarizability can generally be neglected. If the uniform electric and magnetic fields, or the optical field, are in the x-direction,

$$n_x - n_y = \frac{1}{9n}(n^2+2)^2 2\pi \frac{N}{V}[(\alpha_{11}-\alpha_{33})S_{11}+(\alpha_{22}-\alpha_{33})S_{22}+2\alpha_{12}S_{12}+2\alpha_{13}S_{13}+$$

$$2\alpha_{23}S_{23}],$$

$$= \frac{1}{9n}(n^2+2)^2 2\pi \frac{N}{V}\alpha_{\alpha\beta}S_{\alpha\beta}, \tag{22}$$

where $S_{\alpha\beta}$ is one of the components of $n^{(1)}(\mathbf{r},\omega)$ in eqn. (9). Actually, the mean value of the component A_{xx} of any second-rank tensor is $\overline{A_{xx}} = \frac{1}{3}A_{\alpha\alpha}+\frac{2}{3}A_{\alpha\beta}S_{\alpha\beta}$. The different $S_{\alpha\beta}$ coefficients in eqn. (22) could be measured by observing the dispersion of the anisotropy $n_x - n_y$ in the vicinity of absorption bands of known polarization. Birefringence studies are particularly valuable when the molecules possess C_{nv} ($n \geqslant 3$) symmetry when $\alpha_{22} = \alpha_{33} = \alpha_{\perp}$ and only S_{11} is independent. Then eqn. (22) becomes

$$n_x - n_y = \frac{1}{9n}(n^2+2)^2 2\pi \frac{N}{V}(\alpha_{\parallel}-\alpha_{\perp})S_{11}, \tag{23}$$

making S_{11} a directly observable quantity. In electric and magnetic fields E_x and H_x, $(n_x - n_y)$ is related to the Kerr and Cotton-Mouton constants B and C:[10]

$$n_x - n_y = B\lambda E_x^2, \text{ or } C\lambda H_x^2, \tag{24}$$

where λ is the wavelength of the radiation in air at 1 atm. For nitrobenzene, $B = 4 \times 10^{-5}$ e.s.u. and $C = 2 \cdot 4 \times 10^{-12}$ e.m.u. for yellow light at 25°C, so $S_{11} \sim 10^{-8} E_x^2$ or $5 \times 10^{-16} H_x^2$, where E_x and H_x are in e.s.u. and e.m.u.

In a strong magnetic field, diamagnetic molecules are oriented through the anisotropy in their susceptibility tensors χ, and

$$S_{\alpha\beta} = \sum_{i=1}^{N}\langle\chi_{\alpha\beta}^{(i)}-\chi^{(i)}\delta_{\alpha\beta}\rangle H_x^2/10kT, \tag{25}$$

where $\langle\chi_{\alpha\beta}^{(i)}\rangle$ is the mean susceptibility of molecule i in the direction of the $\alpha\beta$ axes of molecule 1 and $\chi^{(i)} = \frac{1}{3}\chi_{\gamma\gamma}^{(i)}$ is the mean susceptibility of molecule i.

If the orienting field is that of an intense beam of light polarized in the x-direction,

$$S_{\alpha\beta} = \sum_{i=1}^{N}\langle a_{\alpha\beta}^{(i)}-a^{(i)}\delta_{\alpha\beta}\rangle\frac{(n^2+2)^2}{9n}2\pi I_x/5ckT, \tag{26}$$

where I_x is the intensity (energy crossing unit area in unit time) of the light beam, and $a^{(i)}$ is the polarizability for the frequency of the orienting light beam.

In strong static electric fields, the difficult question of the local field arises, but for non-polar media the Lorentz field $\frac{1}{3}(\varepsilon+2)E_x$ is reliable and

$$S_{\alpha\beta} = \sum_{i=1}^{N}\langle\alpha_{\alpha\beta}^{(\circ)(i)}-\alpha^{(\circ)(i)}\delta_{\alpha\beta}\rangle\frac{1}{9}(\varepsilon+2)^2 E_x^2/10kT, \tag{27}$$

where $\alpha^{(\circ)}$ is the static polarizability tensor. In polar liquids [11]

$$S_{\alpha\beta} = \sum_{i=1}^{N}\left\langle\alpha_{\alpha\beta}^{(\circ)(i)}-\alpha^{(\circ)}\delta_{\alpha\beta}+\frac{1}{kT}(m_{\alpha}^{(i)}M_{\beta}-\frac{1}{3}m_{\gamma}^{(i)}M_{\gamma}\delta_{\alpha\beta})\right\rangle\frac{1}{9}(\varepsilon+2)^2 E_x^2/10kT, \tag{28}$$

where $\mathbf{M}$ is the total dipole moment of the macroscopic sphere *in vacuo* in the field $E_0 = \frac{1}{3}(\varepsilon+2)E_x$. The short and long-range contributions to the mean value of $\langle M_{\alpha}M_{\beta}-\frac{1}{3}M^2\rangle$ must be evaluated in a similar way to that used by Kirkwood [4] for analyzing $\langle M^2 \rangle$. For highly polar axially symmetric molecules satisfying eqn. (19),[11]

$$\langle M_1^2 - \tfrac{1}{3}M^2 \rangle = \frac{90k^2T^2 S_{11}}{(\varepsilon+2)^2 E_x^2} = \frac{27kT}{2\pi n} \frac{\varepsilon(\varepsilon-\varepsilon_\infty)}{(\varepsilon+2)^2(2\varepsilon+\varepsilon_\infty)} + \mu^2(g-1)\frac{6\varepsilon^2(\varepsilon_\infty+2)^2}{(\varepsilon+2)^2(2\varepsilon+\varepsilon_\infty)^2}$$

$$\left\{1 - \tfrac{2}{3}(g-1)\frac{(\varepsilon-1)(\varepsilon-\varepsilon_\infty)}{\varepsilon(\varepsilon_\infty+2)}\right\} + \frac{2\varepsilon(\varepsilon_\infty+2)\mu^2\Omega}{(\varepsilon+2)(2\varepsilon+\varepsilon_\infty)n}\left\{\iint (\tfrac{3}{2}\cos^2\gamma_{12} - \tfrac{1}{2})\right.$$

$$n^{(2)}(\mathbf{r}_2,\omega_2)d\mathbf{r}_2 d\omega_2 + \iiiint (\tfrac{3}{2}\cos\gamma_{12}\cos\gamma_{13} - \tfrac{1}{2}\cos\gamma_{23})$$

$$\left. n^{(3)}(\mathbf{r}_2,\omega_2;\mathbf{r}_3,\omega_3)d\mathbf{r}_2 d\omega_2 d\mathbf{r}_3 d\omega_3 \right\}, \tag{29}$$

so the Kerr constant of a dipolar liquid depends on the two- and the three-particle distribution functions.[12]

Eqn. (25), (26) and (27) reduce to expressions of the following form for symmetric top molecules:

$$S_{11} = \tfrac{2}{3}(\chi_\| - \chi_\perp)[1 + n\Omega^{-1}\iint P_2(\cos\gamma)g(\mathbf{r},\omega)d\mathbf{r}d\omega] H_x^2/10kT. \tag{30}$$

Birefringence experiments therefore yield valuable information about angular correlation.

The field dependence of the dielectric constant of a liquid is proportional to $3\langle M^4 \rangle - 5\langle M^2 \rangle^2$, and this could similarly be related to the two, three and four particle distribution functions.

RAYLEIGH LIGHT SCATTERING BY DENSE FLUIDS

If there is correlation between the positions of scattering centres, the waves coherently scattered interfere and affect the intensity of the radiation emitted. If the incident beam travelling in the x-direction is plane polarized in the z-direction, then the intensities scattered by dipole radiation in the y direction with x and z-polarization have the ratio [13]

$$\frac{I_x}{I_z} = \frac{\sum_{i,j}\langle \alpha_{xz}^{(i)} \alpha_{xz}^{(j)} \cos\psi_{ij}\rangle}{\sum_{k,l}\langle \alpha_{zz}^{(k)} \alpha_{zz}^{(l)} \cos\psi_{kl}\rangle} \tag{31}$$

where $\psi_{ij} = (2\pi/\lambda)(x_{ij} - y_{ij})$ is the difference of phase at the detector between the waves scattered from molecules i and j. If correlation extends over distances that are short compared to the wavelength λ (this condition does not apply near the critical point), eqn. (31) becomes

$$\frac{I_x}{I_z - \tfrac{4}{3}I_x} = \frac{(\alpha_{\alpha\beta}\alpha_{\alpha\beta} - 3\alpha^2) + n\Omega^{-1}\iint (\alpha_{\alpha\beta}^{(1)}\alpha_{\alpha\beta}^{(2)} - 3\alpha^{(1)}\alpha^{(2)})g(\mathbf{r},\omega)d\mathbf{r}d\omega}{10\alpha^2 nkT\kappa}, \tag{32}$$

where

$$\kappa = 1 + n\Omega^{-1}\iint \{g(\mathbf{r},\omega) - 1\}d\mathbf{r}d\omega \tag{33}$$

is the isothermal compressibility $-V^{-1}(\partial V/\partial p)_T$ provided the configurational energy U is the sum of pair contributions.

When λ is comparable to, or shorter than, the correlation distances, it is no longer possible to use the dipole approximation. The scattering of X-rays or neutrons of wavelength ~ 1 Å, gives valuable information about structure in a fluid—the Fourier transform of the intensity of scattering at various angles gives the radial distribution of the scattering centres. The observable is therefore the number of atoms at a distance r from a given atom, and this can be interpreted in terms of distribution functions. The technique is most valuable when applied to very simple molecules.[14]

HARMONIC SCATTERING

In strong electric fields, the dipole moment of a molecule can be written [15]

$$m_\alpha = \mu_\alpha + \alpha_{\alpha\beta}E_\beta + \tfrac{1}{2}\beta_{\alpha\beta\gamma}E_\beta E_\gamma + \tfrac{1}{6}\gamma_{\alpha\beta\gamma\delta}E_\beta E_\gamma E_\delta + \ldots, \tag{34}$$

where β and γ are hyperpolarizabilities describing the non-linear polarization. If E has the frequency ω, then β and γ produce dipoles oscillating, and therefore radiating, at the second and third harmonic frequencies. If the molecules are centro-symmetric, μ and β are zero. The second harmonic analogue of eqn. (31) is

$$\frac{I_x(2\omega)}{I_z(2\omega)} = \frac{\sum_{i,j}\langle \beta^{(i)}_{xzz}\beta^{(j)}_{xzz} \cos(2\psi_{ij})\rangle}{\sum_{k,l}\langle \beta^{(k)}_{zzz}\beta^{(l)}_{zzz} \cos(2\psi_{kl})\rangle}. \tag{35}$$

If $\tfrac{1}{2}\lambda \gg$ the extent of correlation, the numerator and denominator in this equation can be reduced to expressions similar to the numerator in eqn. (32).[16] However, the result is complicated and is limited by the uncertain effects of the environment on the hyperpolarizability β.

Unlike $I_z(2\omega)$, the third harmonic component $I_z(3\omega)$ is reduced similarly to I_z in the liquid. This is because α_{zz} and γ_{zzzz}, unlike β_{zzz}, have non-vanishing mean values.

MAGNETIC RESONANCE OF PARTIALLY ORIENTED MOLECULES

The magnetic resonance spectra of molecules in anisotropic fluids show interesting effects, which can be interpreted in terms of the orientation coefficients $S_{\alpha\beta}$ of Saupe.[3,17] All five independent coefficients could, in principle, be obtained for a molecule of low symmetry possessing sufficient magnetic nuclei in known positions. Successful studies have been made in strong electric fields [18] and particularly in liquid crystal solvents. In nematic liquid crystals, the magnetic field aligns the solvent molecules and the solute derives its alignment through the angular dependence of the distribution function $g_{ab}(\mathbf{r},\omega)$. Large degrees of alignment, $|S_{\alpha\beta}| \sim 10^{-1}$, and as high as 0·7, have been achieved.

[1] J. de Boer, *Rep. Progr. Physics.*, 1949, **12**, 305.
[2] J. O. Hirschfelder, C. F. Curtiss and R. B. Bird, *Molecular Theory of Gases and Liquids*, (Wiley, New York, 1954).
[3] A. Saupe, *Z. Naturforsch.*, 1964, **19a**, 161.
[4] J. G. Kirkwood, *J. Chem. Physics*. 1939, **7**, 911.
[5] G. Oster and J. G. Kirkwood, *J. Chem. Physics*, 1943, **11**, 175.
[6] L. Onsager, *J. Amer. Chem. Soc.*, 1936, **58**, 1486.
[7] H. Fröhlich, *Theory of Dielectrics*, (Oxford University Press, Oxford, 2nd ed., 1958).
[8] A. D. Buckingham, *Proc. Roy. Soc. A*, 1956, **238**, 235.
[9] J. A. Pople, *Proc. Roy. Soc. A*, 1951, **205**, 163.
[10] J. W. Beams, *Rev. Mod. Physics*, 1932, **4**, 133.
[11] A. D. Buckingham and R. E. Raab, *J. Chem. Soc.*, 1957, 2341.
[12] J. M. Deutch and J. S. Waugh, *J. Chem. Physics*, 1965, **43**, 2568; 1966, **44**, 4366.
[13] A. D. Buckingham and M. J. Stephen, *Trans. Faraday Soc.*, 1957, **53**, 884.
[14] E. E. Bray and N. S. Gingrich, *J. Chem. Physics*, 1943, **11**, 351.
[15] A. D. Buckingham and J. A. Pople, *Proc. Physic. Soc. A*, 1955, **68**, 905.
[16] R. Bersohn, Y.-H. Pao and H. L. Frisch, *J. Chem. Physics*, 1966, **45**, 3184.
[17] A. D. Buckingham and K. A. McLauchlan, *Progress in N.M.R. Spectroscopy*, Vol. II, (ed. J. W. Emsley, J. Feeney and L. H. Sutcliffe), (Pergamon Press, Oxford, 1967), p. 63.
[18] A. D. Buckingham and K. A. McLauchlan, *Proc. Chem. Soc.*, 1963, 144; *Chem. in Britain*, 1965, **1**, 54.

Frequency-Dependent Direct Correlation Function

BY J. STECKI

Institute for Physical Chemistry, Polish Academy of Sciences,
Warszawa 42, Poland

Received 23rd January, 1967

Generalization of the Ornstein-Zernike direct correlation function to a frequency-dependent function appropriate for a description of time-dependent fluctuations in an equilibrium fluid, is discussed.

The standard distribution functions of equilibrium statistical mechanics can be represented as single-time averages of microscopic density functions taken at different points of the fluid. Thus if

$$\rho(\mathbf{r},t) = \sum_{i=1}^{N} \delta(\mathbf{r}-\mathbf{R}_i(t)), \qquad (1)$$

where $\mathbf{R}_i(t)$ is the position of particle i at time t,

$$\langle \rho(\mathbf{r},t) \rangle = \rho = N/V, \qquad (2)$$

$$\rho^{-1}\langle \rho(\mathbf{r},t)\rho(\mathbf{r}',t) \rangle = \delta(\mathbf{r}-\mathbf{r}') + \rho g(|\mathbf{r}-\mathbf{r}'|), \qquad (3)$$

and so on. Here $g(r)$ is the radial distribution of the fluid and the angular bracket denotes the equilibrium average. In terms of Fourier-transformed quantities $\rho_k = \Sigma_i \exp(i\mathbf{k}\cdot\mathbf{R}_i)$,

$$\rho^{-1}\langle \rho_k(t)\rho_{-k}(t) \rangle = 1 + \rho\sigma_k = I(k,0). \qquad (4)$$

The direct correlation function is introduced via an integral equation which in terms of Fourier coefficients is [1]

$$(1+\rho\sigma_k)(1+\beta\rho v_k) = 1, \qquad \beta = (kT)^{-1}. \qquad (5)$$

This may be taken as a definition of v_k although (5) was derived as an approximate relation and v_k were interpreted as parameters of the effective interaction. Relation (5) is an important element of the original derivation of the Percus-Yevick equation [1] for $g(r)$ in terms of the true intermolecular potential $V(r)$.

The generalization of expressions like (3) or (4) to the time-dependent description is generally achieved by taking the microscopic densities not only at two different spatial points but also at two different times. Thus, the l.h.s. of (3) is generalized to the average of $\rho(rt)\rho(r't')$ and the van Hove function $G(r,t)$ with its double Fourier transform $S(k,\omega)$, the "scattering law" of neutron or light scattering, make their appearance. These quantities, of fundamental importance for the molecular dynamics of equilibrium systems, have been widely discussed and their properties have been listed, e.g., by Martin.[2] However, as for $g(r)$ some time ago, formal relations and limiting properties are known and explicit calculations are possible for systems such as the Boltzmann gas, slightly anharmonic solid, etc. Several detailed models have been proposed which will not be discussed here. One can also write down formal (linearized) kinetic equations [3] applying the procedures of Prigogine-Résibois [4] or of Zwanzig.[5] What one lacks, are approximations that would form the counterpart of the known integro-differential equations for $g(r)$ such as Born-Green, Kirkwood-Salsburg, or Percus-Yevick equation.

One also lacks a virial expansion in powers of density and recent developments of kinetic equations seem to prove convincingly [6] that such a virial expansion is not possible for the autocorrelation functions. Moreover, the three-particle contribution in a moderately dilute gas is composed of two parts. One corresponds to the Enskog correction and is well-behaved; the other part contains re-collisions of the same particles, was always neglected in earlier work as a minor correction, and yet is divergent for the hard-sphere potential This, to me, casts serious doubts on the attempts to use Enskog-type kinetic equations for systems of hard spheres even if one did not have such doubts before. This can also be viewed as a one reason more for a search for a collective description of the fluctuations in a fluid. The direct correlation function may enter in such a description.

Thus, we would like to see eqn. (5) as connecting two single-time quantities and as a particular case to which a relation between two double-time (or frequency-dependent) quantities would reduce. Also, eqn. (5) becomes an exact relation for a dilute equilibrium (Debye) plasma if the true (Coulomb) potential is substituted for the effective potential v_k. Thus, conversely, v_k is the effective potential to use if the electron-gas relations are forced to fit any other system. This effective potential will guarantee that at least the static pair-distribution function is given correctly. We also note that the dilute plasma is one more example of the few physical systems for which $S(k\omega)$ can be calculated. One obtains [7]

$$S(k\omega) = \frac{1}{2\pi}\int_{-\infty}^{+\infty} d\omega \exp(i\omega t) I(k,t) = \frac{1}{\pi\omega}(\varepsilon^+(k0)-1)^{-1} Im\left(\frac{1}{\varepsilon^+(k\omega)}\right) \qquad (6)$$

with

$$I(k,t) = \rho^{-1}\langle \rho_k(t)\rho_{-k}(0)\rangle. \qquad (7)$$

Here ε^+ is the frequency-dependent dielectric function of the plasma. Explicitly,

$$\varepsilon^+(k,\omega) = 1 - \beta\rho V_k \int_{-\infty}^{+\infty} dp(kv)\phi(p)\frac{1}{\omega-kv}, \quad Im\omega \to 0^+. \qquad (8)$$

The one-dimensional Maxwellian is $\phi(p)$ and $p = mv$. This quantity ε^+ is of fundamental importance; it enters the short-time reversible Vlassov equation as well as the irreversible long-time Balescu-Lenard equation. It is directly related to the density (potential) response to an external perturbing charge density (potential) and can be generally defined by

$$\frac{1}{\varepsilon^+(k\omega)} - 1 = \beta\rho V_k[i\omega Q^+(k,i\omega) + I(k,0)], \qquad (9)$$

with

$$Q^+(k,i\omega) = \int_0^\infty d\tau \exp(i\omega\tau) I(k,\tau), \quad S = \pi^{-1} Re Q^+, \quad Im\omega \to 0^+. \qquad (10)$$

Despite the simplicity of (6) and (8), these results [7] are far from trivial.

Just as $S(k\omega)$ and ε^{-1} are, so is $I(k,0)$ directly related to a density response to a (static now) external potential $U(r)$ and the r.h.s. of (3) can be represented [8] as a functional derivative $\delta\rho(r_1)/\delta\beta U$. Wertheim's relations become ordinary algebraic in terms of Fourier coefficients. The direct correlation function or rather $(1+\beta\rho v_k)$, was expressed by Wertheim as a functional derivative inverse to that just quoted. Thus, if $S(k\omega)$ is associated with ε^{-1}, a proper frequency dependent $v(k\omega)$ should be associated with the inverse response function, i.e., with ε. In fact, for an electron gas, relation (5) is simply rewritten as

$$[\varepsilon^+(k,0)]^{-1}[\varepsilon^+(k,0)] = 1, \qquad (11)$$

because

$$I(k,0) = 1 + \rho\sigma_k = \int_{-\infty}^{+\infty} d\omega S(k,\omega) = [\varepsilon^+(k,0)]^{-1} \qquad (12)$$

by Kramers-Kronig relations, and

$$\varepsilon^+(k,0) = 1 + \beta\rho V_k. \qquad (13)$$

An immediate generalization of eqn. (11) and thus of (5) is then obvious:

$$[e^+(k\omega)]^{-1}[e^+(k\omega)] = 1, \qquad (14)$$

with

$$e^+(k\omega) = 1 + \beta\rho v(k,\omega), \qquad (15)$$

where $e(k\omega)$ is a suitably defined screening function that should generalize the dielectric function for a system with Coulomb intermolecular potential. The function $v(k\omega)$ generalizes the direct correlation function $v_k = v(k,\omega = 0)$. Thus, at zero frequency

$$e(k0) = 1 + \beta\rho v_k. \qquad (16)$$

A general set of definitions involving $\varepsilon^+(k\omega)$ independently of the nature of the interparticle potential and of the external perturbing potential, has been described by Glick.[9] His definitions lead directly to (8), V_k being now the intermolecular potential. However, (13) is not preserved and the quantity $\beta\rho V_k$ is thus not eliminated in a simple way. It is, however, possible to define $e(k\omega)$ so as to preserve the appearance of eqn. (6); thus setting

$$S(k,\omega) = (\pi\omega)^{-1}[e^+(k0) - 1]^{-1}Im[e^+(k\omega)^{-1}]. \qquad (17)$$

Hence

$$[e^+(k\omega)]^{-1} - 1 = \beta\rho v_k[i\omega Q^+(k,i\omega) + I(k,0)]. \qquad (18)$$

Eqn. (15) then defines $v(k\omega)$. The bracketed expression in (18) fulfils Kramers-Kronig relations. The static structure factor is thus always given correctly as

$$I(k,0) = [e^+(k0)]^{-1} = (1 + \beta\rho v_k)^{-1}. \qquad (19)$$

One can also presume that in a stable system, $e(k\omega) - 1$ fulfils Kramers-Kronig relations.

Rewriting now eqn. (14) in the form

$$\left[\left(\frac{1}{e} - 1\right) + 1\right][1 + \beta\rho v(k\omega)] = 1, \qquad (20)$$

one can invert this relation to the $\mathbf{k}t$ and to the $\mathbf{r},t$ space, thus obtaining integral equations relating the inverse transform of v to $G(r,t)$ and its time derivative, or to $I(k,t)$ or $I'(k,t)$. Moment relations can be investigated, the hydrodynamic limit examined, and so on. These calculations will not be recorded here; the usefulness of $C(r,t)$ or $v(k,\omega)$ and of the particular choice of the definitions, are to be judged by the feasibility of proposing simple approximations to v. One such approximation is suggested by Zwanzig [10] and is also straightforward in the present context. We are investigating now a particular form

$$v(k\omega) = -v_k \langle kv(\omega-kv)^{-1}\rangle, \qquad Im\omega \to 0^+, \qquad (21)$$

in which the ω-dependence is the same as in true plasma and we hope to report soon on the results to which this form may lead. In any case, a relatively simple expression for $e(k\omega)$ ought to give already sufficiently interesting results for S. Also, other possibilities of simple approximations to v seem to be present in the subtracted dispersion relations, of Kadanoff and Martin and of Puff,[11] which involve $\hat{S}^{-1}$.

[1] J. K. Percus and G. J. Yevick, *Physic. Rev.*, 1958, **110**, 1.
[2] P. C. Martin, *Proc. Int. Symp.* (Aachen 1964).
[3] J. Stecki, unpublished.
[4] I. Prigogine and P. Résibois, *Physica*, 1961, **27**, 621.
[5] R. Zwanzig, 1959 *Boulder (Colorado) Lectures in Theoretical Physics*, 1960, vol. III.
[6] J. M. J. van Leeuwen and A. Weijland, reported at *I.U.P.A.P. Int. Symp.* (Copenhagen, 1966). K. Kawasaki and I. Oppenheim, *ibid.* E. G. D. Cohen, *ibid.* J. Stecki, *ibid.* J. Sengers, preprints, 1965. L. K. Haines, J. R. Dorfman and M. H. Ernst, *Technical Note BN*-619 (University of Maryland), Oct. 1965, where further references can be found.
[7] D. C. Montgomery and D. A. Tidman, *Plasma Kinetic Theory* (1964) where further references can be found.
[8] M. Wertheim, *Lecture Notes on Percus-Yevick Equation*, (Los Alamos).
[9] A. J. Glick in *Lectures on the Many-Body Problem*, ed. E. R. Caianello (1962).
[10] R. Zwanzig, *Physic. Rev.*, 1966, **144**, 170.
[11] R. D. Puff, *Physic Rev.*, 1965, **137**, 407.

Influence of Molecular Rotation on Some Physical Properties of Liquids

By D. B. Davies and A. J. Matheson

Department of Chemistry, University of Essex, Colchester

Received 2nd January 1967

In those liquids which show an Arrhenius temperature dependence of viscosity, molecules are able to rotate many times about at least two axes during the time between translational jumps. In the higher temperature non-Arrhenius region molecules can rotate about only one axis during this time, while in the lower temperature non-Arrhenius region molecular rotation occurs primarily as a result of translational motion. The distribution of shear relaxation times in liquids at low temperatures arises from this restriction of molecular rotation, as does the structural contribution to the heat capacity of non-associated liquids.

TEMPERATURE DEPENDENCE OF VISCOSITY OF LIQUIDS

The temperature dependence of the viscosity η of liquids at temperatures well above their melting points is precisely described by the Arrhenius equation

$$\log \eta = A + E/RT, \tag{1}$$

where A is a constant, R is the gas constant, T is the absolute temperature, and E is the activation energy for viscous flow. This equation applies to some liquids over the whole normal liquid range. The viscosity of most liquids is greater than that predicted by eqn. (1) at lower temperatures in the liquid range. In this region the viscosity is described by the free volume equation,

$$\log \eta = A' + B'v_0/v_f, \tag{2}$$

or the equivalent T_0 equation

$$\log \eta = A'' + B''/(T - T_0). \tag{3}$$

Here v_0 is the limiting specific volume of the liquid at the second-order transition temperature T_0, v_f is the expansion free volume, and A', B', A'' and B'' are constants. The change from Arrhenius to non-Arrhenius viscosity behaviour occurs over 10 or 20° at viscosities of approximately 1 cpoise. We define the Arrhenius temperature T_A as that temperature at which the viscosity deviates from eqn. (1). T_0 is the fundamental reference temperature for molecular transport and relaxation processes in liquids, being that temperature at which there is no expansion free volume in the equilibrium glassy liquid and at which the viscosity becomes infinite.

In order to fit the observed viscosity data in a few non-associated molecular liquids, eqn. (3) has to be applied to two regions with two sets of the constants A'', B'' and T_0.[1] This change in non-Arrhenius viscosity behaviour occurs over about 10° at or below the liquid melting point at a viscosity which is typically 1 poise. We define the intersection temperature T_K as that temperature at which this viscosity changeover occurs. T_0 of the higher temperature non-Arrhenius region is always greater than T_0 of the lower temperature region. Since the liquid density is linear with temperature, this implies an increase in expansion free volume on cooling through T_K.

MOLECULAR ROTATION AND VISCOSITY OF LIQUIDS

The viscosity of a liquid is a measure of the ease of translational movement of the molecules in the liquid. Eyring [2] suggests that this translational motion occurs as a series of jumps by a molecule from one site in the liquid to another. The viscosity is approximately related to the average time between jumps or shear relaxation time τ_s by Maxwell's relation

$$\eta = \tau_s G_\infty, \qquad (4)$$

where G_∞ is the limiting rigidity modulus of the liquid.

It is likely that molecular rotation has a considerable influence on the translational motion of molecules in a liquid. In considering liquid viscosities we say that a molecule exhibits free rotation about a given axis if it is able to rotate through 360° or more during the time between translational jumps, while if a molecule makes several translational jumps before rotation through 360° can occur we say that rotation about that axis is restricted. A molecule whose rotation is restricted is able to translate less readily than one whose rotation is free: the restricted molecule is unable to rotate to align itself into a favourable orientation to squeeze past its neighbours so that the observed viscosity is greater than it would have been if rotation were free.

This suggests that liquids which are composed of spherical atoms or molecules should show an Arrhenius temperature dependence of viscosity throughout the normal liquid range. The atoms or molecules are always in a suitable orientation to make a translational jump, and the probability that they do so is determined solely by the probability that they have sufficient energy to jump. For example, the viscosities of the liquid inert gases and of liquid metals show Arrhenius viscosity behaviour. The same is true of those molten salts which contain only monatomic ions.[3]

In molecular liquids the translational motion is severely restricted in comparison with the gas phase. In certain liquids such as H_2, O_2, N_2 and CH_4, however, Raman spectroscopy has shown [4] that molecular rotation occurs as freely as in the gas phase. Hence many molecular rotations will occur per translational jump in the liquid, and so the viscosity of these liquids should show Arrhenius behaviour, as observed.[3] There is little direct evidence on the rotational behaviour of other quasi-spherical liquid molecules, though it is reasonable that those molecules whose shapes are approximately spherical should have relatively free molecular rotation. A useful measure of molecular sphericity is the ratio σ of the longest to the shortest van der Waals' radii of the molecule. Smyth [5] found that when σ is close to unity, as in the tetra-substituted methanes, molecules are able to rotate in the crystalline solid. A comparison of the liquid viscosity behaviour with σ is shown in table 1. The liquid viscosity shows Arrhenius behaviour [3] throughout the normal liquid range when the molecules are approximately spherical and σ is less than 1·5: on the other hand, when σ is greater than 1·5 and the molecules are non-spherical, non-Arrhenius viscosity is found at lower temperatures in the liquid range.[3]

Further insight into the influence of molecular rotation on viscosity may be obtained from a calculation of the volumes required for rotation of a molecule about its three axes. These volumes have been calculated from molecular models [6] and table 2 contains a comparison of these volumes, R_A, R_B and R_C with the average volume available to a molecule in a liquid at its melting-point, V_M, at the Arrhenius temperature, V_A, and at the boiling-point, V_B. Although the approximations involved in this comparison do not allow detailed, quantitative predictions to be made from table 2, some qualitative points emerge. Those substances which show Arrhenius viscosity behaviour throughout the normal liquid range have sufficient volume available to a liquid molecule at the melting-point to permit molecular rotation about at least two molecular axes. In contrast to this, those substances which have non-Arrhenius viscosity behaviour at lower temperatures have free rotation about only one axis at temperatures in the region of the melting-point, while at higher temperatures rotation is possible about two or three axes. This suggests that the onset of non-Arrhenius viscosity behaviour occurs at that temperature at which rotation about two molecular axes becomes restricted, while rotation about the third remains free.

TABLE 1.—VISCOSITY BEHAVIOUR AND MOLECULAR SHAPE

Arrhenius		non-Arrhenius	
substance	σ	substance	σ
N_2H_4	1·2	cyclohexyl chloride	1·8
C_2H_4	1·4	cyclohexanone	1·8
C_2H_6	1·2	cyclohexanol	1·8
$C(CH_3)_4$	1·0	ethanol	1·6
$C(NO_2)_4$	1·0	glutaronitrile	2·2
$(CH_3)_3CCl$	1·0	methyl cyclopentane	1·6
$(CH_3)_3CBr$	1·0	methyl cyclohexane	1·8
$(CH_3)_3CCN$	1·1	benzene	2·0
$(CH_3)_3CNO_2$	1·0		
CH_3CCl_3	1·0		
cyclopentane	1·3		
cyclohexane	1·5		
camphene	1·1		

In some liquids free rotation about all three axes is not possible even at the normal boiling-point, and the Arrhenius region coincides with the region in which the molecules have two axes with free rotation. It is probably not important that one axis of rotation is restricted, since rotation occurring simultaneously and rapidly about the other two is equivalent to rotation about the third axis.

By analogy with the change from Arrhenius to non-Arrhenius viscosity behaviour, it seems possible that the change in the non-Arrhenius viscosity behaviour at the

TABLE 2.—MOLECULAR VOLUMES IN LIQUIDS (Å³)

liquid	R_A	R_B	R_C	V_M	V_A	V_B
ethane	58	72	72	76	—	91
propane	82	105	136	100	107	122
butane	87	158	196	126	142	153
ethylene	52	61	68	71	—	82
propylene	84	102	136	91	100	141
benzene	143	137	127	145	140	160
o-xylene	202	225	178	192	200	227
p-xylene	182	265	203	203	—	233
cyclohexane	167	158	132	176	—	194

intersection temperature is also caused by the restriction of the rotation of the molecules in the liquid. To test this hypothesis, the minimum volumes required for rotation by molecules of some alkyl benzenes have been calculated: these substances have been chosen because the lower and higher members of the series do not show two regions of non-Arrhenius viscosity behaviour, while intermediate members do have two such regions.[1] For the purposes of this calculation it has been assumed that the molecules exist in a fully extended configuration. Table 3 contains a comparison of the volumes required for rotation of a molecule about its three axes with the average volume available to a molecule in the liquid at its melting-point and at the intersection temperature. The one rotational mode which remains free in the non-Arrhenius region is still unrestricted at the melting-points of toluene, ethyl benzene and n-hexyl benzene. These liquids show a single type of non-Arrhenius viscosity behaviour throughout the experimentally accessible liquid range, including the supercooled region. In contrast to this, the lowest rotational volumes of n- and i-propyl benzene and n- and sec-butyl benzene are all about the same as the volumes available to a liquid molecule at the temperature at which the change in non-Arrhenius viscosity behaviour occurs. Although this correlation is less satisfactory for n-pentyl benzene, the figures for the other four liquids suggest that in the lower temperature non-Arrhenius region free rotation is not possible about any molecular axis, and that this restriction of rotation around the intersection temperature leads to the change in the non-Arrhenius viscosity behaviour in liquids.

TABLE 3.—MOLECULAR VOLUMES IN AROMATIC HYDROCARBONS ($Å^3$)

liquid	R_A	R_B	R_C	V_K	V_M
toluene	149	210	167	—	158
ethyl benzene	164	240	223	—	182
n-propyl benzene	210	331	273	208	207
i-propyl benzene	211	260	245	206	208
n-butyl benzene	227	409	316	235	235
s-butyl benzene	254	246	277	237	238
n-pentyl benzene	252	~530	~420	264	264
n-hexyl benzene	278	~680	~500	—	293

The origin of the two T_0 values for certain liquids is now clear. In the non-Arrhenius region at temperatures above the intersection temperature, molecules are rotating freely on the definition given above. Hence the T_0 which governs viscosity in this region is that temperature at which translational motion would cease although molecular rotation about one axis would still be possible. The lower temperature T_0 is that temperature at which both molecular translation and rotation are impossible. It follows that the apparent increase in expansion free volume on cooling through the intersection temperature corresponds to the difference between the rotational envelope of a molecule and its van der Waals volume.

This argument requires that only one change in viscosity behaviour can occur in the non-Arrhenius region. Hence, if we define the glass transition temperature T_g of a liquid as occurring when the viscosity attains 10^{13} poise, we would expect that observed T_g values would correspond to values predicted for the lower temperature region of the liquid by eqn. (3). Experimentally this is so for the twelve liquids for which sufficient viscosity data for the two non-Arrhenius regions are available.[7]

We conclude that at high temperatures in the liquid range where molecules are able to rotate several times about at least two axes during the time between translational jumps, the viscosity of a liquid may be described by the Arrhenius eqn. (1). At lower temperatures molecular rotation is possible about only one axis on this time scale, and the viscosity is governed by the T_0 eqn. (3). If the liquid can be cooled to sufficiently low temperatures, the remaining rotational mode becomes restricted, and a change in the non-Arrhenius viscosity behaviour is observed.

MOLECULAR ROTATION AND RELAXATION IN LIQUIDS

If the times required for a liquid molecule to translate and rotate are different, it would be expected that the dielectric (τ_D) and shear (τ_S) relaxation times would also be different. In the non-Arrhenius region rotation about the short molecular axes occurs less frequently than does molecular translation. Since dielectric relaxation generally requires molecular reorientation about a short axis, τ_D should be longer than τ_S in the non-Arrhenius region. This has been observed by Litovitz [8] in a number of liquids. In the Arrhenius region, however, several molecular rotations occur per translational jump and hence τ_D should be less than τ_S. Experimental difficulties preclude the measurement of τ_S in the low viscosity Arrhenius region, but it is significant that the ratio τ_D/τ_S in the non-Arrhenius region of n-propanol decreases as the temperature is increased.[9]

This concept of restricted molecular rotation in liquids also offers a possible explanation of the distribution of shear relaxation times observed in liquids.[10] In order to separate the true relaxation region from the non-relaxing contribution caused by the dependence of G_∞ on temperature, it is experimentally necessary to work at low temperatures where molecular rotation about all three axes is usually restricted. The translational motion of a molecule is the vector sum of three mutually perpendicular translational motions, one along the long axis of the molecule which occurs relatively easily and two at right angles to this. One can envisage the translational motion perpendicular to the long axis of the molecule occurring either directly as a translational jump or as a molecular rotation about a short axis followed by a translation along the long axis of the molecule. Either type of motion has a relaxation time longer than that for translation along the long axis of the molecule: in the former case three distinct processes contribute to the distribution of shear relaxation times, and in the latter case five. The observed [10] distribution may be precisely described by summing five single relaxation times. It may also be described to within the experimental error by a summation of three single relaxation times in the ratio 480 : 35 : 1. The ratio of the longest to the shortest relaxation time is comparable to the observed τ_D/τ_S at low temperatures in n-propanol.[9]

As the temperature increases and the various molecular rotations occur more rapidly than translation, the molecule is more readily able to align itself into a favourable position for translation to occur. In the Arrhenius region a molecule rotates many times about at least two molecular axes during the time between jumps, and so it can translate equally readily in any direction. Experimentally, a single relaxation time is adequate to describe the shear relaxation in the Arrhenius region.[11]

MOLECULAR ROTATION AND THE HEAT CAPACITY OF LIQUIDS

In order to examine further this suggestion that molecular rotation is of importance in determining the properties of liquids, some studies have been made of the temperature dependence of the heat capacity of liquids at constant volume, C_V. C_V of a liquid contains contributions from four sources: [12] (i) motion of the centre of gravity of the molecule, C_{tr}; (ii) molecular rotation, C_{rot}; (iii) internal molecular vibrations, C_{vib}; and (iv) changes in the structure of the liquid, C_{st}. C_{tr} can lie between the ideal gas value of $3R/2$ and $3R$, the latter corresponding to the motion of a classical three-dimensional harmonic oscillator with potential and kinetic energy. Likewise C_{rot} of a nonlinear molecule can be between $3R/2$ corresponding to free rotation and $3R$ corresponding to fully restricted libration about the three molecular axes. C_{vib} is assumed to have approximately the same value in the liquid as in the ideal gas. The origin of C_{st} is obscure in liquids where molecular association (e.g., hydrogen bonding) is absent.

The following discussion refers to C_V at atmospheric pressure since liquid viscosities are usually measured at this pressure. Few data are available for C_V of liquids over a large range of temperature and accordingly C_V has been calculated [13] from known values of the heat capacity at constant pressure, the expansion coefficient, and the velocity of sound. In order to investigate the effect of molecular interactions in the liquid on C_V, C_V of the ideal gas has been subtracted from C_V of the liquid to give the residual C_V. Figs. 1 and 2 show the temperature dependence of the residual C_V for some Arrhenius and non-Arrhenius substances. From fig. 1, those substances

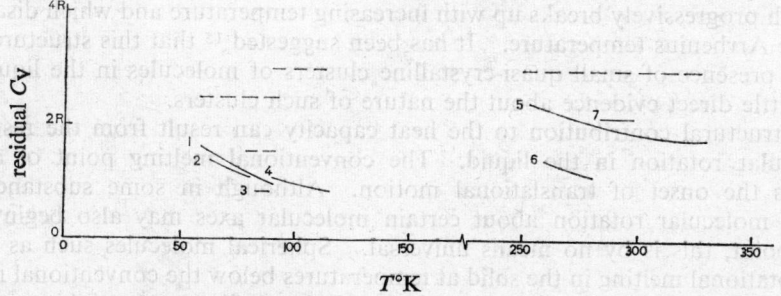

FIG. 1.—Variation with temperature of the residual heat capacity of liquids with Arrhenius viscosity behaviour: — —, maximum contribution from fully restricted rotation and translation: 1, O_2; 2, N_2; 3, A; 4, CH_4; 5, CCl_4; 6, neopentane; 7, cyclohexane.

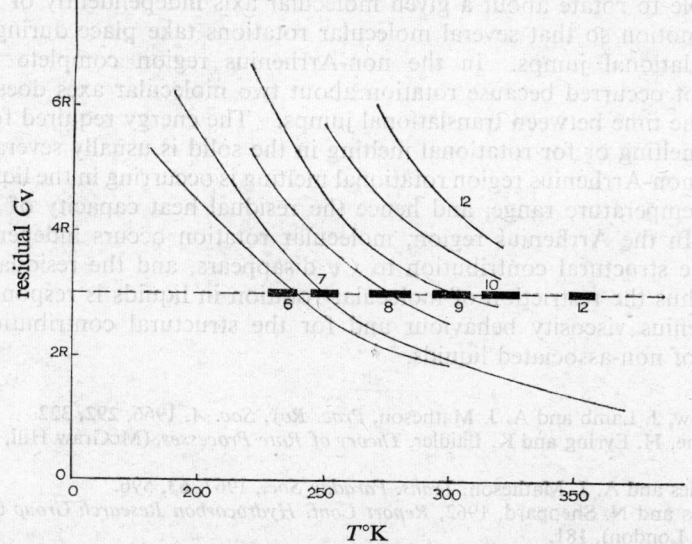

FIG. 2.—Variation with temperature of the residual heat capacity of liquids with non-Arrhenius viscosity behaviour: — —, maximum contribution from fully restricted rotation and translation: —, Arrhenius temperature: 6, n-hexane; 7, n-heptane; 8, n-octane; 9, n-nonane; 10, n-decane; 12, n-dodecane.

which have Arrhenius viscosities throughout the normal liquid range [3] have residual C_V values which are less than those corresponding to fully restricted molecular rotation and translation.

It was argued that, at the Arrhenius temperature, two molecular rotations become fully restricted while one remains free on the time scale of the translational time between jumps; and also that restricted rotation leads to restricted translation. Hence at the Arrhenius temperature the residual C_V should have a value close to $3R$.

Fig. 2 shows that this is approximately true for several n-alkanes to within the uncertainty of at least $\pm 10°$ involved in estimating the Arrhenius temperature. The same effect is found in other non-associated liquids such as CS_2, $CHCl_3$, diethyl ether, benzene, toluene, hept-l-ene and oct-l-ene.[7, 14]

At temperatures below T_A there is a substantial structural contribution to C_V. Thus we require that there exist in the liquid at low temperatures some type of structure which progressively breaks up with increasing temperature and which disappears about the Arrhenius temperature. It has been suggested [15] that this structure arises from the presence of small quasi-crystalline clusters of molecules in the liquid, but there is little direct evidence about the nature of such clusters.

The structural contribution to the heat capacity can result from the restriction of molecular rotation in the liquid. The conventional melting point of a solid represents the onset of translational motion. Although in some substances unrestricted molecular rotation about certain molecular axes may also begin at the melting point, this is by no means universal. Spherical molecules such as CH_4 [51] exhibit rotational melting in the solid at temperatures below the conventional melting point. Other substances such as benzene and the n-alkanes [16] exhibit rotational melting about one molecular axis in the solid, while some quasi-spherical molecules such as cyclohexane have two rotational melting points in the solid.[16]

It seems reasonable to state that complete rotational melting has occurred when a molecule is able to rotate about a given molecular axis independently of molecular translational motion so that several molecular rotations take place during the time between translational jumps. In the non-Arrhenius region complete rotational melting has not occurred because rotation about two molecular axes does not take place during the time between translational jumps. The energy required for normal translational melting or for rotational melting in the solid is usually several 100 cal/mole. In the non-Arrhenius region rotational melting is occurring in the liquid over a considerable temperature range, and hence the residual heat capacity of the liquid exceeds $3R$. In the Arrhenius region, molecular rotation occurs independently of translation, the structural contribution to C_V disappears, and the residual C_V falls below $3R$. Thus the restriction of molecular rotation in liquids is responsible both for non-Arrhenius viscosity behaviour and for the structural contribution to the heat capacity of non-associated liquids.

[1] A. J. Barlow, J. Lamb and A. J. Matheson, *Proc. Roy. Soc. A*, 1966, **292**, 322.
[2] S. Glasstone, H. Eyring and K. Laidler, *Theory of Rate Processes*, (McGraw Hill, New York, 1941).
[3] D. B. Davies and A. J. Matheson, *Trans. Faraday Soc.*, 1967, **63**, 596.
[4] W. J. Jones and N. Sheppard, 1962, *Report Conf. Hydrocarbon Research Group* (Institute of Petroleum, London), 181.
[5] C. P. Smyth, *J. Physics Chem. Solids*, 1961, **18**, 40.
[6] D. B. Davies and A. J. Matheson, *J. Chem. Physics*, 1966, **45**, 1000.
[7] D. B. Davies and A. J. Matheson, unpublished work.
[8] T. A. Litovitz and C. M. Davis, 1965, *Physical Acoustics*, Vol. IIA. ed. W. P. Mason, (Academic Press, New York).
[9] R. Kono, T. A. Litovitz and G. E. McDuffie, *J. Chem. Physics*, 1966, **45**, 1790.
[10] A. J. Barlow, J. Lamb, A. J. Matheson and J. Richter, 1966, *Chem. Soc. Spec. Publ.*, no. 20, 203.
[11] P. Macedo and T. A. Litovitz, *Physics Chem. Glasses*, 1965, **6**, 69.
[12] D. Harrison and E. A. Moelwyn-Hughes, *Proc. Roy. Soc. A*, 1957, **239**, 230.
[13] J. S. Rowlinson, *Liquids and Liquid Mixtures*, (Butterworths, London, 1959).
[14] L. A. K. Staveley, K. R. Hart and W. I. Tupman, *Disc. Faraday Soc.*, 1953, **15**, 130.
[15] A. R. Ubbelohde, *Melting and Crystal Structure* (Clarendon, Oxford, 1965).
[16] E. R. Andrew, *J. Physics Chem. Solids*, 1961, **18**, 9.

Viscoelastic Relaxation in Supercooled Liquids

By A. J. Barlow and J. Lamb

Dept. of Electrical Engineering, The University of Glasgow, Glasgow, W.2

Received 2nd January, 1967

A study has been made of the viscoelastic behaviour of a range of supercooled liquids each of which has a steady-flow viscosity η fitting the equation,

$$\ln \eta = A' + B'/(T-T_0),$$

where T_0 is the reference temperature at which no free-volume is available for molecular translational motion. For all the liquids investigated, the limiting shear rigidity modulus G_∞ varies with temperature according to the relationship,

$$\frac{1}{G_\infty} = \frac{1}{G_0} + \frac{a_0}{G_1}(T-T_0),$$

where a_0 is the coefficient of thermal expansion and G_0 the shear modulus at temperature T_0, and G_1 is a shear modulus associated with the weakening of the intermolecular force field due to an increase in free-volume with increasing temperature. The complete linear viscoelastic behaviour can be calculated from a knowledge of the dependence upon temperature of the density, steady-flow viscosity and limiting shear rigidity modulus. Details are given of the new liquid model on which these predictions are based, together with ample experimental confirmation.

Viscoelastic relaxation in liquids can be observed by using alternating shear stress in which the frequency is an experimental variable. At sufficiently low frequencies of the applied shear, all liquids behave as Newtonian, the response being entirely viscous with a phase difference of 90° between the sinusoidal oscillations of shear stress and the resulting strain. At sufficiently high frequencies it is possible to achieve conditions such that the molecules of the liquid are sensibly unable to flow during the short time period of the rapid stress alternations. Stress and strain are then in phase and the liquid behaves essentially as an elastic solid with a shear rigidity modulus G_∞, which is of the order 10^{10} dyne/cm^2. At intermediate frequencies the phase angle between stress and strain changes progressively with increasing frequency from 90° at low frequencies to zero at high frequencies and this constitutes the viscoelastic relaxation region.

In practice, by use of the principle of time-temperature superposition, it is possible to employ temperature as an equivalent and supplementary variable to frequency, thereby enabling measurements to be made over the complete region of viscoelastic relaxation. This implies that the variation with temperature of the limiting parameters η, the steady-flow viscosity, and G_∞, the shear rigidity modulus, must be determined over the temperature range employed. Although the frequency range which can be covered by the experimental systems developed in this laboratory extends from approximately 10^4 to 10^9 c/sec [1-5] better accuracy is obtained for the techniques operating above 10^6 c/sec provided that the liquid has a steady-flow viscosity η exceeding 10 cpoise. For this reason it is generally necessary to work with liquids which can be appreciably supercooled.

The Arrhenius equation fails to describe the relatively steep temperature dependence of the viscosity of most liquids having viscosities above about 0·1 poise and is completely inapplicable to supercooled liquids. The viscosities of such liquids can be described by the Doolittle free-volume equation [6]:

$$\ln \eta = A + B(V_0/V_f), \qquad (1)$$

where A and B are constants, V_f is the free-volume in the liquid and V_0 is the occupied volume. For the supercooled liquids considered here, the density is a linear function of temperature and under this condition, eqn. (1) can be modified to give

$$\ln \eta = A' + B'/(T-T_0), \qquad (2)$$

an equation identical with one proposed empirically by Tammann and Hesse [7] and subsequently established on theoretical grounds.[8,9]

The temperature T_0, which can be calculated from viscosity data for the liquid over the non-Arrhenius region, is considered as the fundamental reference temperature for all transport and relaxation processes and, at this temperature, no free-volume would be available for molecular translational motion in the equilibrium liquid. However, in practice, the slowness of molecular motion below the glass transition temperature T_g, precludes the attainment of an equilibrium liquid at $T_0(<T_g)$ in an experiment of finite duration. For present purposes, T_g is evaluated as that temperature at which the steady-flow viscosity reaches 10^{13} poise, this temperature being close to values of T_g recorded by differential thermal analysis.[10]

Complete information on the details of the work reported here, is given in two forthcoming papers.[11,12] The purpose of the present paper is to review the present state of knowledge in this field and to outline the information which can be obtained from measurements of viscoelastic relaxation.

VISCOELASTIC PARAMETERS

It is convenient to describe the Maxwell model for viscoelastic behaviour although subsequently a new model is presented which supercedes previous analyses based on the assumption of a summation of Maxwell elements. Consider a simple shear in the $X-Y$ plane with transverse displacement u, caused by the shear stress T, and a shear strain $S = \partial u/\partial z$. In order to account for viscoelastic behaviour, Maxwell postulated the stress-strain relationship,

$$T + \tau \partial T/\partial t = \eta \partial S/\partial t, \qquad (3)$$

where τ is the viscoelastic relaxation time.

For alternating shear stress of the form $\exp(j\omega t)$ we replace $\partial/\partial t$ by $j\omega$ and obtain

$$T(1+j\omega\tau) = j\omega\eta S. \qquad (4)$$

At low frequencies where $\omega\tau \ll 1$, $T = j\omega\eta S$, and the response is entirely viscous. At high frequencies such that $\omega\tau \gg 1$, $T = (\eta/\tau)S$, and the response is purely elastic. The elastic modulus G_∞ is therefore equal to (η/τ), or $\eta = \tau \cdot G_\infty$.

Defining the ratio T/S as the complex shear modulus, $G^* = G' + jG''$, we obtain

$$G' = G_\infty \omega^2\tau^2/(1+\omega^2\tau^2); \quad G'' = G_\infty \omega\tau/(1+\omega^2\tau^2), \qquad (5)$$

and the dynamic viscosity,

$$\eta' = G''/\omega = \eta/(1+\omega^2\tau^2). \qquad (6)$$

In practice the quantities G', G'' or η' are not measured directly but are obtained from the components R_L and X_L of the shear mechanical impedance Z_L which are experimentally determined. This impedance is defined by $Z_L = R_L + jX_L = -T\left/\dfrac{\partial u}{\partial t}\right.$, and solution of the wave equation, which is given by equating the net force on a volume element to the product of mass and acceleration, gives the general relationship:

$$Z_L^2 = \rho G^*. \tag{7}$$

Hence

$$\rho G' = R_L^2 - X_L^2 \text{ and } \rho G'' = 2R_L X_L. \tag{8}$$

For a Newtonian liquid, $R_L = X_L = (\pi f \eta \rho)^{\frac{1}{2}}$; $G' = 0$ and $\eta' \equiv \eta$, the steady flow viscosity.

The predicted behaviour obtained from the Maxwell model for a single relaxation time, $\tau = \eta/G_\infty$, is shown in fig. 1; the viscosity ratio η'/η falls from 0·9 to 0·1 in

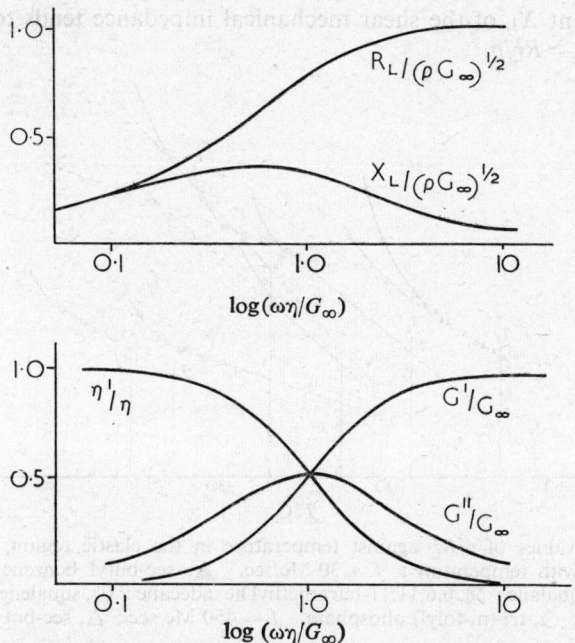

FIG. 1.—Calculated behaviour of the viscoelastic relaxation parameters according to the Maxwell model with a single relaxation time, $\tau = \eta/G_\infty$.

approximately one decade of frequency. In order to represent experimental results in the normalized form shown for the Maxwell model in fig. 1 it is necessary to know the variation with temperature of the density ρ, the steady-flow viscosity η, and the shear rigidity modulus G_∞. Both ρ and η can be measured by conventional methods but the determination of the temperature dependence of G_∞ requires shear-wave measurements to be made at temperatures above T_g in the region where $(\omega \eta/G_\infty)$ is much greater than unity.

EXPERIMENTAL

The liquids were obtained from various suppliers and were samples of high purity. All samples were dried before use in a desiccator containing P_2O_5. Densities were measured to an accuracy of ±0·1 % by the standard procedure of weighing a calibrated flask of known volume. Viscosities were measured with calibrated suspended-level viscometers according to B.S.S. no. 188. Values obtained are estimated to be accurate to ±0·5 %

below 100 poise and to ±1 % above 100 poise. Measurements of the shear mechanical impedance were carried out by using techniques described previously.[1-6, 11] The estimated accuracy of measurement for R_L and X_L is ±500 dyne sec/cm³, these being the c.g.s. units in which the shear mechanical impedance is expressed.

RESULTS

DEPENDENCE ON TEMPERATURE OF SHEAR RIGIDITY MODULUS, G_∞

The shear rigidity modulus G_∞ can only be studied by making measurements in the region where the liquid is exhibiting purely elastic behaviour, i.e., at relatively high frequencies and in the temperature range between the glass transition temperature and that at which viscoelastic relaxation becomes significant. In this region the reactive component X_L of the shear mechanical impedance tends to zero and hence from eqn. (8), $G_\infty \simeq R_L^2/\rho$.

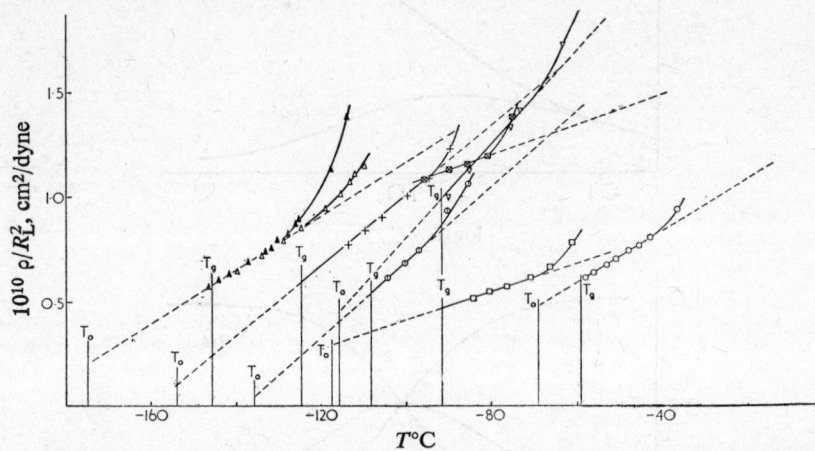

FIG. 2.—Measured values of ρ/R_L^2 against temperature in the elastic region, showing the linear variation of $1/G_\infty$ with temperature; $f = 30$ Mc/sec. ▲, sec-butyl benzene; +, tetra-(2-ethyl hexyl) silicate; ▽, squalane; ⊠, 6,6,11,11-tetramethyl hexadecane : ◐, squalene ; ☐, tri-chloroethyl phosphate ; ○, tri (m-tolyl) phosphate. $f = 450$ Mc/sec ; △, sec-butyl benzene.

Measurements made under these conditions on a wide range of different liquids have all been found to give results which within experimental accuracy obey the relationship,

$$(1/G_\infty) = (1/G_0) + (a_0/G_1)(T - T_0). \tag{9}$$

Values of T_0 are obtained from viscosity data, a_0 is the thermal expansion coefficient and G_0 the modulus of the close-packed state at temperature T_0 and G_1 is a constant modulus for a given liquid. Since the density can be expressed as

$$\rho = \rho_0[1 - a_0(T - T_0)], \tag{10}$$

and with the valid approximation that $G_0 \gg G_1$, eqn. (9) can be written as

$$V/G_\infty = (V_0/G_0) + (V_f/G_1). \tag{11}$$

The modulus G_1 is therefore associated with the weakening of the intermolecular force field due to an increase of free-volume. Typical plots of ρ/R_L^2 against T are shown in fig. 2 : values of G_1 are obtained from the slope of the straight line and G_0 is the intercept at $T = T_0$. Behaviour represented by eqn. (9) has been confirmed for over 20 liquids measured.

RELAXATIONAL BEHAVIOUR

Having determined the dependence of G_∞ upon temperature according to eqn. (9)-extrapolated values for G_∞ can be obtained for somewhat higher temperatures covering the relaxation region. It is then possible to normalize the measured values of R_L

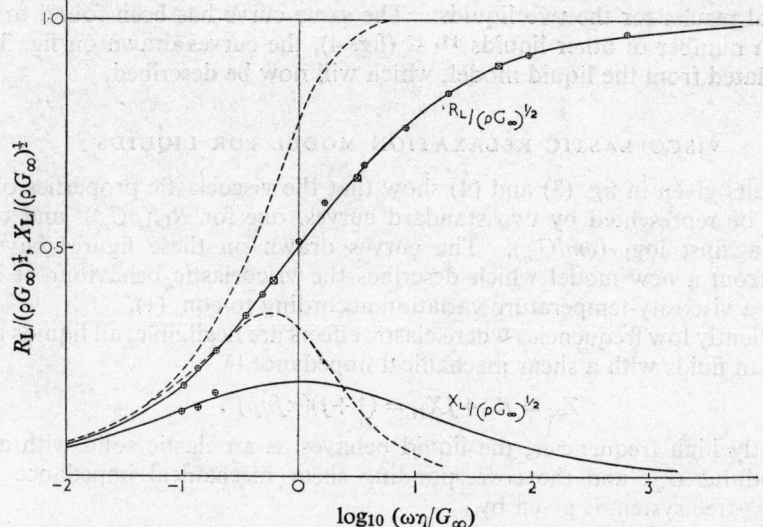

Fig. 3.—Normalized plots of $R_L/(\rho G_\infty)^{\frac{1}{2}}$ and of $X_L/(\rho G_\infty)^{\frac{1}{2}}$ against $\log_{10}(\omega\eta/G_\infty)$ for squalene (⊕), and for 6,6,11,11-tetramethyl hexadecane (⊠). The full curves are calculated from the liquid model using eqn. (14) and (15). The corresponding predictions from the Maxwell model are shown by the dashed curves.

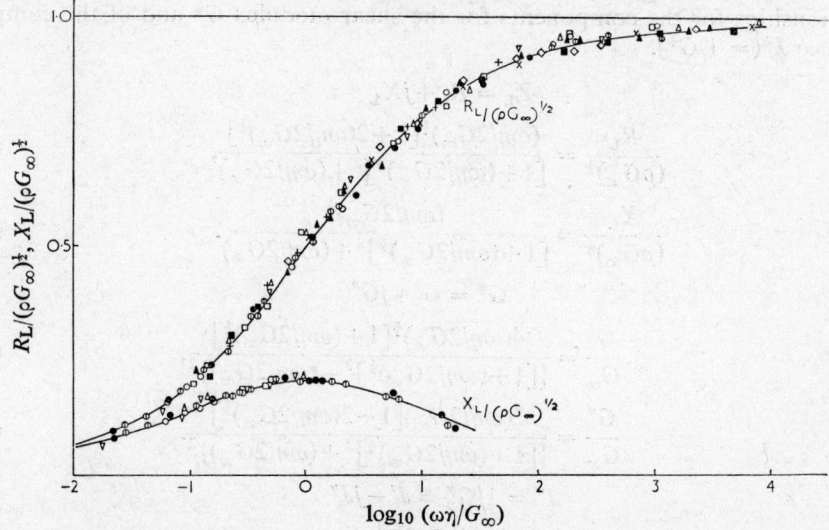

Fig. 4.—Normalized plots of $R_L/(\rho G_\infty)^{\frac{1}{2}}$ and $X_L/(\rho G_\infty)^{\frac{1}{2}}$ against $\log_{10}(\omega\eta/G_\infty)$. The curves are calculated according to the liquid model from eqn. (14) and (15); ▽, squalane; □, trichloroethyl phosphate; ○, tri(m-tolyl) phosphate; ×, tris(2-ethyl hexyl) phosphate; +, tetra (2-ethyl hexyl) silicate; △, bis (m-phenoxy phenoxy) phenyl ether; ◐, di(isobutyl) phthalate; ●, di (n-butyl) phthalate; ■, iso-propyl benzene; ◇, n-propyl benzene; ▲, sec-butyl benzene.

and X_L by dividing by $(\rho G_\infty)^{\frac{1}{2}}$ and plotting the quantities $R_L/(\rho G_\infty)^{\frac{1}{2}}$ and $X_L/(\rho G_\infty)^{\frac{1}{2}}$ against $(\omega\eta/G_\infty)$. Experimental results for squalene and for 6,6,11,11-tetramethyl hexadecane,* represented in this manner, are shown in fig. 3 and compared with the corresponding behaviour according to the Maxwell model. Clearly the observed relaxation extends over a wider range of frequency than does that given by the Maxwell model and moreover, a single curve for $R_L/(\rho G_\infty)^{\frac{1}{2}}$ can be drawn through the experimental results for the two liquids. The same curve has been found to fit the results for a number of other liquids [11, 12] (fig. 4), the curves drawn on fig. 3 and 4 being calculated from the liquid model, which will now be described.

VISCOELASTIC RELAXATION MODEL FOR LIQUIDS

The results given in fig. (3) and (4) show that the viscoelastic properties of these liquids can be represented by two standard curves, one for $R_L/(\rho G_\infty)^{\frac{1}{2}}$ and one for $X_L/(\rho G_\infty)^{\frac{1}{2}}$ against $\log_{10}(\omega\eta/G_\infty)$. The curves drawn on these figures have been calculated from a new model which describes the viscoelastic behaviour of liquids which have a viscosity-temperature variation according to eqn. (1).

At sufficiently low frequencies where elastic effects are negligible, all liquids behave as Newtonian fluids with a shear mechanical impedance,[13]

$$Z_N = R_N + jX_N = (1+j)(\pi f\eta\rho)^{\frac{1}{2}}. \tag{12}$$

At sufficiently high frequencies, the liquid behaves as an elastic solid with a shear rigidity modulus G_∞, and the corresponding shear mechanical impedance for an assumed loss-free system is given by

$$Z_S = R_S = (\rho G_\infty)^{\frac{1}{2}}. \tag{13}$$

It is found that the behaviour of the liquids studied is represented by a parallel combination of Z_N and Z_S, leading to the following expressions for the shear mechanical impedance of the liquid $1/Z_L = (1/Z_N + 1/Z_S)$ from which are derived corresponding relationships for the components for the shear modulus G^* and of the complex compliance $J^*(=1/G^*)$.

$$Z_L = R_L + jX_L$$

$$\frac{R_L}{(\rho G_\infty)^{\frac{1}{2}}} = \frac{(\omega\eta/2G_\infty)^{\frac{1}{2}}[1+2(\omega\eta/2G_\infty)^{\frac{1}{2}}]}{[1+(\omega\eta/2G_\infty)^{\frac{1}{2}}]^2 + (\omega\eta/2G_\infty)}, \tag{14}$$

$$\frac{X_L}{(\rho G_\infty)^{\frac{1}{2}}} = \frac{(\omega\eta/2G_\infty)^{\frac{1}{2}}}{[1+(\omega\eta/2G_\infty)^{\frac{1}{2}}]^2 + (\omega\eta/2G_\infty)}. \tag{15}$$

$$G^* = G' + jG''$$

$$\frac{G'}{G_\infty} = \frac{4(\omega\eta/2G_\infty)^{\frac{3}{2}}[1+(\omega\eta/2G_\infty)^{\frac{1}{2}}]}{\{[1+(\omega\eta/2G_\infty)^{\frac{1}{2}}]^2 + (\omega\eta/2G_\infty)\}^2}, \tag{16}$$

$$\frac{G''}{G_\infty} = \frac{2(\omega\eta/2G_\infty)[1+2(\omega\eta/2G_\infty)^{\frac{1}{2}}]}{\{[1+(\omega\eta/2G_\infty)^{\frac{1}{2}}]^2 + (\omega\eta/2G_\infty)\}^2}. \tag{17}$$

$$J^* = 1/G^* = J' - jJ''$$

$$G_\infty J' = 1 + (\omega\eta/2G_\infty)^{-\frac{1}{2}}, \tag{18}$$

$$G_\infty J'' = (G_\infty/\omega\eta) + (\omega\eta/2G_\infty)^{-\frac{1}{2}}. \tag{19}$$

* This compound was prepared by R. M. Schilsa, Monsanto Chemical Co., St. Louis, U.S.A.

The curves of fig. 3 and 4 have been plotted by calculation from eqn. (14) and (15); there is no disposable parameter.

DISCUSSION

The work reviewed here establishes that the viscoelastic relaxation curves for a wide range of pure liquids are identical when represented in terms of normalized co-ordinates. The standard curves can be predicted from a simple model involving only density, viscosity and the limiting shear modulus of the liquid without any disposable parameter. Many different types of liquid have been studied, including simple benzene derivatives, phosphate silicate and phthalate esters, polyphenyl ethers, and relatively long-chain hydrocarbons. Moreover, this general pattern of viscoelastic relaxation is not confined to liquids which are normally regarded as supercooled. The same behaviour has been found for a poly-l-butene liquid [14] of low molecular weight, this being monodisperse material with eight repeat units per molecule.

It follows that viscoelastic relaxation is governed only by physical variables and does not depend directly on the type of molecule involved. All of the liquids which have been found to conform to the proposed model have a viscosity-temperature dependence given by eqn. (1). It is therefore reasonable to suppose that this form of free-volume equation for viscosity must hold for the model to apply.

At low frequencies ($\omega\eta/G_\infty \ll 1$) the variation with frequency of the components of the complex shear modulus according to the Maxwell model are given from eqn. (5) as $G'/G_\infty \propto \omega^2$ and $G''/G_\infty \propto \omega$. However, according to the liquid model described here the corresponding variations given by eqn. (16) and (17) are $G'/G_\infty \propto \omega^{3/2}$ and $G''/G_\infty \propto \omega$. Hence measurements of the frequency-dependence of G'/G_∞ in this region of the spectrum indicate which model is applicable.

It has been suggested that liquids, which have a viscosity given by the Arrhenius equation

$$\ln \eta = A + B/T, \qquad (20)$$

should exhibit viscoelastic properties which conform to the simple Maxwell model. Unfortunately most such liquids have values of viscosity which are too low for their viscoelastic relaxation to be studied by existing experimental techniques. However, certain molten compounds are exceptional in that they have viscosities described by eqn. (20) with values exceeding 100 poise. Two such liquids are molten zinc chloride and molten boron trioxide, and in each of these a single relaxation process has been found, the measured behaviour conforming to the Maxwell model.[15, 16]

Since the liquids reviewed here have viscosities which at higher temperatures are described by the Arrhenius equation, it follows that if this approach is of general validity then a single relaxation time would be expected if the viscoelastic relaxation could be studied in this region. With decreasing temperature a gradual transition from the Maxwell model to that described by the present liquid model would be expected to occur as the degree of co-operative molecular motion increases. Evidence for such a transition may be obtainable from measurements of the relaxation region made at high frequency atnd at temperatures close to the lower limit of Arrhenius behaviour.

Recent measurements on mixtures of two liquids, each component of which conforms to the model for supercooled liquids have shown that a small departure from liquid purity, amounting to only a few percent, can give rise to significant deviations of the values of $R_L/(\rho G_\infty)^{1/2}$ and $X_L/(\rho G_\infty)^{1/2}$ from the standard curves over the viscoelastic relaxation region. However, large amounts of impurity do not give gross deviations, and preliminary evidence indicates that for certain critical mixture ratios the relaxational behaviour reverts to the standard curves. This suggests that for such compositions the mixture behaves as a homogeneous liquid as far as the propagation of shear waves is concerned.

This research has been supported in part by a contract with the National Engineering Laboratory, Ministry of Technology. Assistance has also been given by Shell Research Ltd. and by Imperial Chemical Industries Ltd. Many helpful discussions have been held with Dr. G. Harrison and Dr. A. J. Matheson, and thanks are due to Miss A. Erginsav for her diligent experimental work.

[1] A. J. Barlow and J. Lamb, *Proc. Roy. Soc. A*, 1959, **253**, 52.
[2] A. J. Barlow, G. Harrison, J. Richter, H. Seguin and J. Lamb, *Lab. Pract.*, 1961, **10**, 786.
[3] A. J. Barlow, G. Harrison and J. Lamb, *Proc. Roy. Soc. A*, 1964, **282**, 228.
[4] J. Lamb and J. Richter, *Proc. Roy. Soc. A*, 1966, **293**, 479.
[5] J. Lamb and J. Richter, *J. Acoust. Soc. Amer.*, 1967, to be published.
[6] A. J. Barlow, J. Lamb and A. J. Matheson, *Proc. Roy. Soc. A*, 1966, **292**, 322.
[7] G. Tammann and W. Hesse, *Z. anorg. Chem.*, 1926, **156**, 245.
[8] M. H. Cohen and D. Turnbull, *J. Chem. Physics*, 1959, **31**, 1164.
[9] S. F. Kumar, *Physics and Chem. of Glasses*, 1963, **4**, 106.
[10] M. R. Carpenter, D. B. Davies and A. J. Matheson, *J. Chem. Physics*, 1967, to be published.
[11] A. J. Barlow, J. Lamb, A. J. Matheson, P. R. K. L. Padmini and J. Richter, *Proc. Roy. Soc. A*, 1967, **298**, 467.
[12] A. J. Barlow, A. Erginsav and J. Lamb, *Proc. Roy. Soc. A*, 1967, **298**, 481.
[13] W. P. Mason, *Piezoelectric Crystals and their Applications to Ultrasonics*, chap. 14 (Van Nostrand, Princeton, 1950).
[14] A. J. Barlow, R. A. Dickie and J. Lamb, *Viscoelastic Relaxation in Poly-1-Butene Liquids of Low Molecular Weight*, 1967, *Proc. Roy. Soc. A*, 1967, in press.
[15] G. J. Gruber and T. A. Litovitz, *J. Chem. Physics*, 1964, **40**, 13.
[16] P. Macedo and T. A. Litovitz, *Physics and Chem. of Glasses*, 1965, **6**, 69.

Euclidean Geometry and the Flow of Generalized Liquids

By F. W. Smith

Division of Mechanical Engineering, National Research Council, Ottawa

Received 14th November, 1966

This paper is a review of recent research on liquid viscosity, derived from structural studies based on aggregates of spheres in space, and from non-linear continuum mechanics. The use of Voronoi polyhedra and the Delaunay graph to characterize irregular aggregates is briefly described, and the theory due to Bernal of a liquid as an aggregate of spheres is reviewed. The Bernal polyhedra, and an elementary rate theory where the activation volume is essentially a second rank tensor, give expressions for viscosity and for stress in lineal flow that are compatible with the non-linear theory of stress of Coleman and Noll.

---

1. AGGREGATES—VORONOI AND DELAUNAY STRUCTURES

In this section are reviewed some concepts in the geometry of irregular aggregates in euclidean space. These concepts underlie, or are derived from, the work of Bernal described in § 2.

The instantaneous structure of a simple liquid or other irregular aggregate can be represented as an array of points in space. The most familiar way of concisely characterizing such an array is by means of its radial distribution function of density; we deal here with a different characterization, that based on the Voronoi construction.[1, 2] If lines are constructed between each point and all other points in its general vicinity, the planes which perpendicularly bisect these lines cause each point to be enclosed in a polyhedron, the Voronoi polyhedron of the point. The dimensions and topology of these polyhedra give a characterization of the aggregate.

Each face of a polyhedron serves to relate two points as "geometric neighbours" of each other. The set of all lines between neighbouring points forms a network in space. For irregular aggregates (or of regular aggregates whose points have been slightly translated in a suitable fashion) this network of lines is the edges of tetrahedra which pack to fill space, and may be termed the Delaunay simplices, Delaunay graph, or simplicial graph of the aggregate.[3-5] The average number of lines meeting each point may be termed the "primitive coordination number" of the aggregate. This graph is a purely geometric structure, whose lines in a physical case do not necessarily imply a physical interaction between the particles connected by the line; for the diamond lattice, for example,[5] the primitive coordination number is 20. It is convenient, therefore, to define a "structural graph" of a physical aggregate as a subset of the simplicial graph such that its lines are the vectors of a significant interaction. The structural graph of the diamond crystal is thus the familiar diagram which connects each atom to four neighbours.

2. BERNAL LIQUID

Bernal has described and reviewed experiments and calculations on irregular aggregate having varying degrees of geometric resemblance to monatomic liquids.[6-13] This work elucidates many structural features of liquids, such as radial distribution, coordination, nucleation, and crystallization; we mention here only certain aspects with a bearing on the theory of viscosity.

These experiments have included a study of the polyhedra obtained when an aggregate of plastic spheres is compressed into a compact mass.[7] These shapes give an impression of some features of the Voronoi polyhedra of a monatomic liquid, such as a prevalence of 5-sided faces, and indicate a primitive coordination number of about 14. Further observations on masses of steel balls and models of connected rods led essentially to a description of the structural graph of a prototype liquid of spherical molecules, the Bernal liquid, whose principal features are that its arrangement is irregular and that no cavities occur that are large enough to contain an additional molecule.

This structural graph connects all "near neighbours"—pairs of molecules which are separated by distances ranging up to about 15 % above the minimum separation. The lines of this graph were shown to form the edges of a space-filling by polyhedra of only five types. These "Bernal polyhedra" comprise the tetrahedron, the octahedron, and 10, 14 and 16-faced figures, all faces of which are triangles. This series of polyhedra encloses cavities of progressively greater size, surrounded by 4, 6, 8, 9 and 10 molecules respectively. The dynamic behaviour of these cavities will be discussed in the following section in connection with the theory of liquid viscosity.

3. FLOW OF A BERNAL LIQUID

The structural graph of a Bernal liquid which is not flowing but whose molecules have kinetic motion is a dynamic network of polyhedra which are continuously interchanging their identities, but whose overall population statistics remain constant. For example, an octahedron may transform into four tetrahedra by the approach of two molecules along a diagonal, while compensating changes occur elsewhere in the liquid.

This concept has been used to develop a theory of viscosity, along the following route.[4] First, it is assumed that each step in which a polyhedron changes to the next polyhedron in order of size can be treated as an activation process by the techniques of chemical rate theory,[14] and that an "activation volume" is involved which is the difference in volume of the cavities of the two polyhedra. For the Bernal liquid this activation volume is about 10 % of the molar volume. Secondly, these local changes in free volume are related to the overall shear of the liquid by using the concept of "volume production" described in the next section. Thirdly an expression is derived for viscosity by relating the rates of local events in the liquid to a macroscopic stress tensor. This stress tensor can be either that given by the classical linear Navier-Stokes theory,[4] or that given by the non-linear Coleman-Noll theory, mentioned below.

These procedures yield expressions for a liquid viscosity which decreases with increasing temperature and with high shear stress, and which increases with pressure and which exhibits the normal stresses discussed in § 5. Because of the many assumptions and simplifications in these theories, their possible field of application seems at present to be in inter-relating macroscopic parameters—e.g., high stress viscosities in terms of low-stress viscosities—rather than in the *ab initio* calculation of flow properties from molecular properties.

4. ACTIVATION VOLUME; THE KINEMATICS OF AGGREGATES

The treatment of liquid viscosity requires an analysis of the way local changes in intermolecular cavities combine into the macroscopic flow of a liquid which in principle need possess no cavity large enough to contain an additional molecule. The basic concept used is that the creation or change in shape of a cavity in an aggregate is a process that involves *direction* as well as *magnitude*. The process has been termed "volume production" or "volume destruction",[4] and "tensor displacement".[16] For example, in the Bernal liquid, an octahedron may collapse into tetrahedra along any of three directions, in a process of volume destruction.

In a liquid at rest but undergoing thermal kinetic motion, such processes are uniformly distributed in space; the total volume production and destruction are isotropic. In a flowing liquid, the macroscopic shearing motion causes a perturbation of this distribution, so that the volume production is *anisotropic*; more cavities are created in one direction than another, and more destroyed in the second direction than the first.

The local flow process must be represented mathematically as a second rank tensor in order to be integrated into the tensor representing the macroscopic flow of the liquid. In current applications of the theory a simplification has been necessary in which it is assumed that the local tensor has a single eigenvalue—the activation volume.[4, 15] For example, the three-directional motion by which an octahedron collapses is represented by a one-directional volume change aligned in a particular direction in space.

Towards generalization of the Bernal liquid, some discussion has been given of the flow of a "general aggregate", whose members are arbitrary closed surfaces in euclidean space.[16] Such a structure would be a useful basis for discussing the flow of more complicated molecules such as those of lubricating oils, and would seem necessary as a basis for more detailed treatments of the intermolecular cavities in the Bernal liquid. One likely result in the latter case is that more than one "activation volume" may be needed to describe a local flow event in any liquid, or to express the macroscopic response of the liquid to deformation.

5. MODERN CONTINUUM MECHANICS—THEOREM OF COLEMAN AND NOLL

Modern non-linear continuum mechanics is a subject that has developed from extensive analyses of the nature of deformation.[17] As the "modern natural philosophy" of Truesdell, this subject has implications for wider problems in physical chemistry.[18] The description of a liquid in continuum mechanics is different from that given by the space-filling ideas underlying the previous sections, but the two methods perhaps have in common that they each seek to incorporate completely the relevant properties of the euclidean space in which the liquid exists: generalized symmetry properties in continuum mechanics, metric properties in space-filling.

For present purposes, a single result from modern continuum mechanics will be used. The classical, linear, or Navier-Stokes theory of the stress accompanying a steady lineal flow (simple shear) of a liquid is that a shear stress τ acts across the planes of shear, in combination with an isotropic pressure p. The modern non-linear theory of Coleman and Noll regards this pressure as essentially non-isotropic, or as an isotropic pressure p combined with two additional components of pressure—the "normal stresses".[17, 19] The latter stresses decrease with the rate of shear in such a way that the Navier-Stokes theory is obeyed in sufficiently slow motions. These normal stresses can be readily manifested as the Weissenberg effect in certain polymeric liquids; in liquids of simple molecular structure it may be difficult or impossible to reach rates of shear at which normal stresses can be observed, but they retain theoretical significance.[20]

The rate theory of local activation-dependent volume production processes described in § 3 and 4 gives rise to a non-linear stress system whose normal stresses decrease with decreasing rate of shear in a manner functionally consistent with the theory of Coleman and Noll.[15] Essentially, the flow of a liquid is treated as a perturbation of its kinetic motion. If this perturbation is small, i.e., a " sufficiently slow " motion, it produces a linear response in the form of a Navier-Stokes stress field with a Newtonian viscosity; a larger perturbation produces a non-linear response in the form of a Coleman-Noll stress field with a non-Newtonian viscosity.

[1] G. F. Voronoi, *J. Reine Angew. Math.*, 1908, **134**, 198.
[2] H. S. M. Coxeter, *An Introduction to Geometry*, (Wiley, New York, 1961).
[3] B. N. Delaunay (B. N. Delone). *Bull Acad. des Sci. URSS, Classe Sci. Math. Naturelles*, 1933, **6**, 793.
[4] F. W. Smith, *Can. J. Physics*, 1964, **42**, 304.
[5] F. W. Smith, *Can. J. Physics*, 1965, **43**, 2052.
[6] J. D. Bernal, *Trans. Faraday Soc.*, 1937, **33**, 27.
[7] J. D. Bernal, *Nature*, 1959, **183**, 141.
[8] J. D. Bernal, *Nature*, 1960, **185**, 68.
[9] J. D. Bernal and J. Mason, *Nature*, 1960, **188**, 910.
[10] J. D. Bernal, *Sci. Amer.*, 1960, **203**, 125.
[11] J. D. Bernal, J. Mason, and K. R. Knight, *Nature*, 1962, **194**, 957.
[12] J. D. Bernal, *Proc. Roy. Soc. A*, 1964, **280**, 299.
[13] J. D. Bernal in *Liquids, Structure, Properties, Solid Interactions* (Ed. T. J. Hughel), (Elsevier, Amsterdam, 1965.)
[14] S. Glasstone, K. J. Laidler and H. Eyring, The *Theory of Rate Processes*, (McGraw-Hill, New York, 1941).
[15] F. W. Smith, *Can. Congr. Appl. Mechanics* (Quebec, 1967).
[16] F. W. Smith, in *Modern Developments in Mechanics of Continuum*. (ed. S. Eskinazi), (Academic Press, New York, 1967).
[17] C. A. Truesdell and W. Noll, in *Encyclopedia of Physics* (ed. S. Flügge), (Springer, Berlin-Heidelberg, 1965, 3, part 3).
[18] C. A. Truesdell, *Six Lectures on Modern Natural Philosophy*. (Springer, Berlin-Heidelberg, 1966).
[19] B. D. Coleman, H. Markovitz, and W. Noll, *Viscometric Flows of non-Newtonian Fluids*. (Springer, Berlin-Heidelberg, 1966).
[20] C. A. Truesdell, in *Second Order Effects in Elasticity, Plasticity, and Fluid Dynamics*. (ed. M. Reiner and D. Abir). (MacMillan, New York, 1964).

GENERAL DISCUSSION

Dr. Mansel Davies (*Aberystwyth*) said: Prof. Pople has reviewed the various of nuclear spin relaxations in n.m.r. spectra and mentioned also molecular dipole relaxations. It seems appropriate to offer a reminder of the large body of evidence on molecular behaviour in liquids provided by dielectric relaxation methods.

Three factors have to be distinguished: (i) an inertial effect which persists for the very short time ($\approx 10^{-13}$ sec) needed for a molecule to achieve constant angular momentum under the joint influence of an applied torque and viscous damping. It was neglected in Debye's treatment (1913) and has the effect of pulling the dielectric loss factor ε'' down to zero at a frequency depending on $[I/2kT\tau^2]$.[1] As this occurs where the loss is already very low and the frequency high ($\bar{\nu} \sim 30$ cm^{-1}) it has only recently been directly observed. (ii) The angular reorientation of the (rigid) dipole. For this, Debye introduced the simple exponential factor $\exp(-t/\tau)$ with an unique time constant τ. The single valued τ-function accurately represents the behaviour of a considerable number of polar liquids and of polar solutes in many different solvents. In the complex compliance (dielectric) plane the simple Debye relation leads to a semicircular arc (fig. 1a). Increasing the inhomogeneity of the local field around a molecule (i.e., at lower temperatures; at higher viscosities; with increased molecular anisotropy; etc.) an apparent range of relaxation times whose incidence is weighed by a distribution function $G(\tau)$ appears. This leads to a " depressed circular arc " and the corresponding distribution functions can be deduced in alternative forms

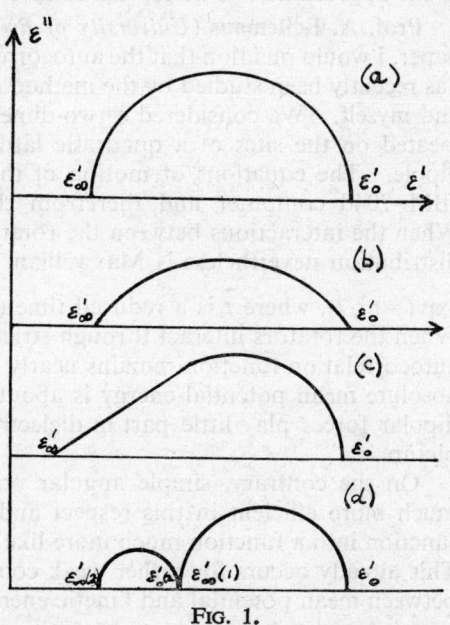

FIG. 1.

(Cole–Cole; Fuoss–Kirkwood; etc.). Further departures are found in some liquids often (not always) of complex structural character (di- and trihydroxylic molecules) or in a supercooled (i.e., glassy) state. These lead to " skewed-arc " plots in the complex plane (c). Their analytical representation and the corresponding $G(\tau)$ has been given by Davidson and Cole, and alternative functions considered by Higasi.

Important models for the co-operative molecular relaxation in liquids have been given by Kirkwood, Frohlich and others. Most significant is the development by Cole and Glarum of a model where re-orientation is partly a localized molecular rotation promoted by the near presence of a " defect " that also diffuses through the liquid. Cole has shown how the treatment based on Kubo's statistical formalism suffices to represent many of the types of behaviour encountered in liquids.

(iii) Some non-rigid polar molecules show distinctly separate dipole relaxations: usually from the essentially well-separated rates of component (orthogonal) dipole

[1] J. G. Powles, *Trans. Faraday Soc.*, 1948, **44**, 802.

elements (*d*). These can lead to the direct evaluation of, e.g., energy barriers restricting rotations of hydroxyl groups within a molecular framework. By transferring such molecules to a very " viscous " medium (e.g., a polystyrene matrix) it becomes possible greatly to increase the separation of component motions, i.e., an intermolecular rotation can be fully resolved from the whole-molecule re-orientation. The individual activation energies of these motions can be evaluated.

Dipolar relaxations have been characterized from 10^{+3} to 10^{-13} sec. Whilst most have dispersions broader than that for the Debye single relaxation-time, absorptions intimately related to the structure in the liquid state have been found [1] in the 10-60 cm^{-1} region of the infra-red which are of a degenerate resonance form: as such, they are appreciably sharper than the Debye type. The approximate positions of these absorptions which are characteristic of the liquid state were predicted by Hill in 1963.[2] It is suggested that dielectric absorption results offer a major contribution to the appreciation of molecular behaviour in the liquid state.[3]

Prof. A. Bellemans (*University of Brussels, Belgium*) said: In relation to Pople's paper, I would mention that the autocorrelation function of the electric dipole moment has recently been studied by the method of molecular dynamics by Gancberg, Köhler and myself. We considered a two-dimensional circular array of about 400 rotators located on the sites of a quadratic lattice and provided with a permanent electric dipole. The equations of motion of this system were integrated numerically on a IBM 7040 computer and therefrom the autocorrelation function was obtained. When the interactions between the rotators are negligible, but the angular momenta distribution nevertheless is Maxwellian, the autocorrelation function is of the form $\exp(-\tilde{t}^2/2)$, where $\tilde{t}$ is a reduced time (with the mean period of rotation as unity). When the rotators interact through strictly dipolar forces only, we observed that the autocorrelation function remains nearly the same as for free rotators, even when the absolute mean potential energy is about equal to the kinetic one. This shows that dipolar forces play little part in dielectric relaxation and do not lead to the Debye picture.

On the contrary, simple angular potential other than the dipolar one may be much more efficient in this respect and transform the free rotator autocorrelation function into a function much more like the exponential decaying function of Debye. This already occurs for rather weak coupling, e.g., an absolute ratio of about 20 % between mean potential and kinetic energies.

Prof. H. G. Hertz (*Technical University, Karlsruhe*) said: Dr. Dwek introduced the concept of a distribution of correlation times. In addition to the reference to a paper by Waugh given by Dr. Dwek, I would point out that the formulation of a distribution of correlation times should not be used too easily in future n.m.r. work. First, we almost never have a precise knowledge of the time correlation functions of the spherical harmonics of second order—or other functions—entering in the theory of nuclear relaxation. Then, usually one starts from a simple model and the deviation of the experimental results from those predicted by this model are ascribed to a distribution of correlation times.

However, the intramolecular and intermolecular relaxation rates are generally of equal magnitude; they clearly have different dispersion behaviour. The intramolecular relaxation rate may be caused by anisotropic rotational motion, the latter being determined in a complicated way by two or three microdynamic time constants

[1] G. W. Chantry and H. A. Gebbie, *Nature*, 1965, **208**, 398; and later publications.
[2] N. E. Hill, *Proc. Physic. Soc.*, 1963, **82**, 723.
[3] for further references, see C. P. Smyth, *Ann. Rev. Physic. Chem.*, 1966, **17**, 433.

even if one uses the most simple rotational diffusion model. The intermolecular relaxation rate depends as well on the special form of translational motion. There may be a finite jump—or infinitesimal jump-mechanism, there may be a superposition of molecular rotation on the translation or partial rotational contribution to the intermolecular rate caused by association effects. These more detailed models are characterized by a small number of well-defined microdynamic time constants—with different temperature dependence. All these facts produce a dispersion behaviour which generally is not explicitly known. Thus, if one uses the concept of a distribution of correlation times too easily one may veil the information buried in the dispersion behaviour of the relaxation time in the form of a small number of microdynamic time constants.

Moreover, even if one considers the name " distribution of correlation times " to be another word for the more precise formulation of non-exponential decay of the correlation functions, the distribution of correlation times thus determined is not necessarily the distribution of correlation times in the various environments in the system under consideration. The latter correlation times are those one would obtain if the particle is trapped for a sufficiently long time in a given environment. The two distributions are no longer equal if the residence times of a molecule in the various environments are shorter than the corresponding correlation times. Thus, in pure liquid, a distribution of correlation times should not be ascribed to different environments.

Finally, even for a purely translational intermolecular relaxation rate in a highly fluid liquid we have a " distribution of correlation times " because the correlation time for a spin-spin vector depends on the length of this vector. Writing $\tau = d^2/D$ in the case of the most simple diffusion-determined intermolecular rate is only a formal abbreviation; what determines the relaxation mechanism is the macroscopic self-diffusion coefficient D and the distance of closest approach d. The relation $\tau = d^2/D$ only transcribes the diffusion coefficient into a quantity of dimension time and " microscopic " magnitude.

Another comment—which is related to the first one—concerns the separation of the motion of toluene in solutions of free radicals into translational and rotational motion of a solvation complex formed by the free radical and the toluene as reported by Krüger, Müller-Wahrmut and van Steenwinkel. One should be sceptical about such a procedure if it yields an activation energy of the rotational motion $2\frac{1}{2}$ times as great as the one for translational motion. The correlation time τ_c of the rotational motion of the complex is roughly given by $\tau_c \sim 4\pi\eta a^3/3kT$, a being the radius of the complex, thus we would expect to find the activation energy for the rotation to be about equal to that of the viscosity η which is not very different from the one for translational motion.

Furthermore, if for acetonitrile we find the correlation time for the rotational motion of the CN-bond to be equal to the correlation time of the rotational motion of the proton-proton vectors, then we must conclude that the rotation of the whole molecule is isotropic. This is so because for an isotropic rotational motion of a rigid body the correlation time for the rotation of one selected vector is identical with the correlation time of any other vector within the rigid body (the molecule). If we had very rapid motion about the C—CN bond, then we would find a smaller correlation time for the proton relaxation. With acetonitrile one other possibility is that the proton relaxation is partly due to spin-rotational interaction. This would mean that the correlation time as determined for the proton-proton vector considering only magnetic dipole-dipole interaction is not correct. This question seems not to be settled experimentally as yet.

Prof. A. D. Buckingham (*University of Bristol*) (*partly communicated*): In reply to Magat and Davies, it is true that if a larger value for ε_∞ were used in the approximate equation for the dielectric polarization of a polar liquid (see eqn. (20) of my paper), the corresponding value of g would be smaller. The equation is based on a separation of the " distortion " and " orientation " polarizations, and for water there may be some ambiguity in this separation. The " distortion " polarization is the mean polarization induced in the system for fixed molecular orientations, and the concept depends on the molecule retaining its integrity when the field is applied; if proton exchange were induced by the field, the resulting polarization could not properly be included as distortion polarization. The librational motion of a molecule in interaction with its neighbours does not contribute to the distortion polarization which arises from electronic and nuclear motion at optical frequencies. This is the reason that, in my table 1, ε_∞ for water is only about 1·8. The fact that the resulting values of g are in agreement with the Pople model for water lends support to this interpretation of the dielectric polarization of the liquid.

The difficulty in assigning a correct value to ε_∞ for water has been discussed by Hill.[1] She concluded that the infra-red dispersion in water should be attributed to distortion polarization and that the hydrogen bonding raises the dielectric constant by enhancing the polarizability rather than by modifying the dipole distribution. The ambiguity stems from simplifications inherent in the Onsager model in which the molecular dipole in the liquid is related to the permanent moment μ and polarizability $\alpha^{(0)}$ of the molecule:

$$m = \mu + \alpha^{(0)}R,$$

where R is the " reaction " field. The high-frequency dielectric constant enters the theory through the equation

$$\frac{\varepsilon_\infty - 1}{\varepsilon_\infty + 2} = \frac{4\pi}{3} n\alpha^{(0)}.$$

Normally $\alpha^{(0)}$ is approximately independent of state, but in water it may not be. However, if the interaction is so strong that $\alpha^{(0)}$ is increased by a factor of about 2·5, it is difficult to believe that the gas value of μ is relevant.

In reply to Stecki, it is true that the Kerr constant of a dipolar fluid is dependent on the three-particle distribution function. Studies of the relaxation of the Kerr constant would give information about the time dependence of both $P_2(\cos \gamma_{12})$ and $(\frac{3}{2} \cos \gamma_{12} \cos \gamma_{13} - \frac{1}{2} \cos \gamma_{23})$, and might be a useful source of information about correlation times in liquids. It would be interesting to compare the results with studies of dielectric relaxation (which depends on $P_1(\cos \gamma_{12})$) and nuclear magnetic relaxation which is also related to $P_2(\cos \gamma_{12})$.

The three-particle distribution function is also involved in dielectric relaxation in monatomic fluids, for in this case, an interacting pair of molecules has no dipole moment, whereas a trio does. However, we have little knowledge of the dependence of the dipole moment on the positions of the three atoms, and the effect may be largely determined by short-range interactions.

Dr. G. H. Findenegg (*Bristol University*) said: I wish to ask Dr. Matheson what assumptions are made as to hindered rotation around the C—C bonds of the n-alkane molecules in the calculation of the residual heat capacities given in fig. 2 of their paper. In the liquid state these internal librational modes are affected not only by the intramolecular potential barriers but also by surrounding molecules; this may

[1] N. E. Hill, *Trans. Faraday Soc.*, 1963, **59**, 344.

alternatively be described in terms of a great number of conformational isomers of different potential energy. By raising the temperature, conformations of low energy will be converted into others of higher energy. The corresponding contribution to the heat capacity cannot be calculated at present, and this forms a major problem for an interpretation of C_v of these compounds. However, it is improbable that chain molecules can rotate as one unit in the liquid state.

Dr. A. J. Matheson (*University of Essex*) said: In " simple " liquids such as chloroform or toluene it is unlikely that the vibrational heat capacity will be significantly different from that of the substance in the ideal gas phase at the same temperature. In such liquids a structural contribution to the residual heat capacity exists only below the Arrhenius temperature. We have assumed that in the n-alkanes also, the vibrational heat capacity is little affected by the transition from the gas to the liquid: it is then found that, as in the "simple" liquids, a structural heat capacity exists only below the Arrhenius temperature.

Dr. R. A. Dwek (*Oxford University*) said: Hertz comments on the use by some authors of a distribution of correlation times to interpret results which cannot be explained on the Kubo and Tomita theory with a single value of τ_c. It is true that there must be other models which could equally well be made to fit the experimental results. All that can be said is, that in many of the systems concerned, the postulate of a random distribution about a mean correlation time is a plausible one on which to base an interpretation. Some examples are to be found under ref. (3) of our paper.

Dr. I. Henderson (*University of Southampton and Defence Research Board, Ottawa*) (*partly communicated*). Smith has noted the importance of determining the effect of volume changes on transport properties. Recently developed techniques for high-pressure studies have already given rise to many data relating to isothermal pressure coefficients and isochoric temperature coefficients, the interpretation of which is likely to lead to further insight into the structural features of liquids. The transport process most amenable to precise measurement is that of conductance, and over the last few years, Hills and his co-workers have studied the variation over a wide range of pressure and temperature of the conductance of a number of aqueous and non-aqueous systems.

Presented here are some preliminary results of a numerical analysis in progress at Southampton of these and other data relating to transport processes. The influence of isothermal volume changes, and in particular of changes of " free volume ", on fluidity, conductance and diffusion, has been the subject of several semi-empirical theories, one of the most recent being that of Macedo and Litowitz [1] who related the jump probability to the product of a free volume term and a Boltzmann factor. Following Cohen and Turnbull,[2] they expressed the free volume term as $\exp([V-V_g]/V_g)$, where V is the molar volume and V_g a corresponding limiting volume characteristic of a glassy state. This relationship has not been found to be appropriate for ionic transport in a wide range of systems in which the free volume defined as $(V-V_0)$ (where V_0 is the low temperature volume of the solid) represented a large fraction (8-20 %) of the total volume. With solutions for which Walden's rule is a good approximation, namely those for which the solute ions are large in

[1] P. B. Macedo and T. A. Litowitz, *J. Chem. Physics*, 1965, **42**, 245.
[2] M. H. Cohen and D. Turnbull, *J. Chem. Physics*, 1959, **31**, 1164.

comparison with the probable size of solvent voids, a simple relation similar to that of Batchinski [1]

$$1/\eta = A(V-V_0)/V \qquad (1)$$

should be valid. This model assumes that concurrently with ionic displacement there occurs a co-operative motion of solvent molecules and that the hydrodynamic properties of the system are therefore involved.

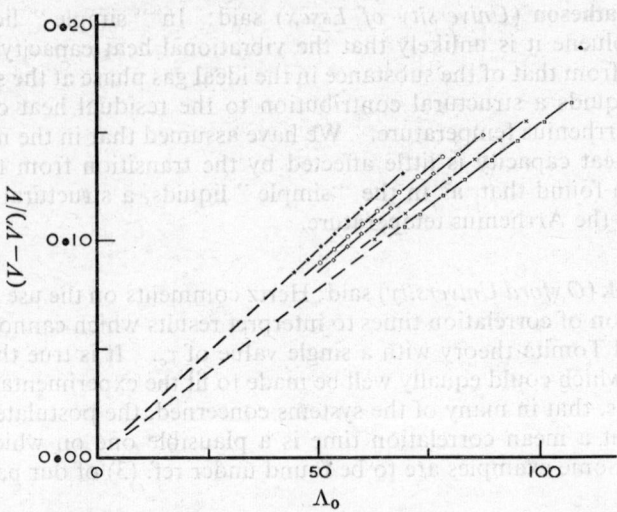

FIG. 1.—Limiting equivalent conductance of potassium picrate in dimethyl formamide against $(V-V')/V$. *, 25°C; ○, 35°C; ◇, 45°C; ×, 55°C; □, 65°C.

In the present analysis, values of a parameter V' were determined to yield the best fit to the isothermal relations.

$$\Lambda = K(T)(V-V')/V, \qquad (2)$$

where Λ is the equivalent conductance and $K(T)$ a density-independent proportionality factor. The resultant values of V' were substantially temperature-independent, so that $K(T)$ could be further expressed as

$$K(T) = K' \exp(-E_v/RT), \qquad (3)$$

where E_v is an isochoric energy of activation. Fig. 1 shows the isothermal data of Brummer [2] for potassium picrate in dimethyl formamide plotted as a function of $(V-67.34)/V$ (corresponding to a pressure range of 1000 atm). Fig. 2 shows the same data computer-plotted against values calculated from the equation

$$\Lambda_{(calc)} = 3.33 \times 10^3[(V-67.34)/V] \exp(-1100/RT). \qquad (4)$$

Similar analyses for tetra-methyl and tetra-butyl ammonium picrates in dimethyl formamide [2] and for four tetra-alkyl ammonium picrates in nitrobenzene (using the data of Barreira [3]), showed that all of the data for each system could be fitted by a similar single relationship.

When the solute ionic species are small in comparison with the dimensions of solvent vacancies, Walden's rule is a poor approximation. Ionic motion can then

[1] A. J. Batchinski, *Z. physik. Chem.*, 1913, **84**, 643.
[2] S. B. Brummer, *J. Chem. Physics*, 1965, **42**, 1636.
[3] F. C. Barreira, *D.I.C. Thesis* (Imperial College, London, 1964).

occur without concurrent rearrangement of solvent molecules, although such solvent motion must take place subsequently. In such a situation, the ionic jump probability should be proportional to the probability that a vacancy exists adjacent to an ion in the plane normal to the direction of the applied field. Thus the overall conductance equation should contain a factor $([V-V']/V)^3$, corresponding to the p_v of Macedo and Litowitz.[1] Preliminary calculations using the data of Howard[2] have shown that this analysis is applicable to a number of ionic solutes in methanol.

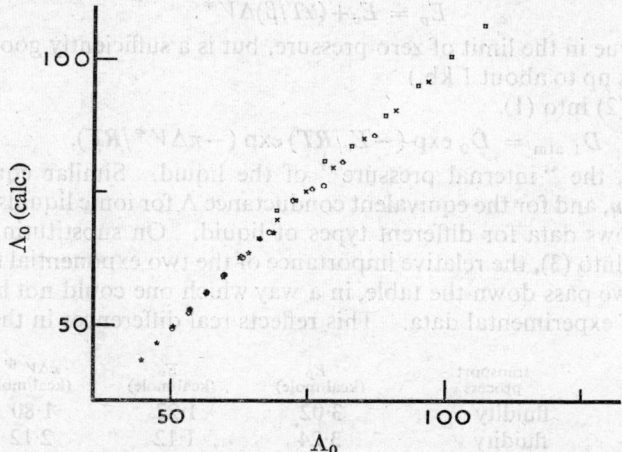

FIG. 2.—Conductance calculated from eqn. (4) against limiting equivalent conductance of potassium picrate in dimethyl formamide. *, 25°C; ○, 35°C; ◇, 45°C; ×, 55°C; □, 65°C.

Dr. F. W. Smith (*N.R.C., Ottawa*) said: I would like to raise a general question of the physical interpretation of volume parameters in liquids, notably activation volume. These parameters are introduced into equations of thermodynamic type as empirical scalars with the dimensions of volume, e.g., 20 cm³/mole. A molecular liquid is an aggregate of closed surfaces moving in euclidean space, and the question is " what is the geometric property or function of this aggregate that can be said to have this value of 20 cm³/mole under the conditions of the experiment? " The answer evidently involves integral or statistical geometry, but a crude analogy suggests that an activation volume function may resemble a deformation tensor, at least to the extent of being characterized by more than one invariant or eigenvalue. Different experiments on the same liquid may therefore yield different scalar " activation volumes " which may be different invariants, or different functions of the invariants, of the underlying geometrical function.

Dr. B. Cleaver (*Southampton University*) (*communicated*): Dr. F. W. Smith has raised the question of the physical meaning of the activation volume for transport processes in liquids. It is wrong to ascribe to experimental activation volumes the simple meaning which the term implies.[3] However, the empirical meaning of this parameter is unambiguous. The relative importance of the isochoric activation energy and the activation volume in determining the temperature dependence of a transport process at atmospheric pressure may be distinguished in the following way.

The variation of the transport parameter with temperature at atmospheric pressure may be represented by an Arrhenius equation. Using the self-diffusion coefficient

---

[1] P. B. Macedo and T. A. Litowitz, *J. Chem. Physics*, 1965, **42**, 245.
[2] B. Howard, *Ph.D. Thesis* (University of London, 1963).
[3] see for e.g., D. Lazarus and N. H. Nachtrieb, *Solids under Pressure* (McGraw Hill, 1963), p. 47.

as an example,

$$D_{1 \text{ atm}} = D_0 \exp(-E_p/RT). \tag{1}$$

Defining the activation volume as

$$\Delta V^{\ddagger} = -RT[\partial \ln D/\partial p]_T,$$

and the isochoric activation energy as

$$E_v = -R[\partial \ln D/\partial(1/T)]_V,$$

then

$$E_p = E_v + (\alpha T/\beta)\Delta V^{\ddagger}. \tag{2}$$

(This is strictly true in the limit of zero pressure, but is a sufficiently good approximation for pressures up to about 1 kb.)

Substituting (2) into (1),

$$D_{1 \text{ atm}} = D_0 \exp(-E_v/RT) \exp(-\pi \Delta V^{\ddagger}/RT), \tag{3}$$

where $\pi = \alpha T/\beta$, the "internal pressure" of the liquid. Similar equations apply for the fluidity $1/\eta$, and for the equivalent conductance Λ for ionic liquids.

The table shows data for different types of liquid. On substituting these values of E_v and $\pi \Delta V^{\ddagger}$ into (3), the relative importance of the two exponential terms changes dramatically as we pass down the table, in a way which one could not have predicted in the absence of experimental data. This reflects real differences in the microscopic

liquid	transport process	E_p (kcal/mole)	E_v (kcal/mole)	$\pi \Delta V^{\ddagger}$ (kcal/mole)	ref.
CCl_4	fluidity	3·02	1·22	1·80	2
benzene	fluidity	3·24	1·12	2·12	2
chlorobenzene	fluidity	2·83	0·95	1·88	2
ethanol	fluidity	3·83	2·10	1·73	2
butanol	fluidity	6·40	4·25	2·15	2
mercury	diffusion	1·00	0·96	0·04	3
gallium	diffusion	1·12	0·98	0·24	3
fused $LiNO_3$	conductance	3·42	3·31	0·11	own work
fused $CsNO_3$	conductance	3·69	1·09	2·60	(unpublished)

mechanisms of transport, but the exact nature of these is obscure until an adequate theory of the liquid state is available. In the meantime, I suggest that the transport processes in these liquids be described as "energy restrained" or "volume restrained" according as E_v is greater, or less, than $\pi \Delta V^{\ddagger}$. This distinction is based directly on empirical data, and can be applied to any type of liquid.

The terms "energy limited" and "volume limited" have been used by Macedo and Litovitz [1] in a slightly different sense to that proposed here. Their usage is based on a model for the transport process and on an expression for the size distribution of holes in the liquid, so it breaks down if these are incorrect. The purely empirical terms suggested above are more appropriate at this stage, when satisfactory theories are lacking for some types of liquid and experimental data are relatively sparse. There seems little chance that successful theories of transport will be developed until experimental investigations have been extended to cover a wider range of liquids. Transport measurements made at atmospheric pressure give no indication that the distinction drawn above even exists, and there is need for more work on pressure dependence of transport processes.

[1] P. B. Macedo and T. A. Litovitz, *J. Chem. Physics*, 1965, **42**, 245.
[2] M. K. Nagarajan and J. O'M. Bockris, *J. Physic. Chem.*, 1966, **70**, 1854.

SUMMARIZING REMARKS

By J. S. ROWLINSON

Dept. of Chemical Engineering and Chemical Technology,
Imperial College, London, S.W.7

This meeting has considered the experimental and theoretical methods now available for determining the structure of fluids. In this attempt at summarizing the discussions, it is perhaps appropriate to recall at each stage the formal notation in which our knowledge is codified. For a fluid of structureless spherical molecules, we start with the pair distribution function $g_2(r)$. At equilibrium this is a function of the separation r of two points in the fluid, and, of course, a function also of density and temperature. It represents the probability that molecules are found at separation r, and is the minimum information that is of any value to us. This value is considerable if the configurational energy of the fluid can be expressed as a sum of pair potentials, for then all the thermodynamic properties can be expressed in terms of $g_2(r)$. If $u_2(r)$ is the pair potential, then we have the well-known results that the configurational energy U is the average of $u_2(r)$ over $g_2(r)$, and that the imperfect part of the pressure is the average over $g_2(r)$ of the intermolecular virial function $v_2(r) = \mathrm{d}u_2(r)/\mathrm{d}\ln r$.

$$U/N = \tfrac{1}{2}n^2 \int u_2(r)g_2(r)\mathrm{d}\mathbf{r}, \qquad (1)$$

$$p - nkT = -\tfrac{1}{6}n^2 \int v_2(r)g_2(r)\mathrm{d}\mathbf{r}, \qquad (2)$$

where N is the number of molecules and n the number density. However, the entropy and free energy cannot generally be written in so simple a way but require a further integration over density or, what is formally equivalent, an integration over a coupling parameter as proposed by Kirkwood.

To determine $g_2(r)$ we turn usually to one of three theories, that of Kirkwood, Born and Green (KBG), that of Percus and Yevick (PY), or the hyper-netted chain (HNC) theory. The first has the disadvantage that it leads at once to the introduction of the triplet function g_3, which has then to be eliminated. The traditional elimination —the superposition approximation of Kirkwood—is now known to be inadequate. Rice and Young have argued that it can be improved by the introduction of a few terms of the expansion of g_3 in powers of the density. Experience with attempts to improve other approximations by this method suggests that we shall be fortunate if this approach is satisfactory at liquid densities.

The PY and HNC approximations are more economical in the sense that they both require and yield information only about the pair functions. The former in particular is closely related to the function $c_2(r)$, the direct correlation function of Ornstein and Zernike. The importance of this function was brought out by Rushbrooke in his Spiers Memorial Lecture. I think that one can use it to answer a question raised in discussion by Levine, namely, what is the physical significance of the PY approximation? The answer is that it is the only self-consistent theory which takes literally the original idea of Ornstein and Zernike that the direct correlation function $c_2(r)$ has a range no greater than that of the intermolecular forces, i.e., the range of $f_2(r) = \exp[-u_2(r)/kT] - 1$.

This restriction on the range of $c_2(r)$ leads inevitably to the PY approximation if one requires also that the virial equation, (2), is to yield a unique value of the pressure for discontinuous potentials as, e.g., for hard spheres or for a square-well potential. This result may be shown as follows.

Define a function $y(r)$ that is related to $g(r)$ by the equation

$$g(r) = [1+f(r)]y(r). \tag{3}$$

(The subscripts 2 are omitted for simplicity.) Now if $u(r)$ is discontinuous, then $v(r)$ in (2) is composed of one or more δ-functions, and if this equation is to yield a unique value of p then it follows that $y(r)$ must be continuous even when $u(r)$, $f(r)$ and hence $g(r)$ are not. The Ornstein–Zernike equation is

$$g(r_{12}) - 1 = c(r_{12}) + n\int c(r_{13})[g(r_{23}) - 1]d\mathbf{r}_3 \tag{4}$$

total = direct + indirect correlation function.

The indirect part of the total correlation function is clearly a continuous function of r_{12}, whatever the discontinuities in $c(r)$ and $g(r)$. Substitute for $g(r)$ from (3), and obtain

$$[1+f(r)]y(r) = 1 + c(r) + \text{indirect term}. \tag{5}$$

Hence if $c(r)$ is to be proportional to $f(r)$, and if the solution of (5) is to lead always to a smooth function for $y(r)$, then there is only one admissible functional form for $c(r)$, viz.,

$$c(r) = f(r)y(r). \tag{6}$$

This is the PY approximation and insertion of (3) and (6) into (4) gives the PY integral equation.

The nature of the HNC approximation is, as its name implies, expressible only in terms of its graphical expansion. PY is certainly the better approximation at high temperatures. Henderson's results and Hutchinson's contribution to the Discussion show that HNC may be the better at low temperatures and in the liquid state, but the question is still open.

Thus, these theories allow us to obtain $g(r)$ from $u(r)$ for fluids at moderate and high temperatures. They all yield qualitatively correct liquid-vapour equilibria if $u(r)$ has a negative portion, but do not apparently describe the solid state. The only indication these equations give of the onset of freezing at high densities are either failure to yield a solution at all (KBG) or the existence of solutions in which $g(r)$ has become negative (PY).

Machine calculations, such as those of McDonald and Singer and those reported in the discussion by Verlet, are now giving us a reasonable "experimental" knowledge of the behaviour of one model fluid of precisely known $u(r)$, viz., that with a Lennard–Jones (12,6)-potential. We have U and p, from eqn. (1) and (2), for the homogeneous fluid at temperatures down to the triple point and for the solid. However, the more difficult task of obtaining the free energy or chemical potential, which requires the further integration mentioned above, has not yet been attempted and is, perhaps, the most urgent task in this field. Until this is done, we have no knowledge of the vapour pressure curve.

Pings has shown us how, in principle, we can obtain $u(r)$ from the X-ray diffraction pattern of a moderately dense gas, and his work with Mikolaj adds to the recent evidence, discussed at the General Discussion of the Society on Intermolecular Forces in 1965, that the true pair potential of the inert gases is deeper and narrower than that of a (12,6)-potential. We have, therefore, the paradox that results such as those of McDonald and Singer show that a (12,6)-potential represents well the properties of liquid argon, whilst studies of the gas phase show that the true pair potential is not of this form. The paradox can be resolved only by assuming that a triplet potential u_3 is acting in the dense state and that the sum of the true u_2 and this triplet term can be treated approximately as an effective pair potential of (12,6) shape.

We still know little about either u_3 or about the triplet distribution function g_3. Pople observed that g_2 gives only the mean number of molecules in, say, the first co-ordination shell around a given molecule, but nothing about the angular distribution of molecules in that shell. This knowledge is formally represented in g_3 and in higher functions, and an increase in our understanding of these functions is an urgent task in equilbrium statistical mechanics. We need to know more about g_3 in order to improve KBG, PY and HNC theories in a systematic way, in order to discuss certain properties of non-spherical molecules (Pople, Buckingham), and in order to make further advances in the theory of mixtures—a field which has scarcely moved for 10 years.

There has been much interest lately in the nature of the singularities in physical properties at the critical point, but we have only touched on this problem here. However, Domb and Sykes have shown that in at least one three-dimensional model the singularity in C_v is not logarithmic as has been widely thought but is a little sharper and varies as $(T-T^c)^{-\frac{1}{8}}$. Fixman has discussed the singularities in viscosity and thermal conductivity. Experimentally the latter singularity is found to be readily observed whilst the former, if present, is scarcely detectable. He suggests the difference is not one of functional form but merely of the size of the numerical coefficients of the singular function $(T-T^c)^{-\frac{1}{2}}$.

With the work on water we reach a fluid that is so different from argon, etc., that our methods of interpretation are much more crude. Narten, Danford and Levy have made perhaps the most thorough study yet reported to the X-ray diffraction pattern and obtained from it what is essentially $g(r)$ for the O—O separations. Page, in the discussion, has shown that neutron diffraction gives us primarily the H—H distribution function. A third technique, with a different balance between O—O, O—H and H—H scattering is needed for a complete study.

One striking difference between water and argon was pointed out by Egelstaff. In argon the first peak in $g(r)$ moves to shorter r as the temperature rises along the orthobaric curve. This peak resembles that in a hard-sphere fluid in that it is a "packing" effect or a manifestation of the repulsive part of the potential. The attractive forces serve merely to provide the "internal pressure" that holds the liquid together. Since the repulsive part of $u(r)$ is not infinitely steep, then the effective size of the argon atoms decreases as the temperature rises.

In water we have the opposite effect. The first peak in $g(r)$ moves to larger r as the temperature rises. Here the maximum of the peak is fixed primarily by the length of the O—H . . . O hydrogen bond, and it is the weakening of this bond at high temperatures that is reflected in the change of position of the maximum. In short, argon is a liquid in which the structure is determined primarily by the repulsive forces and water a fluid in which the structure is determined primarily by the attractive forces. The studies of random close-packing of Bernal and his colleagues tell us something of the geometrical nature of the first problem, at least, in the limit of steep potentials and high pressure.

It was evident from the discussion that the infra-red spectrum of water does not lead to an unambiguous description of the hydrogen-bonding as a function of density and temperature. The words " weaken ", " deform " and " break " were used to describe the effect on these bonds of raising the temperature, whilst the words " non-crystalline ", " quasi-crystalline " and " micro-crystalline " were used to describe the structure. However, it is clear also that studies such as those of Luck and of Franck and Roth provide a substantial body of experimental information with which any proposed structural description of water must conform. Mansel Davies drew attention to the fact that recent work on the far infra-red spectrum is here of great potential value.

The last part of this meeting dealt with the time-dependent properties of fluids. Egelstaff described what is perhaps the most significant experimental advance of the last decade—the use of scattering techniques, and in particular of neutron scattering, to study the evolution in time τ of the pair distribution function. The symbol $\mathscr{G}(r,\tau)$ is generally used for this, rather than $g(r,\tau)$, in order to emphasize that we are interested in two experimentally separable phenomena. The motion of a pair of molecules initially at $\mathbf{r}_1$ and $\mathbf{r}_2$ can be described in terms of the diffusion of the first molecule from position $\mathbf{r}_1$ and in terms of the change with time of the probability that the separation has any particular value $\mathbf{r}_1 - \mathbf{r}_2$. The first motion leads to incoherent scattering of neutrons and the second to coherent scattering. The experimental knowledge of the structure of $\mathscr{G}(r,\tau)$ that we so obtain throws light on those more complex space and velocity correlation functions which are related to the transport properties of a fluid. However, in this discussion, we confined ourselves to the study of $\mathscr{G}(r,\tau)$ and did not explore this link with non-equilibrium statistical mechanics.

The results of Dorner, Plesser and Stiller and those that Cocking reported in discussion show that there is a surprisingly close resemblance between the dynamic properties of solids and of fluids at low temperatures. This resemblance must be supposed to weaken as the temperature rises or as the time scale is extended. The measurements of Aldred, Eden and White and those quoted in discussion by Larsson are of particular interest to chemists, since they show how these scattering techniques can now be used to tell us about the relative motions of different parts of complex molecules.

The earlier part of the discussion has shown how valuable a concept is the direct correlation function at equilibrium $c(r)$. It is, therefore, to be hoped that the efforts made by Stecki to define a time-dependent direct function will be of equal value in non-equilibrium statistical mechanics. Clearly, such a concept need not be restricted to a plasma which he discusses in his paper.

The use of nuclear magnetic resonance to study molecular motions by means of the spin-lattice relaxation time T_1 is probably more familiar to chemists than the neutron scattering work. Pople reviewed the different mechanisms that can lead to relaxation and Dwek and Richards discussed applications to particular molecules. It is often the temperature derivative of T_1, an activation energy, which is of greater interest than its absolute value, since this can be compared with activation energies from other types of translational and rotational relaxation processes. The thermodynamic aspects of molecular rotation were discussed by D. B. Davies and Matheson.

Finally, from Barlow and Lamb we heard how some order can be brought to the complicated field of visco-elastic relaxation. R. O. Davies pointed out in discussion that their analysis, which is based on the assumption that the viscous and elastic components of the mechanical impedance are in parallel (i.e., their reciprocals are to be added), is neither more nor less arbitrary than that of Maxwell. It is, however, equivalent in Maxwell's language to a distribution of times of relaxation rather than to a single time, and this inverse way of looking at the problem may be of value in other fields where more than one time of relaxation has to be invoked to explain the behaviour observed. Unfortunately, no molecular model of the process has yet been developed.

A natural complement of work of this kind is that on Brillouin scattering of light by liquids. This gives the speed and the coefficient of absorption of sound at frequencies above 10^{10} sec^{-1}, whereas the mechanically generated frequencies of Barlow and Lamb are restricted to 10^9 sec^{-1} and below. Brillouin scattering was not discussed at this meeting, although it was the subject of a paper that had to be withdrawn because of the illness of Prof. Litowitz. In spite of many difficulties of interpretation, it is clear that the last decade has seen the development of several new techniques which should soon allow us to describe the time-dependent microscopic properties of fluids with the same confidence that we now have for the equilibrium properties. It will then be for the new field of non-equilibrium statistical mechanics of dense systems to relate this microscopic information on structure to the macroscopic transport properties.

AUTHOR INDEX*

Aldred, B. K., 169
Barker, J. A., 50
Barlow, A. J., 218.
Bellemans, A., 236.
Beresford, R. H., 76.
Bernal, J. D., 60.
Buckingham, A. D., 199, 238.
Cagloti, G., 129.
Cleaver, B., 241.
Cole, G. H. A., 56.
Collins, R., 81.
Corchia, M., 129.
Danford, M. D., 97.
Davies, D. B., 216.
Davies, M., 128, 184, 235.
Domb, C., 85.
Dorner, B., 160.
Dwek, R. A., 191, 239.
Eckstein, B., 148.
Eden, R. C., 169.
Egelstaff, P. A., 149.
Everett, D. H., 82.
Findenegg, G. H., 238.
Finney, J., 83.
Fischer, J., 32.
Fixman, M., 70.
Franck, E. U., 109.
Frank, H. S., 137, 147.
Henderson, D., 26, 50.
Henderson, I., 239.
Hertz, H. G., 236.
Hillier, I. H., 79.
Hutchinson, P., 53.
Hyne, J. B., 148.
Josien, M. L., 142.
Kim, S., 26.
King, S. V., 60.
Kohler, F., 32.
Lamb, J., 218.
Larsson, K.-E., 184.
Levi, A., 190.
Levine, S., 56, 131.
Levy, H. A., 97.
Luck, W. A. P., 115, 132, 133, 141, 144.
Magat, M., 145.
Mason, G., 75.
Matheson, A. J., 216, 239.
McDonald, I. R., 40.
Moreton, A., 56.
Narten, A. H., 97.
Ng, W. Y., 57.
Oden, L., 26.
Padova, J., 141.
Page, D. I., 130.
Perram, J. W., 131.
Pings, C. J., 89.
Plesser, Th., 160.
Pople, J. A., 187.
Rice, S. A., 16, 57.
Richards, R. E., 191.
Rizzi, G., 129.
Roth, K., 109.
Rowlinson, J. S., 55, 56, **243.**
Rushbrooke, G. S., 7.
Sherwood, J. N., 128.
Singer, K., 40.
Smith, F. W., 231, 241.
Smith, B. L., 88.
Stecki, J., 190, 212.
Stiller, H., 160.
Walkley, J., 57, 79.
Weber, U. v., 59.
White, J. W., 169.
Young, D. A., 16, 57.

* The references in heavy type indicate papers submitted for discussion.

GENERAL DISCUSSIONS OF THE FARADAY SOCIETY

Date	Subject	Volume
1907	Osmotic Pressure	Trans. 3
1907	Hydrates in Solution	3
1910	The Constitution of Water	6
1911	High Temperature Work	7
1912	Magnetic Properties of Alloys	8
1913	Colloids and their Viscosity	9
1913	The Corrosion of Iron and Steel	9
1913	The Passivity of Metals	9
1914	Optical Rotary Power	10
1914	The Hardening of Metals	10
1915	The Transformation of Pure Iron	11
1916	Methods and Appliances for the Attainment of High Temperatures in a Laboratory	12
1916	Refractory Materials	12
1917	Training and Work of the Chemical Engineer	13
1917	Osmotic Pressure	13
1917	Pyrometers and Pyrometry	13
1918	The Setting of Cements and Plasters	14
1918	Electrical Furnaces	14
1918	Co-ordination of Scientific Publication	14
1918	The Occlusion of Gases by Metals	14
1919	The Present Position of the Theory of Ionization	15
1919	The Examination of Materials by X-Rays	15
1920	The Microscope: Its Design, Construction and Applications	16
1920	Basic Slags: Their Production and Utilization in Agriculture	16
1920	Physics and Chemistry of Colloids	16
1920	Electrodeposition and Electroplating	16
1921	Capillarity	17
1921	The Failure of Metals under Internal and Prolonged Stress	17
1921	Physico-Chemical Problems Relating to the Soil	17
1921	Catalysis with special reference to Newer Theories of Chemical Action	17
1922	Some Properties of Powders with special reference to Grading by Elutriation	18
1922	The Generation and Utilization of Cold	18
1923	Alloys Resistant to Corrosion	19
1923	The Physical Chemistry of the Photographic Process	19
1923	The Electronic Theory of Valency	19
1923	Electrode Reactions and Equilibria	19
1923	Atmospheric Corrosion. First Report	19
1924	Investigation on Oppau Ammonium Sulphate-Nitrate	20
1924	Fluxes and Slags in Metal Melting and Working	20
1924	Physical and Physico-Chemical Problems relating to Textile Fibres	20
1924	The Physical Chemistry of Igneous Rock Formation	20
1924	Base Exchange in Soils	20
1925	The Physical Chemistry of Steel-Making Processes	21
1925	Photochemical Reactions in Liquids and Gases	21
1926	Explosive Reactions in Gaseous Media	22
1926	Physical Phenomena at Interfaces, with special reference to Molecular Orientation	22
1927	Atmospheric Corrosion. Second Report	23
1927	The Theory of Strong Electrolytes	23
1927	Cohesion and Related Problems	24

GENERAL DISCUSSIONS OF THE FARADAY SOCIETY

Date	Subject	Volume
1928	Homogeneous Catalysis	24
1929	Crystal Structure and Chemical Constitution	25
1929	Atmospheric Corrosion of Metals. Third Report	25
1929	Molecular Spectra and Molecular Structure	25
1930	Optical Rotatory Power	26
1930	Colloid Science Applied to Biology	26
1931	Photochemical Processes	27
1932	The Adsorption of Gases by Solids	28
1932	The Colloid Aspects of Textile Materials	29
1933	Liquid Crystals and Anisotropic Melts	29
1933	Free Radicals	30
1934	Dipole Moments	30
1934	Colloidal Electrolytes	31
1935	The Structure of Metallic Coatings, Films and Surfaces	31
1935	The Phenomena of Polymerization and Condensation	32
1936	Disperse Systems in Gases: Dust, Smoke and Fog	32
1936	Structure and Molecular Forces in (*a*) Pure Liquids, and (*b*) Solutions	33
1937	The Properties and Functions of Membranes, Natural and Artificial	33
1937	Reaction Kinetics	34
1398	Chemical Reactions Involving Solids	34
1938	Luminescence	35
1939	Hydrocarbon Chemistry	35
1939	The Electrical Double Layer (owing to the outbreak of war the meeting was abandoned, but the papers were printed in the *Transactions*)	35
1940	The Hydrogen Bond	36
1941	The Oil-Water Interface	37
1941	The Mechanism and Chemical Kinetics of Organic Reactions in Liquid Systems	37
1942	The Structure and Reactions of Rubber	38
1943	Modes of Drug Action	39
1944	Molecular Weight and Molecular Weight Distribution in High Polymers. (Joint Meeting with the Plastics Group, Society of Chemical Industry)	40
1945	The Application of Infra-red Spectra to Chemical Problems	41
1945	Oxidation	42
1946	Dielectrics	42 A
1946	Swelling and Shrinking	42 B
1947	Electrode Processes	Disc. 1
1947	The Labile Molecule	2
1947	Surface Chemistry. (Jointly with the Société de Chimie Physique at Bordeaux.) Published by Butterworths Scientific Publications, Ltd.	
1947	Colloidal Electrolytes and Solutions	Trans. 43
1948	The Interaction of Water and Porous Materials	Disc. 3
1948	The Physical Chemistry of Process Metallurgy	4
1949	Crystal Growth	5
1949	Lipo-Proteins	6
1949	Chromatographic Analysis	7
1950	Heterogeneous Catalysis	8
1950	Physico-chemical Properties and Behaviour of Nuclear Acids	Trans. 46
1950	Spectroscopy and Molecular Structure and Optical Methods of Investigating Cell Structure	Disc. 9
1950	Electrical Double Layer	Trans. 47
1951	Hydrocarbons	Disc. 10
1951	The Size and Shape Factor in Colloidal Systems	11
1952	Radiation Chemistry	12
1952	The Physical Chemistry of Proteins	13
1952	The Reactivity of Free Radicals	14
1953	The Equilibrium Properties of Solutions of Non-Electrolytes	15
1953	The Physical Chemistry of Dyeing and Tanning	16
1954	The Study of Fast Reactions	17
1954	Coagulation and Flocculation	18

GENERAL DISCUSSIONS OF THE FARADAY SOCIETY

Date	Subject	Volume
1955	Microwave and Radio-Frequency Spectroscopy	19
1955	Physical Chemistry of Enzymes	20
1956	Membrane Phenomena	21
1956	Physical Chemistry of Processes at High Pressures	22
1957	Molecular Mechanism of Rate Processes in Solids	23
1957	Interactions in Ionic Solutions	24
1958	Configurations and Interactions of Macromolecules and Liquid Crystals	25
1958	Ions of the Transition Elements	26
1959	Energy Transfer with special reference to Biological Systems	27
1959	Crystal Imperfections and the Chemical Reactivity of Solids	28
1960	Oxidation-Reduction Reactions in Ionizing Solvents	29
1960	The Physical Chemistry of Aerosols	30
1961	Radiation Effects in Inorganic Solids	31
1961	The Structure and Properties of Ionic Melts	32
1962	Inelastic Collisions of Atoms and Simple Molecules	33
1962	High Resolution Nuclear Magnetic Resonance	34
1963	The Structure of Electronically-Excited Species in the Gas-Phase	35
1963	Fundamental Processes in Radiation Chemistry	36
1964	Chemical Reactions in the Atmosphere	37
1964	Dislocations in Solids	38
1965	The Kinetics of Proton Transfer Processes	39
1965	Intermolecular Forces	40
1966	The Role of the Adsorbed State in Heterogeneous Catalysis	41
1966	Colloid Stability in Aqueous and Non-Aqueous Media	42
1967	The Structure and Properties of Liquids	43

For current availability of Discussion volumes, see back cover.